EXAMKRACKERS MCAT®

# PHYSICS

11TH EDITION

JONATHAN ORSAY

OSOTE
PUBLISHING

**Major Contributors:**

Jennifer Birk-Goldschmidt, M.S.
Erik Davies, M.Ed.
Jay Li
Laura Neubauer
Christopher Stewart

**Contributors:**

Mark Alshak
Daniel Biro
Jacob Chevlen
Winston Crute
Andrew Elson
Spenser Hayward
Austin Mattox
Kate Millington, M.D.
Haares Mirzan
Lauren Nadler
Mohan Natrajan
Sandeep Palepu
Colleen Moran Shannon
John Shumway
Neil Vadhar

**Art Director:**

Erin Daniel

**Designer:**

Dana Kelley
Charles Yuen

**Illustrators:**

Stephen Halker
Kellie Holoski
Justin Stewart

ISBN 13: 978-1-951127-03-9 (6 Volume Set)
11th Edition

To purchase additional copies of this book or the rest of the 5 volume set, call 1-888-572-2536 or fax orders to 1-859-305-6464.

Examkrackers.com
Osote.com

Printed and bound in China.

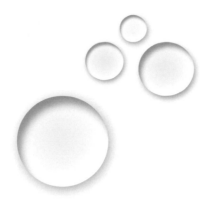

# PHOTOCOPYING & DISTRIBUTION POLICY

The illustrations and all other content in this book are copyrighted material owned by Osote Publishing. Please do not reproduce any of the content, illustrations, charts, graphs, photos, etc., on email lists or websites.

Photocopying the pages so that the book can then be resold is a violation of copyright.

Schools and co-ops MAY NOT PHOTOCOPY any portion of this book. For more information, please contact Osote Publishing: email: support@examkrackers.com or phone 1.888.KRACKEM.

# Acknowledgements

Although I am the author, the hard work and expertise of many individuals contributed to this book. The idea of writing in two voices, a science voice and an MCAT® voice, was the creative brainchild of my imaginative friend Jordan Zaretsky. I would like to thank Scott Calvin for lending his exceptional science talent and pedagogic skills to this project. I also must thank nineteen years worth of Examkrackers students for doggedly questioning every explanation, every sentence, every diagram, and every punctuation mark in the book, and for providing the creative inspiration that helped me find new ways to approach and teach physics. Finally, I wish to thank my wife, Silvia, for her support during the difficult times in the past and those that lie ahead.

## Introduction to the Examkrackers Manuals

The Examkrackers manuals are designed to give you exactly the information you need to do well on the MCAT® while limiting extraneous information that will not be tested. This manual organizes all of the information on the physics tested on the MCAT® conceptually. Concepts make the content both simple and portable for optimal application to MCAT® questions. Mastery of the physics topics covered in this manual will increase your confidence and allow you to succeed with seemingly difficult passages that are designed to intimidate. The MCAT® rewards your ability to read complex passages and questions through the lens of basic science concepts.

An in-depth introduction to the MCAT® is located in the Reasoning Skills manual. Read this introduction first to start thinking like the MCAT® and to learn critical mathematical skills. The second lecture of the Reasoning Skills manual addresses the research methods needed for success on 20% of questions on the science and psychology sections of the MCAT®. Research questions are the most difficult on the MCAT® and are the questions that help students beat the mean and get a high score. Once you have read those lectures, return to this manual to begin your review of the physics you will need to excel on the MCAT®

## How to Use This Manual

Examkrackers MCAT® manuals can be used with the Examkrackers Comprehensive MCAT® Course or as a tool for independent MCAT® study. Examkrackers MCAT® preparation experience has shown that you will get the most out of these manuals when you structure your studying as follows. If you are taking the Examkrackers Comprehensive MCAT® Course, read each lecture twice before the class lecture. During the first reading, you should not write in the book. Instead, read purely for enjoyment. During the second reading, highlight and take notes in the margins. Complete the twenty-four questions in each lecture during the second reading before coming to class. Do not look at the In-Class Exams before class. Immediately after class, read the lecture again, slowly and thoroughly.

If you are studying independently, read each lecture twice (as described above), completing the in-lecture questions during the second reading. Take the In-Class Exam, then read the lecture once more, slowly and thoroughly.

The In-Class Exams are designed to educate. They are similar to an MCAT® section, but are shortened and have most of the easy questions removed. We believe that you can answer most of the easy questions without too much help from us, so the best way to raise your score is to focus on the more difficult questions. The In-Class Exams are designed to help you prepare for test day when you will be faced with an intensity that is difficult to simulate. Technically, the Examkrackers In-Class Exams are timed to take as long as 35 minutes to complete. By practicing with a few minutes less, you will be ready for the pressure and pace of the real exam, and MCAT® day will feel more manageable. These methods are some of the reasons for the rapid and celebrated success of the Examkrackers prep course and products.

With each In-Class Exam you should see the number of questions you answer correctly increase. Do not be discouraged by poor performance on these exams; they are not meant to predict your performance on the real MCAT®. **The questions that you get wrong (or even guess correctly) are the most important ones. They represent your potential score increase.** When you get a question wrong or have to guess, determine why. If content was the problem, target those areas for review. If the issue was your approach to the question, make a commitment to a different approach for the next practice test. As you learn to think like the MCAT®, you will see your score increase.

In order to study most efficiently, it is essential to know what topics are and are not tested directly in MCAT® questions. This manual uses the following conventions to make the distinction. Any topic listed in the AAMC's guide to the MCAT® is printed in **red, bold type**. You must thoroughly understand all topics printed in **red, bold type**. Any formula that must be memorized is also printed in **red, bold type**.

If a topic is not printed in **bold and red**, it may still be important. Understanding these topics may be helpful for putting other terms in context. Topics and equations that are not explicitly tested but are still useful to know are printed in *italics*. Knowledge of content printed in *italics* will enhance your ability to answer passage-based MCAT® questions, as MCAT® passages may cover topics beyond the AAMC's list of tested topics on the MCAT®.

## Features of the Examkrackers Manuals

The Examkrackers manuals include several features to help you retain and integrate information for the MCAT®. Take advantage of these features to get the most out of your study time.

- **The 3 Keys** – The Three Keys unlock the material and the MCAT® by highlighting the most important things to remember from each chapter. The Three Keys are listed at the beginning and end of each lecture with reminders from Salty throughout the text. Examine the Three Keys before and after reading a lecture to make sure you have absorbed the most important messages. As you read, continue to develop your own key concepts that will guide your studying and performance.

- **Signposts** – The MCAT® is fully integrated, asking you to apply the biological, physical, and social sciences simultaneously. The signposts alongside the text in this manual will help you build mental connections between topics and disciplines. This mental map will lead you to a high score on the MCAT®. The post of each sign "brackets" the paragraph to which it refers. When you see a signpost next to a topic, stop and consider how the topics are related. Soon you will begin making your own connections between concepts and topics within and between disciplines. This is an MCAT® skill that will improve your score. When answering questions, these connections give you multiple routes to find your way to the answer.

**Thermodynamics**
CHEMISTRY

- **MCAT® Think** – These sidebars invite deeper consideration of certain topics. They provide helpful context for topics that are tested and will challenge you just like tough MCAT® passages. While MCAT® Think topics and their level of detail may not be explicitly tested on the MCAT®, read and consider each MCAT® Think to sharpen your MCAT® skills. The MCAT® Think sidebars provide essential practice in managing seemingly complex and unfamiliar content, as you will need to do for passages on MCAT® day.

I'm Salty the Kracker. Where you see purple text, that's me. I will show you why the content makes sense and help you develop your MCAT® intuition. My job is to make sure you 1. stay awake and 2. really understand and remember what you're reading. If you think I am funny, tell the boss. I could use a raise. If you get the munchies, reconsider... you'll want me around.

## Additional Resources

If you find yourself struggling with the science or you want more practice, take advantage of the additional Examkrackers resources that are available.

Examkrackers offers a 9-week Comprehensive MCAT® Course to help you achieve a high score on the MCAT®. Whether in person or online, the course includes up to 120 hours with expert instructors, a unique course format, and regular full-length MCAT® exams. Each class includes lecture, a practice exam, and review, designed to help you develop essential MCAT® skills. For locations and registration please visit Examkrackers.com or call 1.888.KRACKEM.

EK-Tests® are Examkrackers full-length, online simulated MCAT® exams that match the AAMC MCAT® in style, content, and skills tested. Written by educators, high-scoring medical students, and physicians, EK-Tests® provide the best MCAT® practice available. To purchase EK-Tests®, please visit Examkrackers.com.

Your purchase of this book new will also give you access to the **Examkrackers Forums** at Examkrackers.com/mcat/forum. These bulletin boards allow you to discuss any MCAT® question with an MCAT® expert at Examkrackers. All discussions are kept on file so you can refer back to previous discussions on any question in this book. Once you have purchased the books you can take advantage of this resource by calling 1.888.KRACKEM to register for the forums.

Examkrackers offers a 9-week Comprehensive MCAT® Preparation Course to help you achieve a high score on the MCAT®. The Examkrackers course includes 66 hours with expert instructors, a unique course format, and regular full-length simulated MCAT® exams. Each class includes lecture, practice exam, and review, designed to help you develop essential MCAT® skills. For locations and registration, visit Examkrackers.com or call 1.888.KRACKEM.

Although we make every effort to ensure the accuracy of our books, the occasional error does occur. Corrections are posted on the Examkrackers Books Errata Forum, also at Examkrackers.com/mcat/forum. If you believe that you have found a mistake, please post an inquiry on the Study with Examkrackers MCAT® Books Forum, which is likewise found at Examkrackers.com/mcat/forum. As the leaders in MCAT® preparation, we are committed to providing you with the most up-to-date, accurate information possible.

Study diligently, trust this book to guide you, and you will reach your MCAT® goals.

# Table of Contents

## LECTURE 4 Electricity 89

## LECTURE 5 Waves: Sound and Light 115

## 30-Minute In-Class Exams    173

## Answers & Explanations to In-Class Exams    213

## Answers & Explanations to Questions in the Lectures    233

## Photo Credits    251

## Index    253

## PHYSICAL SCIENCES

**DIRECTIONS.** Most questions in the Physical Sciences test are organized into groups, each preceded by a descriptive passage. After studying the passage, select the one best answer to each question in the group. Some questions are not based on a descriptive passage and are also independent of each other. You must also select the one best answer to these questions. If you are not certain of an answer, eliminate the alternatives that you know to be incorrect and then select an answer from the remaining alternatives. A periodic table is provided for your use. You may consult it whenever you wish.

---

## PERIODIC TABLE OF THE ELEMENTS

| 1 H 1.0 | | | | | | | | | | | | | | | | | 2 He 4.0 |
|---|---|---|---|---|---|---|---|---|---|---|---|---|---|---|---|---|---|
| 3 Li 6.9 | 4 Be 9.0 | | | | | | | | | | | 5 B 10.8 | 6 C 12.0 | 7 N 14.0 | 8 O 16.0 | 9 F 19.0 | 10 Ne 20.2 |
| 11 Na 23.0 | 12 Mg 24.3 | | | | | | | | | | | 13 Al 27.0 | 14 Si 28.1 | 15 P 31.0 | 16 S 32.1 | 17 Cl 35.5 | 18 Ar 39.9 |
| 19 K 39.1 | 20 Ca 40.1 | 21 Sc 45.0 | 22 Ti 47.9 | 23 V 50.9 | 24 Cr 52.0 | 25 Mn 54.9 | 26 Fe 55.8 | 27 Co 58.9 | 28 Ni 58.7 | 29 Cu 63.5 | 30 Zn 65.4 | 31 Ga 69.7 | 32 Ge 72.6 | 33 As 74.9 | 34 Se 79.0 | 35 Br 79.9 | 36 Kr 83.8 |
| 37 Rb 85.5 | 38 Sr 87.6 | 39 Y 88.9 | 40 Zr 91.2 | 41 Nb 92.9 | 42 Mo 95.9 | 43 Tc (98) | 44 Ru 101.1 | 45 Rh 102.9 | 46 Pd 106.4 | 47 Ag 107.9 | 48 Cd 112.4 | 49 In 114.8 | 50 Sn 118.7 | 51 Sb 121.8 | 52 Te 127.6 | 53 I 126.9 | 54 Xe 131.3 |
| 55 Cs 132.9 | 56 Ba 137.3 | 57 La* 138.9 | 72 Hf 178.5 | 73 Ta 180.9 | 74 W 183.9 | 75 Re 186.2 | 76 Os 190.2 | 77 Ir 192.2 | 78 Pt 195.1 | 79 Au 197.0 | 80 Hg 200.6 | 81 Tl 204.4 | 82 Pb 207.2 | 83 Bi 209.0 | 84 Po (209) | 85 At (210) | 86 Rn (222) |
| 87 Fr (223) | 88 Ra 226.0 | 89 Ac⁼ 227.0 | 104 Unq (261) | 105 Unp (262) | 106 Unh (263) | 107 Uns (262) | 108 Uno (265) | 109 Une (267) | | | | | | | | | |

| * | 58 Ce 140.1 | 59 Pr 140.9 | 60 Nd 144.2 | 61 Pm (145) | 62 Sm 150.4 | 63 Eu 152.0 | 64 Gd 157.3 | 65 Tb 158.9 | 66 Dy 162.5 | 67 Ho 164.9 | 68 Er 167.3 | 69 Tm 168.9 | 70 Yb 173.0 | 71 Lu 175.0 |
|---|---|---|---|---|---|---|---|---|---|---|---|---|---|---|
| ⁼ | 90 Th 232.0 | 91 Pa (231) | 92 U 238.0 | 93 Np (237) | 94 Pu (244) | 95 Am (243) | 96 Cm (247) | 97 Bk (247) | 98 Cf (251) | 99 Es (252) | 100 Fm (257) | 101 Md (258) | 102 No (259) | 103 Lr (260) |

For your convenience, a periodic table is also inserted in the back of the book.

# Motion and Force

## 1.01 | Introduction

Physics concepts are tested in the Chemical and Physical Foundations of Biological Systems Section of the MCAT®. This section asks the test taker to solve problems by combining knowledge of physics and chemistry with scientific inquiry and reasoning skills. The *Physics* manual reviews all of the physics knowledge tested by the MCAT®. Together with the following, it covers the knowledge and skills tested in the Chemical and Physical Foundations of Biological Systems Section:

- the Research and Reasoning Skills for the MCAT®, Lecture ii in the *Reasoning Skills* manual,
- the *Chemistry* manual,
- the *Biology 1: Molecules* manual, and
- the *Biology 2: Systems* manual.

Achieving a high score on the MCAT® requires application of the physics concepts presented in this manual to biological systems. Many physics-related passages and questions on the MCAT® will involve physiological processes.

Pay special attention to connections between physics and biology lectures. For example, while reading the Fluids Lecture in this manual, note connections with the circulatory system, discussed further in *Biology 2: Systems*.

**THE 3 KEYS**

1. Acceleration is required for any change in motion, that is change in direction or speed.

2. See net force, think acceleration. See acceleration, think net force.

3. When forces are acting, draw free body diagrams.

$$\Delta P = P_2 - P_1$$

$P_2$ $P_1$

# Salty's Five Step Never-Fail Method for Solving Physics Problems

Whether they realize it or not, any good physics student has a method for solving physics problems. Some problems are so simple that the entire system can be completed without conscious thought in a fraction of a second. Other times, each step is given careful and deliberate consideration. The following is my method that you can use to solve every single physics problem on the MCAT®. For easy problems you will be able to do the entire method in your head in seconds or less, but the moment you feel any hesitation, start drawing diagrams with your pencil. Remember: first breathe, then DIVE.

### Step 1: Breathe.

Don't let yourself be intimidated by any MCAT® question. Remember that the MCAT® only tests basic physics. After completing this manual, you will have all of the necessary knowledge to handle any physics problem on the MCAT®.

### Step 2: Diagram.

Draw a well-labeled diagram. A good diagram takes the question out of the 'MCAT® environment' and puts it on your terms. The act of drawing a diagram also provides you with new insight into the problem.

### Step 3: Isolate.

Isolate the system of bodies that is of interest for answering the question. This step may seem obvious, but it is the one most often forgotten. Learn to concentrate on only the body or bodies that are relevant to the question and ignore all extraneous information.

### Step 4: Variable.

List all variables that are involved in the problem. Identify the variable(s) that describe the body or system of bodies of interest. Write down any values given for those variables. Identify the variable whose value you are being asked to find.

### Step 5: Equation.

If an equation is needed, brainstorm by writing down equations that include both the variable(s) you know and the one for which you must solve. Select the equation that will allow you to answer the question asked. As necessary, plug in given values and solve for unknowns.

The example problem below will demonstrate every step of my system.

The owner of a warehouse asks an engineer to design a ramp that will reduce the force required to lift boxes to the top of a 0.5 m high step. If there is only room enough for a 4 m ramp, what is the maximum factor by which the lifting force could be reduced?

Breathe
and then:

Diagram

Isolate

Variable

Equation

A. ½

B. 2

C. 4

D. 8

### Breathe:

All of the information needed to solve this problem is covered in the Motion and Force and Energy and Equilibrium Lectures of the *Physics* manual.

### Diagram:

### Isolate:

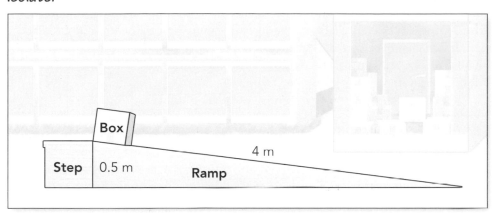

The problem is asking about the degree to which a ramp can reduce the force required to lift a box to the top of a step.

### Variable(s):

Force ($F$): unknown

Displacement ($d$):

$d_{step} = 0.5$ m

$d_{base} = 4$ m

For now, do not worry about the physics knowledge needed to solve this particular problem. We'll get to that later. Focus on the method that is being used to solve the problem.

### Equation:

$$F = ma$$

This equation involves force ($F$). It relates force to mass ($m$) and acceleration ($a$).

$$v = \frac{d}{t}$$

This equation involves displacement ($d$). It relates displacement to velocity ($v$) and time ($t$).

$$\boxed{W = Fd}$$

This equation involves force ($F$) and displacement ($d$). It equates their product to work ($W$).

Ramps do not change the amount of work done. $W = Fd = \Delta PE = mg(\Delta h)$, and $m$, $g$, and $\Delta h$ are constant, so $W$ is constant. However, ramps do change both displacement and force.

Because the product of force and displacement is equal to a constant, these variables are said to be inversely proportional to each other. If one increases by a given factor, the other must decrease by that same factor. The addition of a 4 m ramp would increase displacement by a factor of 8, and force would decrease by that same factor.

If there is only room for a 4 m ramp, the lifting force could be reduced at most by a factor of 8.

## 1.1 Introduction to Motion and Force

This lecture begins with a brief review of vectors and scalars. It then covers motion and the forces that cause and change it. The lecture discusses the basics of translational motion, including displacement, velocity, and acceleration, emphasizing the fact that any change in the direction of motion is a change in velocity and therefore requires acceleration. Next the lecture discusses forces acting at an object's center of mass. Forces create acceleration and cause or change motion. Net force moves an object from rest to motion, from motion to rest, or from one state of motion to another.

## 1.2 Vectors and Scalars

Understanding the difference between vectors and scalars is necessary for solving MCAT® physics problems. This lecture will demonstrate how vectors and scalars can be used to solve problems about motion and force. A **scalar** is a physical quantity that has magnitude but no direction. Distance and speed are scalars commonly used to describe motion. A **vector** is a physical quantity with both magnitude and direction. A vector can be represented by an arrow. The direction of the arrow indicates the direction of the vector; the length of the arrow indicates the magnitude of the vector. Displacement, velocity, and acceleration are vectors commonly used to describe motion. Forces are also vector quantities.

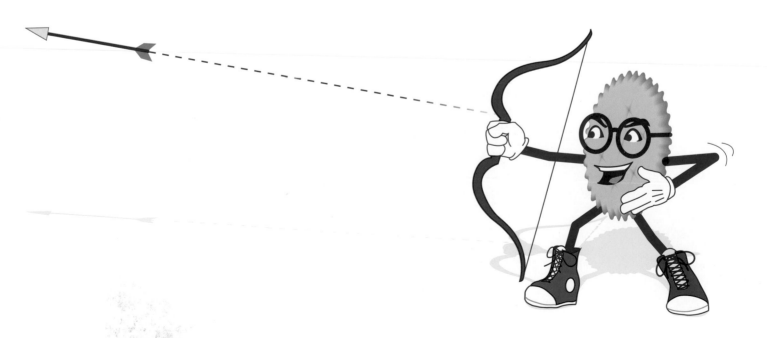

## Adding and Subtracting Vectors

Solving problems with vector quantities often involves adding or subtracting vectors to produce a new vector, such as when forces are added to calculate net force.

To add vectors geometrically, place the first vector such that the head of the arrow meets the tail of the second vector, and draw an arrow from the tail of the first to the head of the second. The resulting arrow is the vector sum of the other two vectors. Notice that the magnitude of the sum of two vectors must be smaller than or equal to the sum of their magnitudes and greater than or equal to the difference of their magnitudes. The sum of two velocity vectors with magnitudes of 10 m/s and 7 m/s will be greater than or equal to a velocity vector with a magnitude of 3 m/s, but smaller than or equal to a velocity vector with a magnitude of 17 m/s.

To subtract vectors geometrically, place the heads of the two vectors together and draw an arrow from the tail of the first to the tail of the second. An alternative method is to find the negative of the vector that is being subtracted and add it to the other vector. The new arrow represents the vector difference between the two original vectors.

> For vector addition, put the vectors head to tail.

> You can subtract vectors the same way you add them. Invert the vector with the negative sign and put the vectors head to tail.

**FIGURE 1.1** | Vector Addition and Subtraction

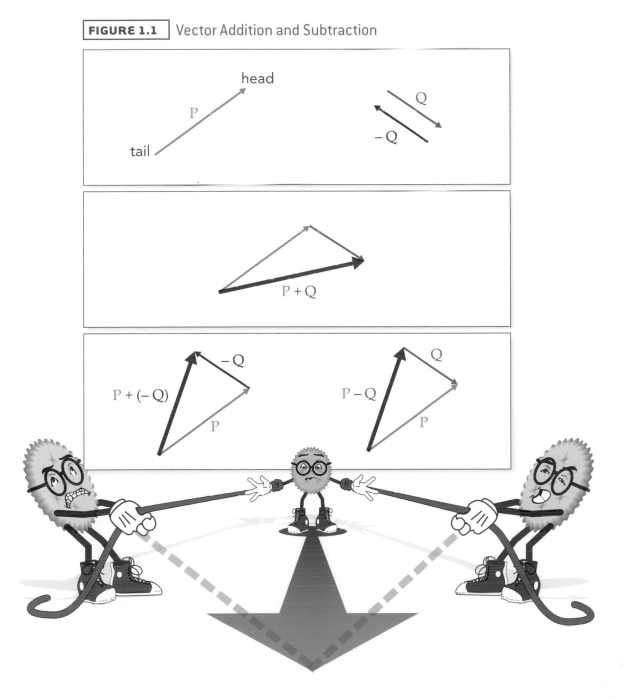

## Component Vectors

Vectors can also be added and subtracted algebraically. This method requires separating each vector into its *x* and *y* component vectors. Any vector can be resolved into infinite numbers of pairs of perpendicular **component vectors** whose vector sum is equal to the original vector. This property of vectors is often convenient, since vectors that are perpendicular to each other, like *x* and *y* component vectors, sometimes affect each other in a limited fashion or not at all.

Figure 1.2 shows three possible pairs of component vectors for one vector. Each component vector is perpendicular to its partner and sums with its partner to equal the original vector. Each of the infinite number of points on the semi-circle represents a possible meeting of the head of one partner and the tail of another. The lengths of the component vectors can be found through simple trigonometry such as the Pythagorean Theorem and SOH CAH TOA.

**FIGURE 1.2** | Component Vectors

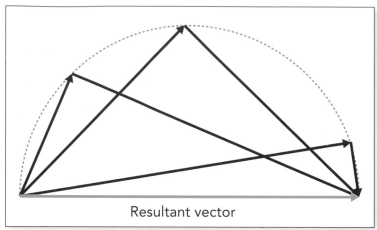

Resultant vector

Any vector can be replaced by component vectors. Component vectors are always at right angles to each other, and their sum is equal to the vector being replaced.

SOH CAH TOA is a little slow for the MCAT®. Memorize the following (where O is Opposite, H is Hypotenuse, and A is Adjacent):

$$O = H\sin\theta$$
$$A = H\cos\theta$$

Except for the ones that you should memorize (as discussed in the Introduction to the MCAT® and Math Lecture), the MCAT® will provide the values of sine and cosine when needed, and, more often, when not needed.

**FIGURE 1.3** | Lengths of Component Vectors

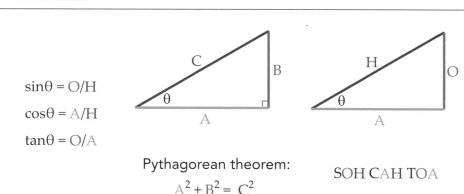

$$\sin\theta = O/H$$
$$\cos\theta = A/H$$
$$\tan\theta = O/A$$

Pythagorean theorem:
$$A^2 + B^2 = C^2$$

SOH CAH TOA

As long as we're thinking about the Pythagorean theorem, we might as well remember one of the most common triangles seen on the MCAT®, the 3-4-5 triangle, and a less common cousin, the 5-12-13 triangle.

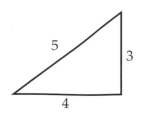

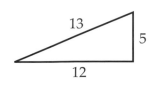

## 1.3 | Translational Motion

Distance, displacement, speed, velocity, and acceleration are all characteristics that describe motion. Distance and displacement are scalar and vector counterparts, as are speed and velocity. Displacement is distance with the added dimension of direction, and velocity is speed with the added dimension of direction. The definitions of average speed and average velocity are represented by the following formulae:

$$\text{speed} = \frac{\text{distance}}{\text{time}} \qquad \text{velocity} = \frac{\text{displacement}}{\text{time}}$$

If a man walks from Point $A$ to Point $B$, his distance traveled can be measured by the number of steps that he takes. His displacement is his final position relative to his starting point, meaning the net distance traveled. If Point $B$ is 10 meters to the right of Point $A$, the man's displacement is 10 meters in the rightward direction. However, the distance is unknown, because he may have taken path $X$, $Y$, or $Z$ (or any other possible path). Notice that the magnitudes of the man's displacement and distance are not necessarily equal.

> The speed and velocity of a moving object will have the same magnitude, but the displacement and distance of a trip taken by that object will not necessarily have the same magnitude. A meandering path from Point A to Point B (described by distance) will differ in magnitude from the shortest path from A to B (described by displacement).

**FIGURE 1.4** | Distance vs. Displacement

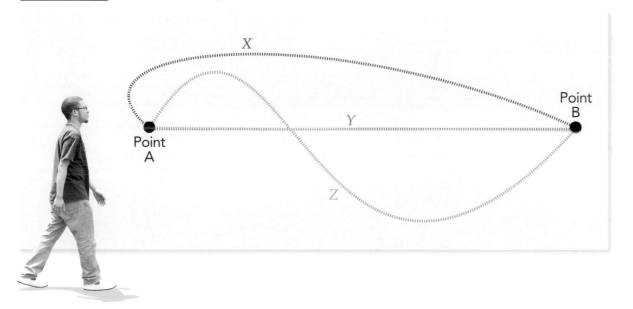

If the entire trip took 100 s, the man's average velocity is his displacement divided by 100 s, or 0.1 m/s to the right. The average velocity does not depend on the path chosen. The man's average vertical velocity during the trip was zero. Since the distance traveled is unknown, the average speed cannot be determined.

The man's **instantaneous speed** and **instantaneous velocity**, that is, his speed and velocity at any one moment during the trip, are also unknown. It is possible that his speed and velocity were constant throughout the trip. Alternatively, he could have covered the first half of the trip in 99 seconds and the second half in 1 second, changing velocity over the course of the trip.

The rate of change in velocity is a vector quantity called **acceleration**, which is defined as follows:

$$\text{acceleration} = \frac{\text{change in velocity}}{\text{time}}$$

Circulatory System
BIOLOGY 2

These equations are helpful for studying the movement of blood throughout the vasculature. As blood leaves arteries and arterioles, it enters capillary beds and its velocity decreases as the combined cross-sectional area of the capillaries increases. This slowing allows sufficient time for $O_2$ to diffuse into the tissue and for $CO_2$ to diffuse into the blood. Blood flow ultimately results from the force of the heart, which accelerates the blood by applying force. Fluid flow will be explained in greater depth in Lecture 3, but it is mentioned here because it will be useful both on the MCAT® and in medical school.

Understand Key 1: You likely have an intuitive understanding of velocity, but not of acceleration. For instance, you probably know what it feels like to move at a velocity of 55 miles/hour, but how does it feel to accelerate at 55 miles/hour²? Are you thrown to the back of your seat, or do you become impatient waiting to speed up? You can understand 55 miles/hour² as a change in velocity of 55 miles/hour every hour. Starting from zero , it would take you one hour to reach a velocity of 55 miles/hour, and another hour to reach 110 miles/hour.

Any change in velocity is acceleration, whether it is a change in magnitude, direction, or both. Therefore a particle must accelerate in order to change the direction of its motion. An object traveling at 10 m/s north one moment and 10 m/s east the next moment has accelerated, even though its speed has not changed. A particle moving at constant velocity has no acceleration; that is, an acceleration equal to zero.

One more point about acceleration: velocity and acceleration do NOT have to be in the same direction. A particle can be moving to the left while accelerating to the right, or moving up while accelerating down. If velocity and acceleration are in opposite directions, the object is slowing down. For instance, a ball thrown upwards is accelerating downwards due to the force of gravity even though it is moving upwards. This is why the ball slows down and eventually starts to fall. The ball is even accelerating the moment it reaches its maximum height, where its velocity is zero, because it is changing direction to start moving downwards.

## Uniformly Accelerated Motion and Linear Motion

The motion – more specifically, the velocity – of a particle experiencing uniform acceleration changes at a constant rate. Recall that acceleration is a vector. Both the direction and magnitude of acceleration must remain constant for the acceleration to be considered constant. This section will examine the rules for the simple case of uniformly accelerated motion along a straight line. Projectile motion, a more complex example, will be discussed later in the lecture.

The motion of a particle in uniformly accelerated motion on a linear path can be described completely by four basic variables: displacement ($x$), velocity ($v$), acceleration ($a$), and time ($t$). The first three of these are vectors, and the last one is a scalar. The values for these variables can be found through three basic equations. These equations can be referred to as the linear motion equations. However, remember that they only apply to objects that are experiencing constant acceleration. The equations are:

TABLE 1.1 > Linear Motion Equations

| Use this... | When this variable is unknown... |
|---|---|
| $x - x_o = v_o t + \frac{1}{2}at^2$ | $v$ |
| $v - v_o = at$ | $x\text{-}x_o$ |
| $v^2 = v_o^2 + 2a(x - x_o)$ | $t$ |

The subscript 'o' indicates a starting value. Note that $x - x_o = \Delta x$ and $v - v_o = \Delta v$, where '$\Delta$' means 'change in.' The equations can be manipulated by substitution of variables. These equations can only be applied to objects that are undergoing constant acceleration and linear motion. When selecting an equation to apply to a particular problem, pick the one in which only one variable is unknown.

The velocities in the equations above are instantaneous velocities. Average velocity in a uniformly accelerated motion problem is given by:

$$v_{avg} = \tfrac{1}{2}(v + v_o)$$

## Questions 1-8 are NOT related to a passage.

### Question 1

A weather balloon travels upward for 6 km while the wind blows it 10 km north and 8 km east. Approximately what is its final displacement from its initial position?

- ○ **A.** 7 km
- ○ **B.** 10 km
- ○ **C.** 14 km
- ○ **D.** 20 km

### Question 2

The Earth moves around the sun at approximately 30 m/s. Is the Earth accelerating?

- ○ **A.** No, because acceleration is a vector
- ○ **B.** No, because the speed is constant
- ○ **C.** Yes, because the speed is not constant
- ○ **D.** Yes, because the velocity is not constant

### Question 3

An airliner flies from Chicago to New York. Due to the shape of the earth, the airliner must follow a curved trajectory. How does the curved trajectory of the airliner affect its final displacement for this trip?

- ○ **A.** The displacement is less than it would be if the airliner flew in a straight line to New York.
- ○ **B.** The displacement is greater than it would be if the airliner flew in a straight line to New York.
- ○ **C.** The displacement is the same as it would be if the airliner flew in a straight line to New York.
- ○ **D.** The final displacement of the airliner is zero.

### Question 4

An automobile that was moving forward on a highway pulled over onto the exit ramp and slowed to a stop. While the automobile was slowing down, which of the following could be true?

- ○ **A.** The velocity was positive and the acceleration was positive.
- ○ **B.** The velocity was negative and the acceleration was negative.
- ○ **C.** The velocity was positive and the acceleration was negative.
- ○ **D.** The velocity and acceleration had the same sign, either positive or negative.

### Question 5

All of the following describe the magnitude and direction of a vector EXCEPT:

- ○ **A.** 10 m/s West.
- ○ **B.** 10 m/s in a circle.
- ○ **C.** 20 m to the left.
- ○ **D.** 20 m straight up.

### Question 6

A car accelerates at a constant rate from 0 to 25 m/s over a distance of 25 m. Approximately how long does it take the car to reach the velocity of 25 m/s?

- ○ **A.** 1 s
- ○ **B.** 2 s
- ○ **C.** 4 s
- ○ **D.** 8 s

### Question 7

A particle moving forward in a straight line slows down at a constant rate from 50 m/s to 25 m/s in 2 seconds. What is the acceleration of the particle?

- ○ **A.** $-12.5$ m/s$^2$
- ○ **B.** $-25$ m/s$^2$
- ○ **C.** $+12.5$ m/s$^2$
- ○ **D.** $+25$ m/s$^2$

### Question 8

A driver moving at a constant speed of 20 m/s sees an accident up ahead and hits the brakes. If the car decelerates at a constant rate of $-5$ m/s$^2$, how far does the car go before it comes to a stop?

- ○ **A.** 10 m
- ○ **B.** 20 m
- ○ **C.** 40 m
- ○ **D.** 100 m

# 1.4 Graphs of Linear Motion

In order to examine changes in the displacement (*d*), velocity (*v*), and acceleration (*a*) of an object in linear motion, we can graph *d*, *v*, or *a* as a function of time (*t*). Such graphs give information only about the object's position and motion along one line in space. For instance, a linear motion graph describing a particle's north and south position or movement would not indicate anything about the particle's position or movement with respect to east and west. This section will describe the significance of the slope of the line and the area under the curve in each type of graph of linear motion.

> Velocity is the rate of change of displacement. Acceleration is the rate of change of velocity.

In a displacement vs. time graph, an object's displacement is plotted as a function of time. The slope at any point is the instantaneous velocity at that particular time. An upward slope indicates positive velocity, while a downward slope indicates negative velocity (i.e. velocity in the reverse direction). A straight line has a constant slope, indicating constant velocity. A straight horizontal line has a slope of zero, indicating that the particle is not moving. A curved line has a changing slope, indicating a changing velocity and therefore acceleration. (Recall that acceleration is the rate of change in velocity). The area beneath the curve has no meaning in a displacement vs. time graph.

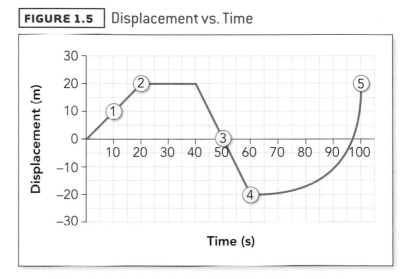

**FIGURE 1.5** | Displacement vs. Time

Suppose that the graph in Figure 1.5 describes the position of a particle with respect to north and south only. If we arbitrarily designate north as positive, we can make the following observations about the particle's motion:

1.  Between zero and 20 seconds, the slope of the line is one, so the particle has a constant velocity of 1 m/s to the north. (The particle's east, west, up, or down velocity cannot be determined from the information given.)

2.  Between 20 and 40 seconds, the particle remains exactly 20 meters to the north of its original position. It is stationary with respect to movement along a north-south axis. The particle may or may not be moving east or west, but we do not have any information that would allow us to determine its movement in those directions.

3.  At 50 seconds, the particle is back where it started with respect to its north-south coordinates. The slope of the line is -2, so it is moving to the south at a velocity of 2 m/s. It has traveled a total distance of 40 meters: 20 meters north and 20 meters south. The particle's total displacement is zero, assuming that it is not moving east or west.

4.  At 60 seconds, the particle changes direction and begins to accelerate north.

5.  The average north-south velocity of the particle after 100 seconds is 20 m/100 s or 0.2 m/s to the north.

> Graphs of linear motion can appear in an MCAT® passage as part of a study about the movement of drugs or other solutes through the body. They can also describe the motion of a body before a crash that results in injury. These graphs could appear in many different contexts.

To practice interpreting displacement vs. time graphs, reexamine Figure 1.5 at each step and try deriving these values.

> One way to visualize the movement represented by a d/t graph is to imagine this machine:

**FIGURE 1.6** | d/t Graph Machine

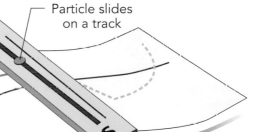

Particle slides on a track

Paper feeds through

**FIGURE 1.7** | Velocity vs. Time

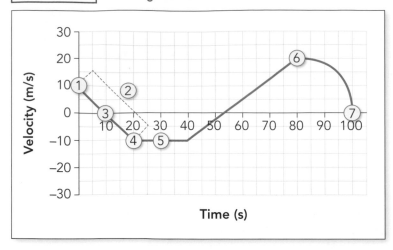

A velocity vs. time graph plots an object's velocity as a function of time. On this type of linear motion graph, the slope at any point is the instantaneous acceleration at that time. An upward slope indicates positive acceleration, while a downward slope indicates negative acceleration. Negative acceleration is not necessarily slowing down. It is simply acceleration in what has been designated the reverse direction. Negative acceleration means slowing down if the velocity is in the positive direction, but speeding up if the velocity is in the negative direction. A straight line indicates constant slope, therefore constant acceleration. A curved line has a changing slope, indicating a changing acceleration. The area beneath the curve can represent distance or displacement. If we label all of the area between the curve and zero velocity as positive, the total area represents distance. If we label the area below zero velocity as negative, the total area represents displacement.

If Figure 1.7 describes the position of a particle with respect to north and south only, and we designate north as positive, we can make the following observations about its motion:

1. The particle begins with a velocity of 10 m/s to the north. Remember, the particle could also be moving up, down, east, or west, but such movement cannot be determined from this particular graph.

2. For the first 20 seconds, the slope of the line is –1, so the particle's acceleration is –1 m/s². The negative sign shows that the particle is accelerating to the south. Note that for the first 10 seconds the particle is moving north but slowing down, and for the next 10 seconds it is moving south and speeding up.

3. At exactly 10 seconds, the particle has traveled 50 meters to the north (not zero meters), as determined by calculating the area under the line.

4. At 20 seconds, the particle has a displacement of zero meters. It is at its starting point with respect to north and south. However, it has travelled 100 meters.

5. Between 20 and 40 seconds, the particle has no acceleration and is moving at a constant velocity to the south.

6. At 80 seconds, the particle begins to decelerate; it is moving north but slowing down. The curved line shows that the deceleration, or negative acceleration, is not constant.

7. At 100 seconds, the particle has a positive, nonzero displacement.

On a displacement versus time graph, the slope is velocity, and the area is meaningless. On a velocity versus time graph, the slope is acceleration, and the area is displacement. Study these graphs and the interpretations in the text until you are completely comfortable with them. The MCAT® is very fond of questions that involve interpretation of graphs.

TABLE 1.1 > **Graphs of Linear Motion**

| Type of graph | Positive slope means: | Negative slope means: | Flat slope means: | Area under the curve indicates: |
|---|---|---|---|---|
| Displacement vs. time | Object is moving toward the positive direction | Object is moving toward the negative direction | Object is at rest | (Not useful!) |
| Velocity vs. time | Object is accelerating in the positive direction | Object is accelerating in the negative direction | Object maintains a constant velocity | The distance the object has traveled in a time interval |
| Acceleration vs. time | (Not tested!) | (Not tested!) | Constant/uniform acceleration | The change in velocity of an object in a time interval |

The displacement is calculated by subtracting the area under the $x$-axis and above the curve from the area above the $x$-axis and below the curve. The total distance traveled is calculated by adding these areas. The area beneath the $x$-axis represents negative displacement. Since distance is a scalar quantity and has no direction, the area above and beneath the curve represents positive distance.

To practice interpreting velocity vs. time graphs, reexamine Figure 1.7 at each step and try deriving the values given above.

The linear motion equations can be used on any of the straight-line sections of a velocity vs. time graph because acceleration for those sections is constant.

---

Want a fast, easy way to solve linear motion problems without using the equations? Use a v/t graph as follows. Draw a line and label the left end with the initial velocity and the right end with the final velocity. If the acceleration is constant, this line represents the line on a v/t graph. The exact midpoint of the line is always the average velocity. Since the displacement is the average velocity multiplied by the time, you know the displacement. If you don't know the time, it is the change in velocity divided by the acceleration; i.e., the difference between the two ends of your line divided by the rate of change in velocity. Remember, acceleration is how fast velocity is changing.

It's not as complicated as it sounds. Use the following examples to practice.

What is the distance traveled by a particle that starts at 30 m/s and accelerates to 50 m/s in 4 seconds? What is the acceleration?

1) Draw and label your line.

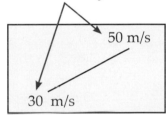

2) Find the average velocity exactly at the middle.

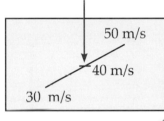

3) Average velocity (40 m/s) multiplied by time (4 s) = 160 m.

4) The acceleration is 50 m/s minus 30 m/s divided by 4 s = 5 m/s².

---

An object is dropped from a plane and falls for 5 seconds. How far does it fall?

1) The vertical velocity for a projectile changes by 10 m/s each second, so final velocity is 50 m/s.

2) Draw and label your line.

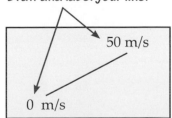

3) Find the average velocity exactly at the middle.

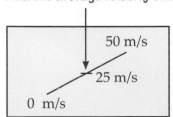

4) Average velocity (25 m/s) multiplied by time (5 s) = 125 m.

# 1.5 | Projectile Motion

The movement of an object through the air along a curved path due to gravity, called *projectile motion*, is a prominent example of uniformly accelerated motion. After an external force puts a projectile into motion — that is, gives it a $v_o$ — the only acceleration the projectile experiences is acceleration due to the force of gravity. Gravitational acceleration, $g$, is a constant approximately equal to 10 m/s².

Projectile motion is not linear motion, but its components are linear. First resolve projectile motion into its vertical and horizontal components. Then apply the linear motion equations.

Acceleration in the vertical direction is constant and equal to gravitational acceleration, 10 m/s². There is no acceleration in the horizontal direction. In the absence of air resistance, horizontal velocity remains constant throughout the object's flight, since acceleration is required for any change in motion.

In projectile motion, the component with acceleration — the vertical component — determines the time for both components. Without the force of gravity pulling the projectile towards the earth, the projectile would travel indefinitely in the horizontal direction.

According to SOH CAH TOA, the initial vertical velocity is always $v\sin\theta$ and the horizontal velocity remains constant at $v\cos\theta$.

> It can be helpful to remember that at the apex of its trajectory, a projectile's vertical velocity, $v_y$, is 0. Acceleration is constant at 10 m/s² downward, even at the apex. As the projectile travels, its vertical velocity, which may have started in a positive direction, is "pulled" downward until it is zero. It is then pulled even further into negative values. A negative vertical velocity means the object is traveling downwards.

**FIGURE 1.8** | Projectile Motion

$$x_{ox} = 0 \qquad x_{oy} = 0$$
$$v_{ox} = v\cos\theta \qquad v_{oy} = v\sin\theta$$
$$a_x = 0 \qquad a_y = -10 \text{ m/s}^2$$

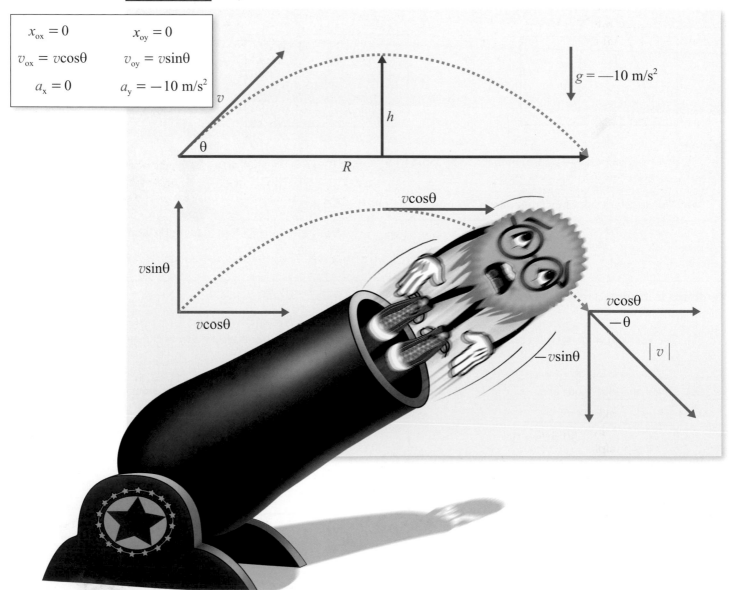

The peak height of the projectile can be found by rearranging the equation:

$$v = \sqrt{2gh}$$

where $g$ is positive 10 m/s². This general equation is derived from the linear motion equations. When using it to find the maximum height of a projectile launched from the ground, $v$ represents the initial vertical velocity, or $v_o\sin\theta$. This equation can also be used to find the final velocity $v$ of a projectile that is dropped straight down from a height $h$. When the object begins to fall, the vertical velocity is zero, and is changing at a rate of $g$ in the downward direction. This means that $v_o$ is zero, and choosing the downward direction as positive gives $g$ a positive value. Solving for $v$ or $h$ results in a positive value as well.

The path of a projectile that is not experiencing air resistance is not influenced by the mass of the projectile. In a vacuum, a golf ball will follow the same path as a ping pong ball if their initial velocities are the same.

Finally, in the absence of air resistance a projectile exhibits symmetry: its path upward is the mirror image of its path downward. For a projectile over a flat plane, time is the same for both halves of the flight, and initial speed is equal to final speed.

In the absence of air resistance, the projectile follows a parabolic path. Its vertical velocity decreases as it moves toward its peak and increases as it moves away from its peak.

---

Studying projectile motion at a conceptual level will simplify projectile motion problems you encounter on Test Day. A projectile moves both up and down in the same flight, but its acceleration is constant. Even when the projectile is motionless, at the instant it reaches its peak, acceleration is still equal to $g$. How can a motionless object have acceleration? The answer lies in the definition of acceleration.

Use the symmetry of projectile motion to help you solve problems. If we use only the second half of the trajectory, for example, vertical $v_o$ is always equal to zero, making calculations easier.

Remember that vertical velocity dictates time of flight. If two projectiles leave the Earth with the same vertical velocity, they will land at the same time, regardless of their horizontal velocities. A bullet shot horizontally from a gun and a rock dropped from the same height will both land at the same time.

Also remember that mass does not affect projectile motion, assuming that there is no air resistance.

---

Projectile motion is unlikely to be tested directly on the MCAT®, but could appear in a passage. The principles that govern projectile motion also underlie the study of fluids and electricity, which ARE both tested by the MCAT®.

## 1.6 | Mass and Weight

Whether they are moving or at rest, all objects have a tendency to remain in their present state of motion. This tendency is called inertia. Mass is the quantitative measure of an object's inertia. An object's mass tells us how much that object will resist a change in its motion. On the MCAT®, mass is usually measured in kilograms (kg).

Weight is the gravitational force that an object experiences when it is close to a much larger body, such as the Earth. Weight is measured in newtons (N). An object's weight at the surface of the Earth is given by the product of its mass and the gravitational constant *g*. In other words, the weight of any object at the surface of the Earth is equal to '*mg*.' Weight and mass are proportional to each other, but they are not the same physical quantity.

On Earth, I have weight.

Here in space, I am virtually weightless, but my mass is the same as it is on Earth. No matter where I go, my mass does not change.

## Center of Mass

The forces discussed in this lecture act at a system's *center of mass*, causing that system to accelerate. The center of mass of a system is the single point at which all of the system's mass can be considered to be concentrated. More precisely, the center of mass is the point through which a single force can be applied in any direction to cause all points in the system to accelerate equally.

If a system is uniformly dense, its center of mass coincides with its geometric center. If the system is not uniformly dense, its center of mass is shifted away from the geometric center toward the denser side. For instance, a cube with one half made of lead and the other half made of Styrofoam would have a geometric center equidistant from its edges. However, its center of mass would be shifted toward the lead side.

The center of mass of an object does not have to be located within that object. A doughnut with uniform density, for instance, has its center of mass at the center of the doughnut hole, a point where there is no mass.

The center of mass of an object is the point where, if the object was hanging by a string, it would be perfectly balanced in any orientation. But center of mass is not limited to systems with only one object. A system with any number of objects also has a center of mass. If the planets shown in Figure 1.9 were of the same mass and density, the center of mass would be in the middle of the three planets. From a distant spaceship, however, the planets would appear to be a single small dot. The ship would be affected by the three planets' gravitational force as if their entire mass was concentrated at the center of mass of the system.

Questions about center of mass on the MCAT® will be intuitive or will involve symmetrical objects. Just look for the perfect balancing point.

---

If force is applied to an object beyond its center of mass, the object will rotate because the force will generate torque (discussed in the next lecture). The center of mass of a human is typically near the navel. Climbing harnesses attach at the hips so that, if the climber falls, the tensional force in the rope can act close to the climber's center of mass. Attaching at that point minimizes the possibility of rotation and injury that could result from a fall.

---

**FIGURE 1.9** | Center of Mass of a Group of Objects

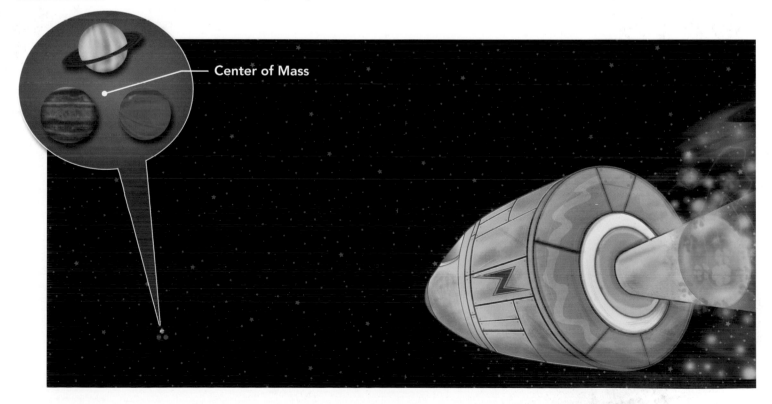

Center of Mass

**Questions 9–16 are NOT related to a passage.**

## Question 9

Which of the following graphs best represents a particle with constant velocity?

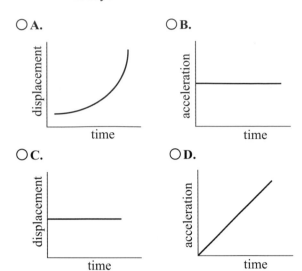

○ **A.**

○ **B.**

○ **C.**

○ **D.**

## Question 10

The graph below represents a particle moving along a straight line. What is the total distance traveled by the particle from $t = 0$ to $t = 10$ seconds?

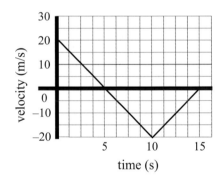

○ **A.**  0 m
○ **B.**  50 m
○ **C.**  100 m
○ **D.**  200 m

## Question 11

Which of the following is the most probable description of the motion of the object depicted by the graph below?

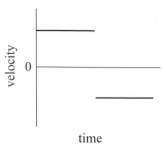

○ **A.**  A person on a bike accelerating in a straight line, and then decelerating
○ **B.**  A baseball thrown by a pitcher and hit by a batter
○ **C.**  A planet in orbit
○ **D.**  One swing on a pendulum

## Question 12

The graph below shows the displacement of a particle over time.

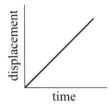

The particle exhibits increasing:

    I.  displacement.
    II.  velocity.
    III.  acceleration.

○ **A.**  I only
○ **B.**  II only
○ **C.**  I and II only
○ **D.**  I and III only

## Question 13

The graph below represents a particle moving in a straight line. When $t = 0$, the displacement of the particle is 0.

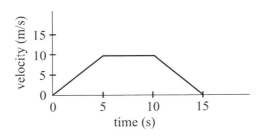

All of the following statements are true about the particle EXCEPT:

○ **A.** the particle has a total displacement of 100 m.
○ **B.** the particle moves with constant acceleration from 0 to 5 seconds.
○ **C.** the particle moves with constant velocity between 5 and 10 seconds.
○ **D.** the particle is moving backwards between 10 and 15 seconds.

## Question 14

A hiker throws a rock horizontally off a cliff that is 40 meters above the water below. If the speed of the rock is 30 m/s, how long does it take for the rock to hit the water? (Ignore air resistance, g = 10 m/s²).

○ **A.** 3 sec
○ **B.** 4 sec
○ **C.** 5 sec
○ **D.** 6 sec

## Question 15

A 10 kg mass is in free fall with no air resistance. In order to slow the mass with an acceleration equal to the magnitude of g, an upward force must be applied with magnitude:

○ **A.** 0 N.
○ **B.** 10 N.
○ **C.** 100 N.
○ **D.** 200 N.

## Question 16

A 50 kg skydiver and a 100 kg skydiver open their parachutes and reach a constant velocity. The net force on the larger skydiver is:

○ **A.** equal to the net force on the smaller skydiver.
○ **B.** twice as great as the net force on the smaller skydiver.
○ **C.** four times as great as the net force on the smaller skydiver.
○ **D.** half as great as the net force on the smaller skydiver.

## The Nature of Force

Force is what causes and changes motion. Distance, displacement, speed, velocity, and acceleration describe motion. Uniformly accelerated motion, linear motion, and projectile motion are types of motion. It is net force that creates acceleration and causes changes in motion. When presented with net force, think of acceleration, and when presented with acceleration, think of net force. Net force moves an object from rest to motion, from motion to rest, and from one state of motion to another.

There are only four types of forces in nature:

1. the strong nuclear force,

2. the weak nuclear force,

3. gravitational force, and

4. electromagnetic force.

The first two forces exist within the nucleus of an atom. Any other force must be either gravitational or electromagnetic. Categorizing a given force would be simple if not for the fact that some electromagnetic forces are difficult to identify. For instance, if a person pushes a book with his finger, the force that moves the book is electromagnetic. Electrostatic repulsion between the atoms in the person's finger and the atoms in the book creates a force that we usually think of as being created by contact. Since it is difficult to think of such contact forces as electromagnetic, we will label them as 'contact forces' instead of electromagnetic forces.

In sum, for any MCAT® problem that does not take place at the level of the atomic nucleus, there are only three possible forces:

1. gravitational,

2. electromagnetic, and

3. contact.

Only gravitational and electromagnetic forces act at a distance. These forces are easy to identify. Gravity is usually just *mg*. Electromagnetic forces require the presence of a charged object or a magnet. In order for contact forces to be acting on a system, something must be making physical contact with the system.

Contact forces must act in at least one of two directions: perpendicular to a surface and/or parallel to a surface. The perpendicular force is also called the normal force. The parallel force requires friction.

---

> Net force is the sum of all forces acting on an object. Two forces that are equal in magnitude but opposite in direction will cancel each other out, leaving zero net force.

---

> You've probably never felt very strong electromagnetic forces, but you've definitely felt the force of gravity. Gravity is actually the weakest of the forces described here. It feels strong on Earth because our mass is so small relative to the planet. All objects with mass exert gravitational force. Think about holding a balloon near your hair. The mass of the balloon does not exert sufficient gravitational force to move individual hairs. If that same balloon carries static charge, the electromagnetic force can make your hairs stand on end.

**FIGURE 1.10** Contact Forces are Electromagnetic

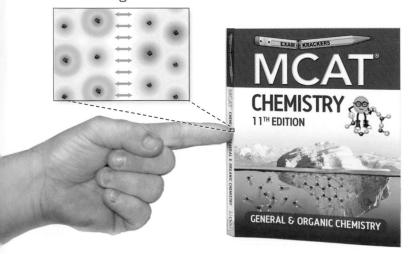

> Remember that the MCAT® will test concepts in physics in the context of biological systems. All of the forces discussed in this lecture occur in the body, but on a very small scale. The action of skeletal muscle is one of the most evident topics for questions that involve forces. These forces are generated by power strokes of myosin heads. This is the fundamental mechanism for the generation of muscular force in the body.

Muscle
BIOLOGY 2

## Free Body Diagrams

Free body diagrams can be used to solve problems involving forces acting on a body or system of bodies. Vectors are used in a free body diagram to isolate the system of interest, show the direction and relative impact of each force, and allow easy addition of forces. Because free body diagrams include vectors that show the direction and relative magnitude of each force, they provide a visual indication of whether or not a net force is acting on the system.

To construct a free body diagram, first remove the body from its environment and draw it as a simple shape. Place a point at its center of mass. Then draw a vector to represent each force acting on the body's center of mass. If the Earth's gravitational force is acting on the body, draw a vector pointing downward from the center of mass. If normal force (discussed in the next section) is present, draw a vector pointing upward from the center of mass. Draw as many vectors as needed to represent all of the forces acting on the object, using longer lines for forces with greater magnitudes. Take note of which force vectors cancel and which do not. Ask yourself if there is a net force on the body. If there is a net force, there will be acceleration.

**FIGURE 1.11** | Free Body Diagrams

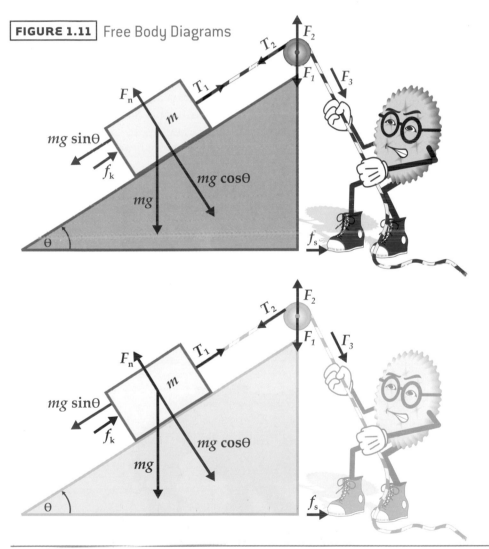

If we are interested in the movement of the box in the diagram above, we should consider only the forces acting on the box. The top diagram contains all kinds of force vectors and is nearly useless. The dark red vectors in the bottom diagram represent only forces acting on the system (the box) and are the only forces that should be considered. First draw the weight forces, then any electromagnetic forces, and then any contact forces, which can only be created by something that has direct physical contact with your system.

1. **BREATHE &**
2. **D iagram**
3. **I solate**
4. **V ariable**
5. **E quation**

Let's go back to my 5 step system. The third step, isolating the system of interest, is particularly relevant to drawing free body diagrams. Define your system carefully, making sure that you know what is your system and what is not. Then consider only the forces that are acting directly on your system. Ask yourself, "Is gravity acting on my system?" If so, label it. "Is my system charged?" Label the electromagnetic forces. Finally, label the normal and frictional contact forces created by objects touching your system. After these steps, you know that you have included all of the relevant forces.

One of the biggest potential pitfalls in drawing free body diagrams is sketching vectors in the wrong direction. Take a moment to check your vectors before tackling a problem. If you don't have a plan for your vectors, they'll have a plan for you!

### MCAT® THINK

A red blood cell is thrown against the wall of a vertical tube as a centrifuge spins, and it maintains its position throughout the cycle. In what direction do the normal force and the frictional force act?

Answer: See page 31

Gravitational force between any two objects is governed by Newton's Law of Universal Gravitation: $F = G\dfrac{m_1 m_2}{r^2}$ where $G$ is a constant, $m_1$ and $m_2$ are the masses of the objects, and $r$ is the distance between the objects. Large changes in the magnitude of gravitational force result from small changes in $r$ because of the squared term in the denominator. This equation is unlikely to show up on the MCAT®, but it is important to understand this relationship between force and distance.

# 1.8 | Newton's Laws in Action

Newton's laws of motion describe how and to what extent forces cause objects to accelerate. Newton's First Law of motion, the law of inertia, states that an object in a state of rest or in a state of motion will tend to remain in that state unless it is acted upon by a net force. Any change in motion requires acceleration, and where there is acceleration, there must be net force.

Newton's Second Law states that when a net force acts on an object, the change in that object's state of motion will be inversely proportional to the mass ($m$) of the object and directly proportional to the net force ($F$) acting on the object. Newton's Second Law can be written as the equation below:

$$F = ma$$

The equation shows that for a given force, the smaller the mass experiencing the force, the greater the acceleration. In other words, a small mass experiences a greater effect of a force than would a larger mass. The effect of the force, acceleration, is a change in the object's velocity – in magnitude, direction, or both. For a given force, a greater mass will experience a smaller resulting acceleration or effect of that force. The direct proportionality between $F$ and $a$ demonstrates that for a given mass, the greater the force, the greater the acceleration.

Newton's Third Law states that for every action, there exists an equal and opposite reaction. When object A applies a force to object B, object A experiences a force that is equal in magnitude but opposite in direction. Such acting and reacting forces never exist within a single system. One system applies a force on another system and experiences a reacting force of equal magnitude.

**FIGURE 1.12** Systems Approach to Newton's Third Law

How can the horse accelerate the cart? No matter how hard the horse pulls, the cart pulls back just as hard. How can it possibly move?

Force on the cart due to the horse

Force on the horse due to the cart

To find the answer, choose your system to be the cart only and then draw only the forces acting on the cart. Notice that the equal and opposite force to the horse pulling on the cart is the cart pulling on the horse. When we choose our system to be the horse, we ignore this force because it is acting on the horse. Now we see that there is a net force on the cart.

## Inclined Planes

Net gravitational force causes an object on the surface of an *inclined plane* to accelerate down the plane. The normal force opposes the component of gravity perpendicular to the surface, and the force of friction opposes the component of gravity parallel to the surface. When the parallel component of gravity is stronger than the force of friction, the object slides down the plane.

In the simplest case (no friction and nothing attached to the block), the only forces acting on a block on an inclined plane are gravity pushing straight downward and the inclined plane pushing back. The force of the inclined plane pushing back against the block is called the **normal force** ($F_n$). The normal force is always perpendicular to the surface that applies it. Figure 1.13 shows a free body diagram of a block on a frictionless inclined plane.

Since gravity and the normal force are the only forces acting on the block, their sum is the net force. The net force can be plugged into Newton's Second Law to find the acceleration of the system. As shown in Figure 1.14, vector addition of the gravitational and normal forces creates a right triangle. This triangle is similar to the triangle of the inclined plane. Similar triangles have equal corresponding angles. Using SOH CAH TOA, we find that the resultant vector has a magnitude of $mg\sin\theta$, where $\theta$ is the angle between the inclined plane and a horizontal surface. The net force due to gravity and the normal force of an inclined plane is always equal to $mg\sin\theta$ and points in a direction that is parallel to the plane.

Remember that $mg\sin\theta$ is the vector sum of the weight and the normal force. Do not label the system with both $mg\sin\theta$ and weight or the normal force, since this would be redundant.

According to the rules of SOH CAH TOA, the normal force is always equal to $mg\cos\theta$.

> Apply Key 3: Free body diagrams help to visualize situations with many forces acting at once. This is especially true in the case of inclined planes, where forces often act at angles. It is worth pausing to draw out a free body diagram any time you run into a problem involving forces.

> If "SOH CAH TOA" doesn't work for you, remember that <u>c</u>osine is used for the component <u>c</u>lose to the angle!

> As the slope gets steeper, the surface provides less normal force. Less normal force means less friction...the struggle is real!

---

**FIGURE 1.13** | Forces on an Object on an Inclined Plane

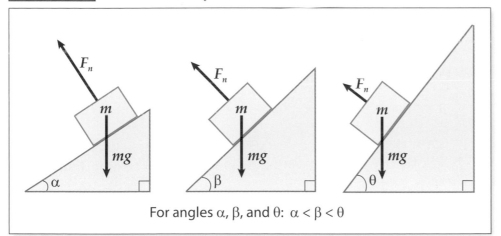

For angles α, β, and θ: α < β < θ

---

**FIGURE 1.14** | Deriving the Net Force on an Object on an Inclined Plane

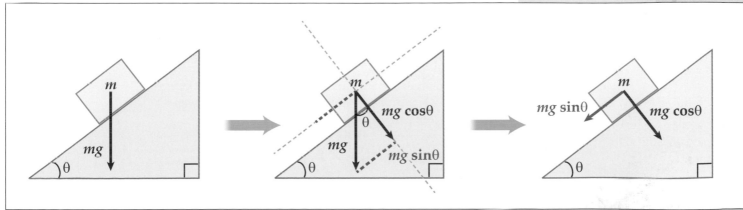

You can remember $mg \sin\theta$ because the mass **S**lides down the incline.

$mg \sin\theta$ **SLIDE**

Whenever you see an inclined plane, think $mg \sin\theta$. This is always the net force down any inclined plane due to gravity and the normal force. Likewise, $mg \cos\theta$ is always the normal force. These formulas work regardless of the angle of the plane.

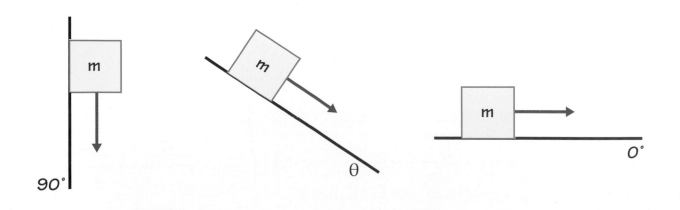

The extreme cases of inclined planes are 90° and 0°. At 90°, $mg \sin\theta = mg$; at 0°, $mg \sin\theta = 0$. An object on a frictionless incline with any angle between 0° and 90° will accelerate at some fraction of $g$.

## Friction and Air Resistance

**Friction** is a force that opposes slipping, also known as relative motion. It is caused by attractive molecular forces between surfaces that are in contact. As one surface moves past the other, the molecules of each surface attract those of the other. Because the surfaces' molecules are attracted to each other, the surfaces do not move past each other as easily as they would in the absence of friction. A frictional force acts parallel to the contact surface, in contrast to a normal force, which acts perpendicularly to the contact surface. Draw frictional force vectors to point in the direction that will prevent surfaces from slipping past each other. For instance, the frictional force on the front tires of an accelerating front wheel–drive car points in the direction of motion of the car because the force prevents the tires from sliding backwards on the road.

Friction occurs in many contexts, but it can be classified into one of two classes. The first class is **static friction**, which occurs when a contact force is applied to an object and the surfaces do not slide past one another. In other words, it occurs only when an object is not in motion relative to its surface. Static friction increases proportionally with the magnitude of the contact force until the object begins moving according to the equation:

$$f_s \leq \mu_s F_N$$

where $\mu_s$ is a constant with a value between 0 and 1. The greater the weight of the object, and by extension its normal force, the greater the frictional force. Note that the frictional force vector increases in magnitude to balance the magnitude of the applied force, so the net force on the object remains zero.

| FIGURE 1.15 | Static and Kinetic Friction

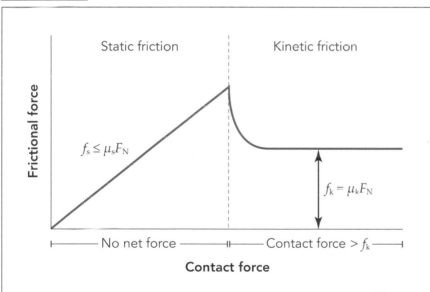

Once the applied force exceeds the threshold of static friction, the forces are no longer balanced and the surfaces begin to move relative to one another. The object is now subject to the second class of friction called **kinetic friction**. Kinetic friction remains constant in magnitude as the two surfaces slide past one another. It behaves according to the equation:

$$f_k = \mu_k F_N$$

where, once again, $\mu_k$ is a constant with a value between 0 and 1.

The MCAT® is unlikely to ask for mathematical differences between kinetic and static friction. Instead, consider the conceptual difference between kinetic and static friction. When a car is moving down a highway, friction from the road opposes slipping of the tires to propel the car forward. Do the wheels experience static or kinetic friction? Counterintuitively, they experience static friction as they roll. Why? Each point on the tire is not sliding along but rather resting on the road. Before a point can begin sliding, it is lifted off the road and replaced by the next point on the tire.

When a driver slams on her brakes, she stops the wheels. Which type of friction occurs now? A single point along the tire is allowed to slide against the road, so this is an example of kinetic friction. Modern cars come equipped with anti-lock braking systems in order to prevent wheels from locking when a driver hits the brakes suddenly, allowing the car to take advantage of the more powerful force of static friction.

Air resistance is unlikely to appear on the MCAT® but if it does, you'll be ready. Air resistance brings together many physics topics, including fluids, collisions, projectiles, force, and acceleration. Remember, the force of air resistance depends on the number of collisions between an object and air molecules per unit time.

A common type of friction is *drag*, also called *air resistance*. Air resistance is usually considered to be negligible in problems involving projectile motion. In reality, it can have a significant effect on motion. Air resistance results from an object's collisions with air molecules. As an object (such as a projectile) moves through a fluid (such as air), or as a fluid moves past an object, fluid molecules collide with and drag past the object. These interactions impede relative motion between the fluid and the object. If the object is a projectile, drag slows the projectile; if the object is a pipe, drag slows the fluid moving through the pipe. The greater the number of molecular collisions that occur each second, the greater the effect of drag.

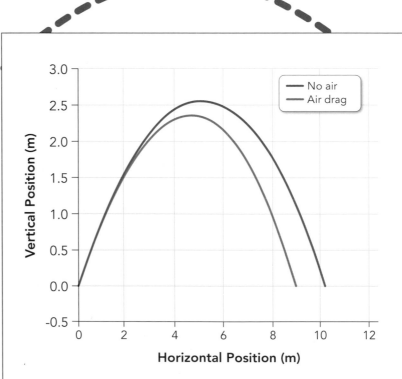

The shape, surface area, and velocity of a projectile change the force of the air resistance that it experiences. Streamlined objects, which are designed to have smooth surfaces and reduced surface area, experience decreased collisions with fluid molecules and therefore decreased drag. Fluid molecules slip by smoother objects more easily than rougher objects, so smoother objects experience less drag. Reduced surface area also leads to fewer collisions and therefore less drag. As the velocity of an object increases, the number of collisions with fluid molecules each second increases, and drag increases.

The mass of an object does not affect the force of air resistance experienced by the object. However, mass does affect the acceleration that results from air resistance. Since the force of air resistance remains constant for any mass (unless the factors discussed above create significant changes), acceleration must decrease as mass increases. Remember, $F = ma$. If force is constant, acceleration and mass must be inversely proportional to one another. For this reason, a golf ball and a ping pong ball, which experience similar forces of air resistance, experience different accelerations due to air resistance. A golf ball experiences lesser acceleration due to air resistance because it is more massive than a ping pong ball.

The direction of air resistance is opposite to the direction of relative motion. When travelling upward, a projectile experiences a downward force of air resistance. Both gravity and air resistance point downward, so net downward acceleration is greater than $g$. When traveling downward, a projectile experiences an upward force of air resistance. Since gravity points downward and air resistance points upward, the net downward acceleration of the projectile is less than $g$. Projectiles are commonly said to be "slowed down" by air resistance because the direction of air resistance is opposite to the direction of motion.

More massive objects are less affected by air resistance than are less massive objects. When a golf ball and a ping pong ball are thrown from the same height, the more massive golf ball will be slowed down less than the ping pong ball.

The key concept behind the idea of friction is that friction always opposes slipping, also known as relative motion. To better understand the notion of relative motion over general motion, return to the example of static and kinetic friction. Static friction prevents any relative motion from occurring, while kinetic friction opposes relative motion of two objects sliding across one another.

## Hooke's Law

Compressing or stretching an object creates another type of force, which follows *Hooke's law*. Solids that have been deformed tend to 'remember' their shape and re-form to it. Hooke's law describes the force that most objects apply against a deforming force. The object's force is directly proportional to the amount of deformation or, more precisely, the change in position ($\Delta x$). Hooke's law is given by the following equation:

$$F = -k\Delta x$$

where $k$ is a constant unique to a given object. The negative sign indicates that the force is in the opposite direction of the displacement. Most solids follow Hooke's law to some extent. All solids violate Hooke's law at some limit of displacement, unique to each object. The point of violation is called the *yield point*. When an object is deformed beyond its yield point, it loses the ability to regain its original shape. At some greater displacement, the object will reach the *fracture point* and break.

On the MCAT®, Hooke's law is most often applied to springs. The force $F$ is the tension in the spring and $\Delta x$ is the change from the spring's position at rest. Rearranging Hooke's Law shows that the spring in Figure 1.16 has a spring constant $k = mg/\Delta x$.

## MCAT® THINK

Describe a situation in which the frictional force vector on an object is the same direction as its velocity vector. What happens to the frictional force when the object moves in the opposite direction?

Answer: See page 31

If Hooke's law comes up on the MCAT®, it will probably be in a problem concerning springs. 'k' is often referred to as the 'spring constant.' The negative sign in the formula can usually be ignored.

**FIGURE 1.16** Hooke's Law

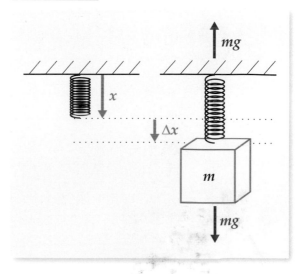

Assuming that my head follows Hooke's law, the force that my head produces against this vise is equal to the change in thickness, $\Delta x$, multiplied by some constant, $k_{salty}$, which is specific to my head. The change in the thickness of my head is negative because I'm getting thinner. If I were being stretched, the change in my thickness would be positive and the force I create would be in the other direction. According to Newton's Third Law, the vise applies an equal but opposite force against me. That's the one that hurts.

$$F = -k_{salty}\Delta x$$

## Question 17

A box starts from rest and slides 40 m down a frictionless inclined plane. The total vertical displacement of the box is 20 m. How long does it take for the block to reach the end of the plane?

○ **A.** 1 s
○ **B.** 2 s
○ **C.** 4 s
○ **D.** 8 s

## Question 18

A box rests on an incline. Which of the following describes the forces on the box as the angle of inclination is increased?

○ **A.** The force parallel to the ramp increases and the force perpendicular to the ramp decreases.
○ **B.** The force parallel to the ramp increases and the force perpendicular to the ramp also increases.
○ **C.** The force parallel to the ramp decreases and the force perpendicular to the ramp also decreases.
○ **D.** The force parallel to the ramp and the force perpendicular to the ramp remain constant.

## Question 19

In many harbors, old automobile tires are hung along the sides of wooden docks to cushion them from the impact of docking boats. The tires deform in accordance with Hooke's law. As a boat is brought to a stop by gently colliding with the tires, the rate of deceleration of the boat:

○ **A.** is constant until the boat stops.
○ **B.** decreases until the boat stops.
○ **C.** increases until the boat stops.
○ **D.** increases and then decreases before the boat stops.

## Question 20

The diagram below shows two different masses hung from identical Hooke's law springs. The Hooke's law constant $k$ for the springs is equal to:

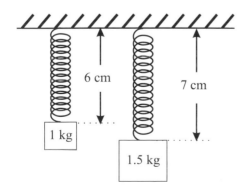

○ **A.** 2 N/cm.
○ **B.** 5 N/cm.
○ **C.** 10 N/cm.
○ **D.** 20 N/cm.

## Question 21

Newton's Third Law states that for every action there exists an equal and opposite reaction. What is the force that acts in reaction to the force of Earth's gravity on an object on its surface?

○ **A.** The normal force that the object exerts on the Earth
○ **B.** The force of gravity that the object exerts on the Earth
○ **C.** The normal force that the Earth exerts on the object
○ **D.** The force of gravity that the Earth exerts on the object

## Question 22

In size exclusion chromatography, molecules are separated on the basis of size using porous beads that only admit the smaller molecules. Which of the following is true of this process?

○ **A.** Large particles elute first because they are subject to fewer frictional forces.
○ **B.** Large particles elute first because they have greater weight.
○ **C.** Small particles elute first because they are subject to weaker normal force .
○ **D.** Small particles elute first because they are subject to a stronger downward net force.

## Question 23

How much force is required to lift a 10 kg box such that it is accelerated from rest to a velocity of 5 m/s within 1 second?

○ **A.** 150 N
○ **B.** 100 N
○ **C.** 50 N
○ **D.** 0 N

## Question 24

Which of the following is true regarding a tennis ball and a feather dropped from the same height? Assume that air resistance acts on both objects.

○ **A.** The tennis ball has more mass so it will fall faster.
○ **B.** The tennis ball has more surface area so it will fall faster.
○ **C.** The tennis ball has less surface area so it will fall faster.
○ **D.** The tennis ball has more weight so it falls faster.

$d$ = distance
$v$ = speed
$\vec{d}$ = displacement

$\vec{v}$ = velocity
$t$ = time
$\vec{a}$ = acceleration

$$v = \frac{d}{t}$$

$$\vec{v} = \frac{\vec{d}}{t}$$

$$\vec{a} = \frac{\Delta\vec{v}}{t}$$

$t$ = time
$x$ = displacement
$h$ = height
$v$ = velocity
$a$ = acceleration

$a$ must be constant

$$x - x_{o} = v_{o}t + \tfrac{1}{2}at^2$$

$$v - v_{o} = at$$

$$v^2 = v^2_{o} + 2a(x - x_{o})$$

$$v_{avg} = \tfrac{1}{2}(v + v_{o})$$

$$v = \sqrt{2gh}$$

$v_{o}$ must be zero

## Newton's Second Law

$$F = ma$$

The net force applied to the center of mass of a system always equals the mass of the system times its acceleration.

## Gravity

$$F = G\frac{m_{1}m_{2}}{r^2}$$

The force of gravity is proportional to the mass of each body and inversely proportional to the square of the distance between their centers of gravity. $G$ is a universal constant.

## Inclined Planes

$$F = mg\sin\theta$$

The sum of the normal force and the force of gravity is $mg\sin\theta$.

$$F = mg\cos\theta$$

The normal force is $mg\cos\theta$.

## Friction

$$f_{s} \leq \mu_{s}F_{n}$$

$$f_{k} = \mu_{k}F_{n}$$

Contiguous surfaces may exert equal and opposite forces against each other parallel to their contiguous surfaces. If the surfaces do not slide relative to each other, this force is static friction. If the surfaces slide relative to each other, this force is kinetic friction.

## Hooke's Law

$$F = -k\Delta x$$

When deformed, objects obeying Hooke's Law will exert a force proportional to their deformity. $k$ is a constant unique to the object.

Acceleration

Average speed

Average velocity

Center of mass

Component vectors

Electromagnetic force

Friction (static and kinetic)

Gravitational force

Inertia

Instantaneous speed

Instantaneous velocity

Mass

Newton's First Law of motion

Newton's Second Law

Newton's Third Law

Normal force ($F_n$)

Scalar

Vector

Weight

## MCAT® THINK Answers

Pg. 21:  The normal force results from contact with a surface, so it extends from the surface of the tube toward the center point of the centrifuge. Gravitational force acts downward, and to oppose the cell's motion relative to the tube, frictional force is directed upward.

Pg. 27:  Impossible! Friction opposes the motion of an object relative to its surroundings. That means that if an object is moving north, its surroundings will exert a frictional force directed south. It may seem like this is not true in the case of a person walking or a car driving, since friction and the "object" velocity are in the same direction, but the actual object is the foot or the wheel, respectively. The velocities of both the foot and the wheel oppose the direction of friction. So when the object changes direction, frictional force will also move in the opposite direction – that is, the original direction of the velocity vector.

**THE 3 KEYS**

1. Acceleration is required for any change in motion, that is change in direction or speed.

2. See net force, think acceleration. See acceleration, think net force.

3. When forces are acting, draw free body diagrams.

# Energy and Equilibrium

## 2.1 | Introduction

This lecture covers the states of equilibrium and then the concept of energy in Physics. To introduce torque, it begins with a discussion of rotational motion. Rotational motion is produced by forces acting at points other than an object's center of mass. Translational motion, in contrast, is produced by forces acting at an object's center of mass. Torque measures the ability of a force to produce rotational motion. Next, equilibrium is discussed. A system in equilibrium experiences no net force, no net torque, and therefore no translational or rotational acceleration. Finally, the lecture will present the topic of energy, emphasizing how energy is never destroyed. It is either converted from one form to another or transferred between a system and its surroundings as heat or work. Energy equations are simply "accounting" used to keep track of where energy came from and where it is going. Most of the energy equations presented in this lecture are versions of one of the following concepts:

1. Energy of system + surroundings before = energy of system + surroundings after.

2. Energy leaving a system = energy entering the surroundings, and
   Energy entering a system = energy leaving the surroundings.

3. Total energy of a system = the sum of all forms of energy in that system.

**THE 3 KEYS**

1. Equilibrium means no net force and no net torque, therefore no acceleration.

2. Energy is conserved but can change forms. Use accounting to build equations: energy before equals energy after, energy in equals energy out.

3. Assume that work in Physics means total change in energy, or force times displacement.

Objects experiencing translational motion have a fixed orientation. Objects experiencing rotational motion change orientation as they rotate about an axis.

Torque

Torque is a measure of a force's ability to cause rotational acceleration. An object accelerates when it is acted on by a net force. If the net force acts at the object's center of mass, the object accelerates translationally. If it acts at any point other than the center of mass, the object also accelerates rotationally.

Like force, torque is a vector. On the MCAT®, it can be thought of as being clockwise or counter-clockwise. The magnitude of torque is given by the following equation:

$$\tau = Fr\sin\theta$$

where $F$ is the force vector, $r$ is the position vector, and $\theta$ is the angle between the force and position vectors. The position vector is the distance from the *point of rotation* to the point of application of the force. If the object is not rotating, any fixed point can be designated as the point of rotation. Since $\sin(90°)$ is equal to 1, it is convenient to make the position vector extend from the point of rotation to the point where the force acts at 90°. This type of position vector is called a lever arm ($l$). When the lever arm is used, the equation for torque can be written as:

$$\tau = Fl$$

The greater the net torque on an object, the greater its rotational acceleration. Torque increases as the following variables increase: 1. the component of the force acting perpendicular to the position vector, and 2. the distance between the point of application of the force and the point of rotation. Door handles are placed perpendicular to the door's surface and far from the door's hinges in order to maximize rotational acceleration for a given force.

**FIGURE 2.1** Torque

The lever arm, $l$, is the position vector, $r$, that is perpendicular to the force vector.

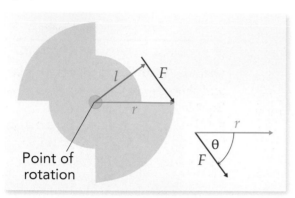

Point of rotation

Notice that force and lever arm are inversely proportional. To keep torque constant while increasing force, the lever arm must decrease, and vice versa. This inverse proportionality is important for equilibrium, as discussed in the next section.

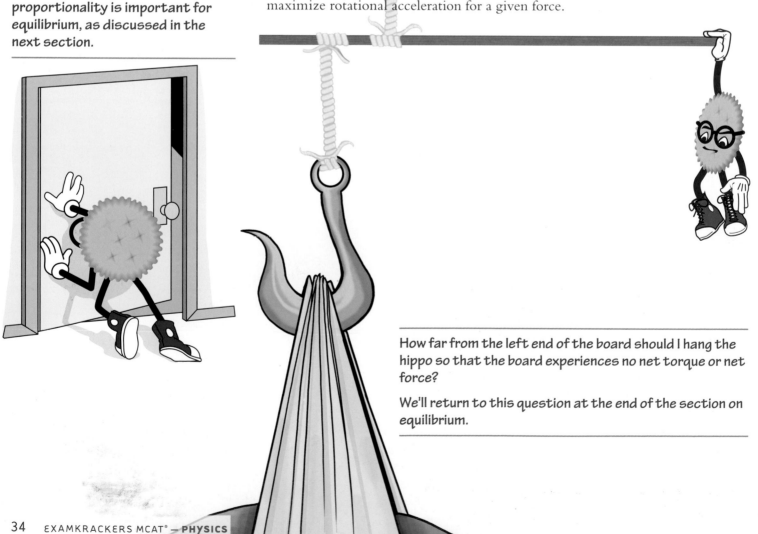

How far from the left end of the board should I hang the hippo so that the board experiences no net torque or net force?

We'll return to this question at the end of the section on equilibrium.

The concept of torque poses an interesting challenge for skeletal muscle in the human body. Consider the case of the biceps muscle, which inserts on the forearm a short distance from the elbow. If an individual needs to lift a heavy object such as a milk jug from a counter, the biceps contracts to raise the forearm. Because the insertion point is so close to the elbow ($l$ is small), the biceps must exert a substantial force to provide sufficient torque to rotate the forearm and lift the jug. Of course, if the biceps inserted near the wrist, yielding a much larger $l$, that would pose its own physiological challenges.

Muscle
BIOLOGY 2

## 2.3 | Equilibrium

In physics, equilibrium is a state in which there is no net force and no net torque. Objects in equilibrium may be moving, but they are not accelerating. A system is in equilibrium if the translational velocity of its center of mass and the angular velocities of all its parts are constant (in other words, if it is moving and rotating at a constant velocity). If all velocities are zero, the system is in static equilibrium. If any velocities are nonzero, but all velocities are constant, the system is in dynamic equilibrium.

Remember Key 1: In equilibrium there is no net force, no net torque, and therefore no acceleration. Equilibrium does not mean motionless. It means that velocity is constant because all forces are balanced.

Static and dynamic equilibrium are both defined by constant velocity. The only difference is that in static equilibrium, the constant velocity is zero. Problems involving static or dynamic equilibrium are solved in exactly the same way.

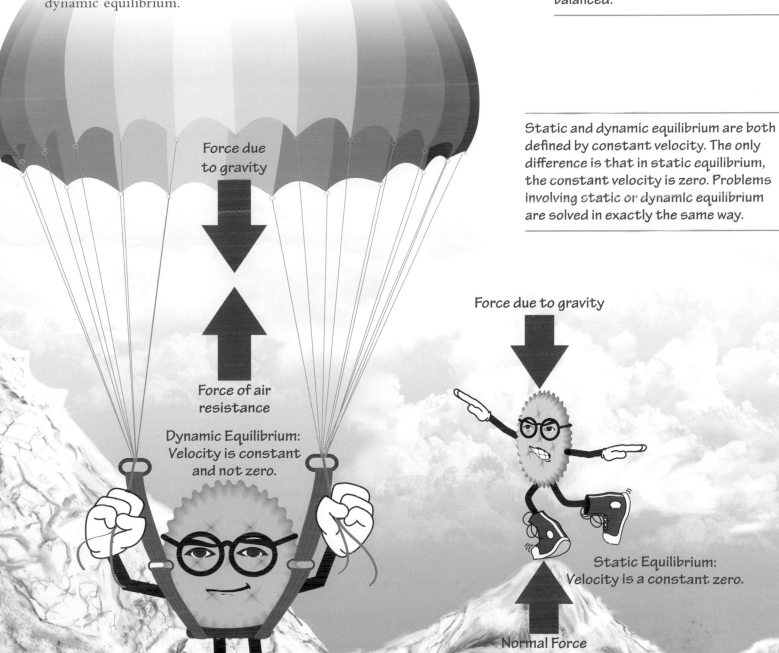

Force due to gravity

Force of air resistance

Dynamic Equilibrium: Velocity is constant and not zero.

Force due to gravity

Static Equilibrium: Velocity is a constant zero.

Normal Force

For a system in equilibrium, the sum of all the forces and torques acting on the system equals zero. In other words, the net force and net torque acting on a system in equilibrium are equal to zero. A reliable and simple method of viewing systems in equilibrium on the MCAT® is as follows: the sum of the magnitudes of the upward forces equals the sum of the magnitudes of the downward forces, the sum of the magnitudes of the rightward forces equals the sum of the magnitudes of the leftward forces, and the sum of the magnitudes of the clockwise torques equals the sum of the magnitude of the counterclockwise torques. With this method, it is possible to use positive numbers for all forces. It is no longer necessary to decide if $g$ is positive or negative 10; $g$ is always said to be positive.

This is not the method taught in physics class, but it is faster and more intuitive for simple problems, so it is an effective method for the MCAT®. The three formulae that describe a system in equilibrium are:

$$F_{upward} = F_{downward}$$
$$F_{rightward} = F_{leftward}$$
$$\tau_{clockwise} = \tau_{counterclockwise}$$

## Systems Not in Equilibrium

If a system is not in equilibrium, its center of mass is accelerating translationally or its parts are accelerating rotationally. The MCAT® does not test angular acceleration, where parts are accelerating rotationally, so a system not in equilibrium on the MCAT® must have only translational acceleration. For a system not in equilibrium, the sum of the forces equals the mass of the system multiplied by the acceleration of the system, or $\Sigma F = ma$.

On the MCAT® there is a faster and more effective way to solve non-equilibrium problems. When faced with any system not in equilibrium, follow these five steps:

Step 1: Assume that you have the knowledge to solve the problem.

Step 2: Draw your diagram.

    A. Ignore the acceleration and lay out the problem as if the system were in equilibrium.

    B. Predict the direction of acceleration and verify that one of your axes is parallel to the direction of acceleration.

Step 3: Choose your system.

Step 4: Find your formulae.

Step 5: Plug and chug (if needed).

---

While the most likely connection of force and torque to the human body involves the skeletomuscular system, unbalanced forces not in equilibrium can disrupt many other systems. The lungs, for instance, are subject to an elastic recoil force that makes them prone to collapse. An opposing force created by the pressure gradient in the pleural cavity prevents them from collapsing. If the forces on the lungs were tossed out of equilibrium – say, from a puncture wound – they would collapse, disrupting their normal function.

---

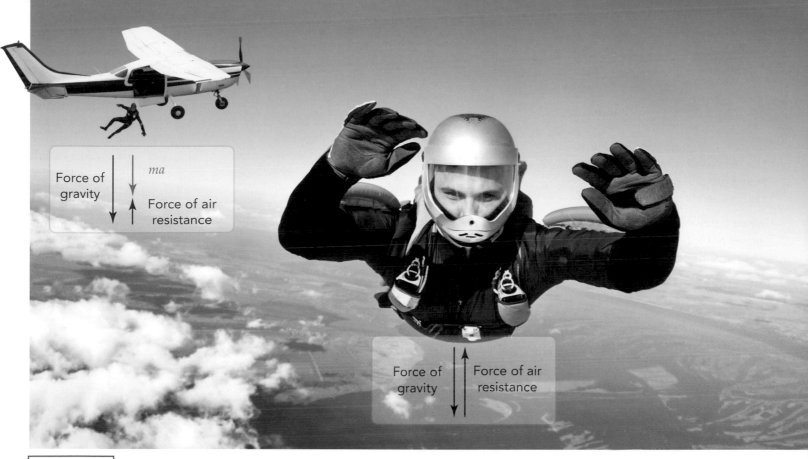

**FIGURE 2.2** | Non-Equilibrium vs. Equilibrium

As an example, we can solve for the acceleration of the skydiver in Figure 2.2. Immediately after the skydiver jumps from the plane, he is not in equilibrium. The downward force on him due to gravity is greater than the upward force due to air resistance. In order to find his acceleration, we pretend that he is in equilibrium by placing all upward forces on one side of the equation and all downward forces on the other. Since he is not in equilibrium, the two sides are not equal.

$$F_{upward} \neq F_{downward}$$

Next we decide which side has greater force. Since he is accelerating downward, the downward force must be greater. In order to balance the two sides of our equation, we add 'ma' to the side with less force.

$$F_{upward} + ma = F_{downward}$$

Now the two sides are equal and we can solve for acceleration.

After a few seconds, the skydiver reaches terminal velocity, where the gravitational force downward is equal to the force of air resistance upward. At this point, he is in equilibrium and his acceleration is zero.

Note again that our method is not the method that you learned in physics class. In physics class, you assign positive and negative values to opposite directions and label your forces accordingly. Then you set the sum of these positive and negative forces equal to *ma*. If the acceleration is positive, the object is accelerating in the positive direction. If the acceleration is negative, the object is accelerating in the negative direction. In our method, all numbers are positive. Our method helps you think about the problem intuitively. Since the MCAT® tends to test your science intuition more than the ability to recall formulae and plug and chug, our method is faster and more effective on the MCAT®. The physics class method works perfectly and is certainly the preferred method if you are an engineer building a bridge! But you have to be careful when using it on the MCAT®. The MCAT® expects you to use the physics class method and has developed questions designed to be confusing when you use it. As is usually the case on the MCAT®, a simplified method is better than lengthy calculations.

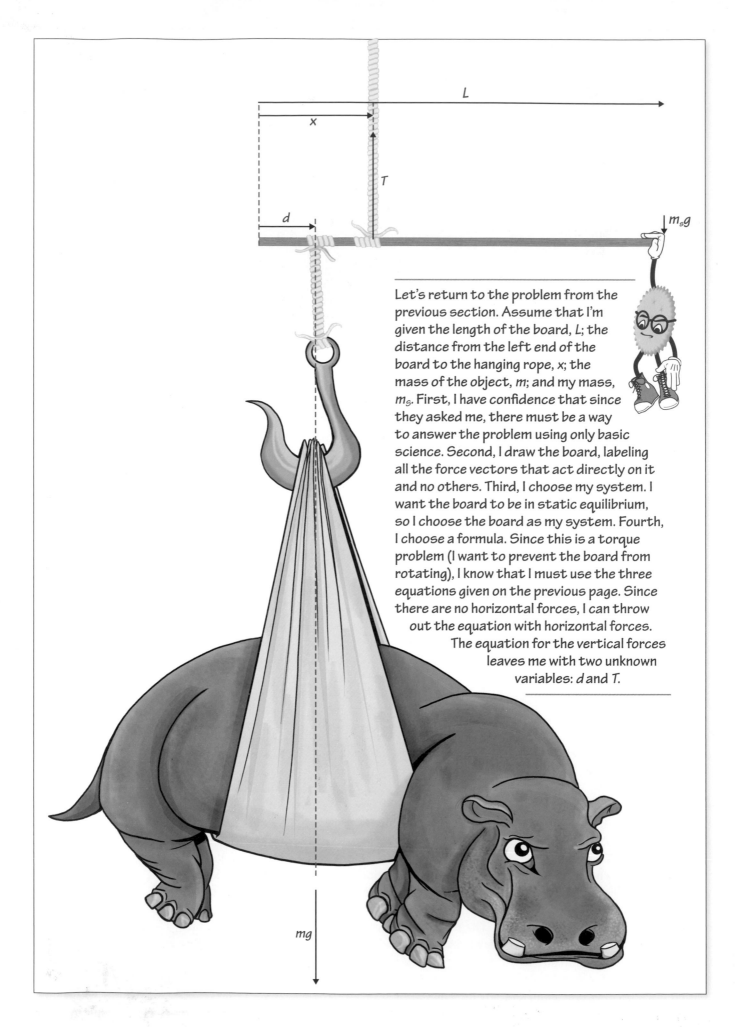

Let's return to the problem from the previous section. Assume that I'm given the length of the board, $L$; the distance from the left end of the board to the hanging rope, $x$; the mass of the object, $m$; and my mass, $m_s$. First, I have confidence that since they asked me, there must be a way to answer the problem using only basic science. Second, I draw the board, labeling all the force vectors that act directly on it and no others. Third, I choose my system. I want the board to be in static equilibrium, so I choose the board as my system. Fourth, I choose a formula. Since this is a torque problem (I want to prevent the board from rotating), I know that I must use the three equations given on the previous page. Since there are no horizontal forces, I can throw out the equation with horizontal forces. The equation for the vertical forces leaves me with two unknown variables: $d$ and $T$.

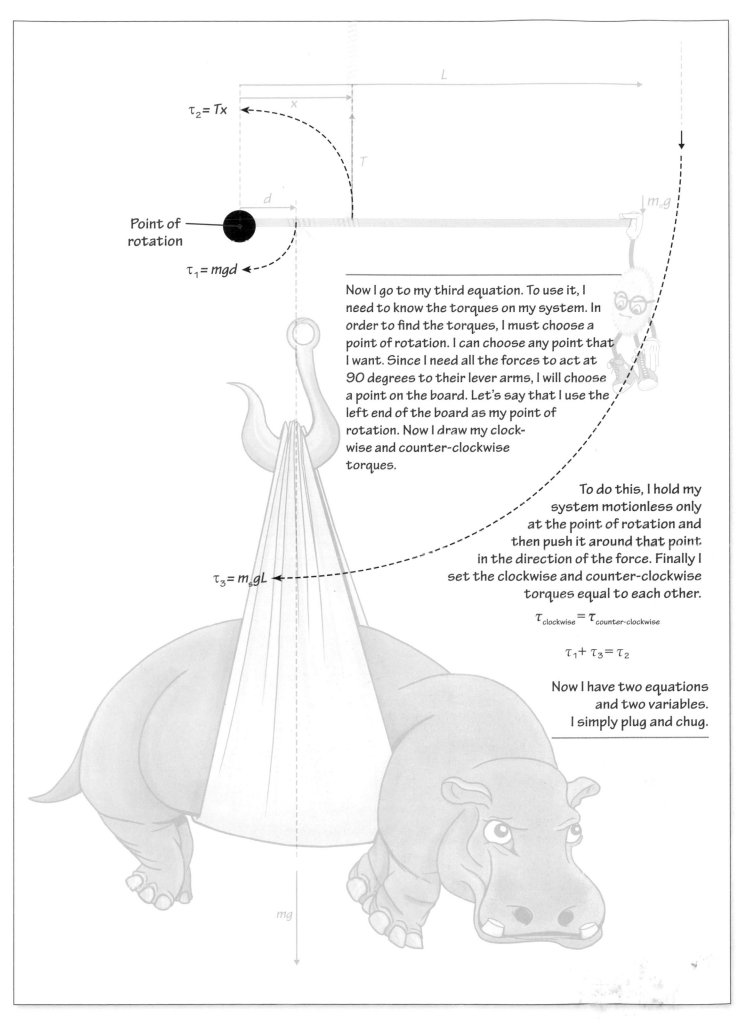

$\tau_2 = Tx$

Point of rotation

$\tau_1 = mgd$

$\tau_3 = m_sgL$

Now I go to my third equation. To use it, I need to know the torques on my system. In order to find the torques, I must choose a point of rotation. I can choose any point that I want. Since I need all the forces to act at 90 degrees to their lever arms, I will choose a point on the board. Let's say that I use the left end of the board as my point of rotation. Now I draw my clockwise and counter-clockwise torques.

To do this, I hold my system motionless only at the point of rotation and then push it around that point in the direction of the force. Finally I set the clockwise and counter-clockwise torques equal to each other.

$$\tau_{clockwise} = \tau_{counter\text{-}clockwise}$$

$$\tau_1 + \tau_3 = \tau_2$$

Now I have two equations and two variables. I simply plug and chug.

## Question 25

A rescue helicopter lifts a 50 kg rock climber by a rope from a cliff face. The rock climber is accelerated vertically at 5 m/s$^2$. What is the tension in the rope?

○ **A.** 350 N
○ **B.** 500 N
○ **C.** 750 N
○ **D.** 1500 N

## Question 26

A skydiver jumping from a plane will accelerate up to a maximum velocity and no greater. This constant velocity is known as terminal velocity. Upon reaching terminal velocity, the net force on the skydiver is:

○ **A.** zero and the skydiver is in equilibrium.
○ **B.** zero and the skydiver is not in equilibrium.
○ **C.** equal to the weight of the skydiver and the skydiver is in equilibrium.
○ **D.** equal to the weight of the skydiver and the skydiver is not in equilibrium.

## Question 27

There are 3 forces acting on an object. Two of the forces are of equal magnitude. One of these forces pulls the object to the north and one pulls to the east. If the object undergoes no acceleration, then in which direction must the third force be pulling?

○ **A.** Northeast
○ **B.** Northwest
○ **C.** Southeast
○ **D.** Southwest

## Question 28

Which of the following describes a situation requiring no net force?

○ **A.** A car starts from rest and reaches a speed of 80 km/hr after 15 seconds.
○ **B.** A bucket is lowered from a rooftop at a constant speed of 2 m/s.
○ **C.** A skater glides along the ice, gradually slowing from 10 m/s to 5 m/s.
○ **D.** The pendulum of a clock moves back and forth at a constant frequency of 0.5 cycles per second.

## Question 29

A telephone pole stands as shown below. Line A is 4 m off the ground and line B is 3 m off the ground. The tensions in line A and line B are 200 N and 400 N respectively. What is the net torque on the pole?

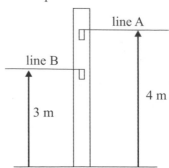

○ **A.** 0 Nm
○ **B.** 400 Nm
○ **C.** 800 Nm
○ **D.** 2000 Nm

## Question 30

If all of the forces below have equal magnitude, which one creates the most torque?

○ **A.**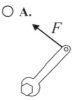

○ **B.**

○ **C.**

○ **D.**

## Question 31

A one meter board with uniform density hangs in static equilibrium from a rope with tension T. A weight hangs from the left end of the board as shown. What is the mass of the board?

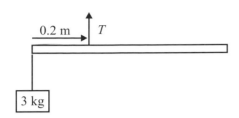

- ○ **A.** 1 kg
- ○ **B.** 2 kg
- ○ **C.** 3 kg
- ○ **D.** 4 kg

## Question 32

A student with a mass of 40 kg sits on the end of a seesaw with a total length of 10 meters as shown in the picture.

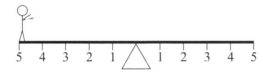

How far to right of the center of the seesaw should a student with a mass of 50 kg sit to achieve the best balance?

- ○ **A.** 1 m
- ○ **B.** 2 m
- ○ **C.** 4 m
- ○ **D.** 5 m

## 2.4 | Systems and Energy

Energy is often transferred between systems and their surroundings. A *system* is any defined area that we choose to consider separately from the rest of the universe. The rest of the universe is called the *surroundings*. Mass and energy define the three basic types of systems in physics: the *open system*, which allows exchange of energy and mass with the surroundings; the *closed system*, which allows exchange of energy with the surroundings but not exchange of mass; and the *isolated system*, which allows no exchange of energy or mass with the surroundings. The form of energy in an isolated system may change, but the energy of the system is conserved. In the First Law of Thermodynamics, which says that the energy of the universe remains constant, the universe is defined as an isolated system.

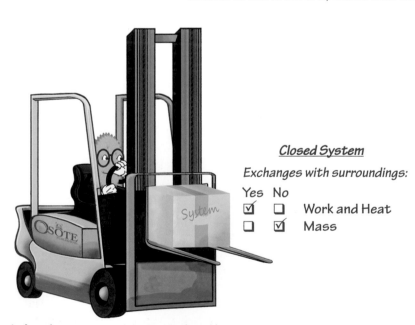

### Isolated System

Exchanges with surroundings:

| Yes | No | |
|-----|-----|------------------|
| ☐ | ☑ | Work and Heat |
| ☐ | ☑ | Mass |

An isolated system cannot exchange work, heat, or mass with its surroundings. This storage unit is securely locked and temperature controlled. No work can be done on the system, no heat can be transferred into or out of it, and no mass can be added to or taken from it.

### Open System

Exchanges with surroundings:

| Yes | No | |
|-----|-----|------------------|
| ☑ | ☐ | Work and Heat |
| ☑ | ☐ | Mass |

### Closed System

Exchanges with surroundings:

| Yes | No | |
|-----|-----|------------------|
| ☑ | ☐ | Work and Heat |
| ☐ | ☑ | Mass |

A closed system can exchange work and heat with its surroundings. This forklift is doing work on the system by lifting it, changing its potential energy. The box remains closed, so no mass can be added to or taken from it. A closed system cannot exchange mass with its surroundings.

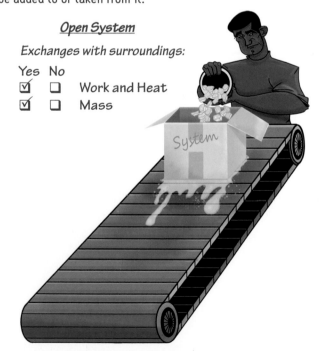

An open system can exchange work, heat, and mass with its surroundings. The conveyer belt is both doing work on the system and transferring heat into it. Because the box is open, ice cubes can be added to it, and the melted ice cubes can leave the system as water; thus mass can be added and removed from the system.

# 2.5 | Energy and Accounting

The **energy** of a system, including that of a closed or open system, is never destroyed. Instead, it is either converted from one form to another or transferred as work or heat. The energy that leaves an open or closed system goes into its surroundings. For energy problems on the MCAT®, think like an accountant and keep careful record of where the energy is coming from and where it is going.

Many equations are presented in this lecture, but most are just versions of one of the following:

1. Energy of system + surroundings before = energy of system + surroundings after.

2. Energy leaving a system = energy entering the surroundings, and Energy entering a system = energy leaving the surroundings.

3. Total energy of a system = the sum of all forms of energy in that system.

---

**Apply Key 2: When you see an energy problem, think like an accountant. Use these equations to "balance the books."**

---

The unit of energy used on the MCAT® is the **joule** (J). One joule is $1 \text{ kg m}^2/\text{s}^2$, which is the same as 1 N m. To remember this combined unit, recognize that the two variables in the work equation each contribute to these two units:

$$W = Fd$$

units are newtons (N)

units are meters (m)

Energy is a scalar quantity, so energy usually provides the most convenient method for solving mechanics problems. Whenever there is a mechanics problem on the MCAT®, first check to see if it can be solved using conservation of energy, which is discussed below.

---

**Mechanics is the study of bodies, the forces that act on them, and the motion that they experience.**

---

Energy can be divided into mechanical and non-mechanical energies. **Mechanical energy** ($\Delta E_m$) is the energy of a macroscopic system. A macroscopic system is a system that can be examined without a microscope. Mechanical energy can be further divided into kinetic and potential energy.

---

**Keep it simple here. Remember that there are two kinds of energy: mechanical and non-mechanical. Mechanical energy is the energy of macroscopic objects. Non-mechanical energy is the energy of microscopic objects.**

---

**Kinetic energy** ($K$) is the energy of motion. Any moving mass has a kinetic energy given by the equation:

$$K = \tfrac{1}{2}mv^2$$

**Potential energy** ($U$) is the energy of position. The potential energy of any object depends on where it is located. The most important types of potential energy on the MCAT® are gravitational potential energy ($U_g$) and elastic potential energy ($U_e$). (Electrical potential energy will be discussed in Physics Lecture 4.)

**Gravitational potential energy** ($U_g$) is potential energy created by the force of gravity. Gravitational potential energy between any two masses is given by

Think of energy as you have always thought about energy. You have an intuitive idea of what is meant by the statement "He is full of energy today." Use that intuition about energy when you work physics problems.

You are about to use energy to turn this page. Where did that energy come from? We can begin with the center of the sun. Nuclear fusion at the sun's core releases solar energy. That energy is trapped by the chloroplasts in plants and converted to chemical energy. All food begins with plant energy. The energy you put into your "system" in the form of calories is converted through the process of cellular respiration to ATP and heat. It is then converted to mechanical energy during muscle contraction, allowing you to turn the page!

$U_g = -Gm_1m_2/r$, where $G$ is the universal gravitational constant, $m_1$ and $m_2$ are the two masses, and $r$ is the distance between their centers of gravity. The negative sign indicates that energy decreases as the distance between objects decreases. The numerical value becomes larger as distance decreases, but because of the negative sign, this increase corresponds to decreasing energy. A limited form of this equation, which is more useful on the MCAT®, gives the gravitational potential energy of an object near the earth's surface. This formula is:

$$U_g = mgh$$

Some MCAT® questions can be solved with either vectors or conservation of energy. It is much faster to solve them using conservation of energy. When faced with a mechanics problem, always consider conservation of energy first.

where $m$ is the mass of the object, $g$ is the free-fall acceleration at the surface of the earth, and $h$ is the height of the object or system above some arbitrary point.

An object is said to have **elastic potential energy** ($U_e$) when a restorative elastic force acts on it. For most objects, the magnitude of the restoring force, $F$, is proportional to the change in position, $\Delta x$. That is, most objects follow Hooke's Law, $F = -k\Delta x$. A deformed object following Hooke's Law has an elastic potential energy given by the formula:

$$U_e = \tfrac{1}{2}k\Delta x^2$$

where $k$ is the Hooke's Law constant for the object and $\Delta x$ is the displacement of the object from its relaxed position. The constant $k$ is an intrinsic property of the material from which the object is made. It measures the extent to which the material resists deformation and is expressed in newtons per meter (N/m). This makes sense since the magnitude of $k$ is equal to $F/\Delta x$.

**Metabolism**
BIOLOGY 1

While the forms of potential energy discussed here are readily observable, potential energy on the molecular scale plays a critical role in bioenergetics. The primary direct source of energy in the body is ATP, an adenosine derivative with three phosphate groups. These three phosphate groups carry a total of four negative charges in close proximity, causing considerable electrostatic repulsion. Their high potential energy makes ATP molecules highly unstable. When ATP donates its phosphate group at the γ position to become ADP, there is less electrostatic repulsion present and the excess charge on the phosphate molecule gains additional resonance stabilization. ATP has become ADP and in the process converted its unstable potential energy into cellular work. Any potential energy exceeding cellular requirements is lost to the environment. There are other molecules in the body such as phosphocreatine that can possess greater potential energy than ATP, but the energy in ATP more closely matches cellular requirements. ATP releases less excess energy to the environment and is the energy carrier of choice in biological systems.

TABLE 2.1 > Equation Summary

**Thermodynamics**
CHEMISTRY

| Type of energy | Equation |
|---|---|
| Kinetic | $K = \tfrac{1}{2}mv^2$ |
| Gravitational potential | $U_g = mgh$ |
| Spring potential | $U_s = \tfrac{1}{2}kx^2$ |
| Total | $E_m = K + U$ |

Make sure to have these equations down cold on Test Day!

Conservation of energy does not mean that a certain type of energy (e.g., kinetic or potential) must be conserved. It means that the sum of all energy types must remain constant in an isolated system. Kinetic energy can be converted to potential energy and vice versa while the total amount of energy remains constant. In a closed system, the change in the sum of all energy types must equal the energy leaving or entering the system. Energy can enter or leave a closed system only as work or heat. Work is discussed in the following section. Heat is discussed in the Thermodynamics Lecture of the *Chemistry* manual.

A ball is pushed off a cliff onto a spring-loaded platform below. Describe the changes in energy states that occur when (a) the ball falls from the cliff and touches the top of the platform and (b) when the spring-loaded platform compresses fully in response to the falling ball.

Answer: See page 59

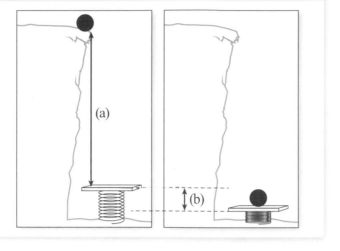

Answer: See page 59

## 2.6 | Work and Power

There are only two types of energy transfer: heat and work. **Heat (q)** is energy that is transferred between a system and its surroundings due to a temperature difference between them. **Work (W)** is energy transferred for any reason other than a temperature difference. All work is energy transfer, but not all energy transfer is work. By "transfer" we mean transfer from the system to the surroundings or vice versa. The energy transferred out of a system equals the energy transferred into its surroundings, and the energy transferred into a system equals the energy transferred out of its surroundings.

When light is shined upon the surface of a metal, it ejects electrons from the metal's surface as long as the photons' energy exceeds a value unique to each metal. This is known as the photoelectric effect. The light that reflects from the surface does not have the same energy as the light that was incident on the surface, suggesting that the incident photons did work on the electrons in the metal. The work done on these electrons can be calculated by subtracting the energy of the reflected photons by their initial energy.

Electrochemistry
CHEMISTRY

Work is a scalar and is measured in units of energy (joules). This makes sense since work is a transfer of energy.

As summarized by the **First Law of Thermodynamics**, any change in the total energy of a system is due to either work or heat.

$$W + q = \Delta E_{\text{total}}$$

This equation shows that in the absence of heat, $q$, any change in a system's total energy must be due to work, $W$.

Recall that the total energy of a system is equal to the sum of all forms of energy in that system. That is, $\Delta E_{\text{total}} = \Delta E_{\text{mechanical}} + \Delta E_{\text{internal}} = \Delta K + \Delta U + \Delta E_{\text{internal}}$. Work changes the total energy of a system, so it changes one or more of the forms of energy that are present in that system. The MCAT® often tests students' knowledge of work through questions that describe a change in the potential or kinetic energy of a system occurring in the absence of heat. To answer such questions correctly, recognize that the change in energy is equal to the magnitude of work done.

*W, E, and U all have the same unit – the joule. Work and energy are essentially synonyms. We typically use the term "work" to describe an input into or output of energy from a system.*

Only frictional forces can change $E_{\text{internal}}$, so assume that $\Delta E_{\text{internal}}$ is equal to zero in the absence of friction, which is typically the case on the MCAT®. A useful simplification for the MCAT® is:

$$W + q = \Delta K + \Delta U$$

*For more on internal energy, see the Thermodynamics Lecture in the Chemistry manual.*

This equation shows that in the absence of heat, any change in the sum of potential and kinetic energies must be due to work.

An even more simplified version tested by the MCAT® is:

$$W = \Delta K$$

This equation is an expression of the **Work-Kinetic Energy Theorem**. It is only true when all energy transfer results only in a change to kinetic energy. In other words, it is a very limited case of the previous equations. As an example, this equation could be used to calculate the work done to stop a moving object. The work, $W$, done on the moving object is equal to the change in kinetic energy, $\Delta K$. For a moving object, this relationship implies that the amount of work done on a system contributes to (or depletes) its kinetic energy. Take the example of a person sledding across a level, snowy plain who hits a rough patch of grass. If the sled–person system possessed 250 J of kinetic energy and the frictional force did 50 J of work in the opposite direction of the sled, it follows that the sled–person system now has 200 J of kinetic energy.

---

Remember, energy equations are accounting tools. Use them to keep track of where energy came from and where it is going. Think of work as the total money transferred into or out of a bank account. Think of forms of energy as the forms that money can take, such as checks, bills, and coins. A hundred dollars can be transferred into a bank account in the form of two fifty-dollar bills or five twenty-dollar bills. In the same way, a hundred joules can be transferred into a system as 20 J of potential energy and 80 J of kinetic energy or 50 J of potential energy and 50 J of kinetic energy. Work changes the total energy of a system. Once within the system, that energy can change forms.

---

A common example of work is the energy transfer that occurs when a force acts over a distance. In this case, the magnitude of work done is given by:

$$W = fd\cos\theta = \Delta K + \Delta U$$

where $F$ is the force on some system, $d$ is the displacement of the system, and $\theta$ is the angle between $F$ and $d$. This equation gives the energy transferred into a system due to a force. The force described by this equation may be one of many forces acting on the system or it may be the net force. Know that only a force or component of force in the direction parallel to the system's direction of displacement, $F\cos\theta$, can do work on the system.

---

Remember Key 3: When work is done on an object, its energy changes. When you see the word "work," think about a force acting over some distance to change the energy of an object.

You have probably seen the formula for work written as:

$$W = Fd$$

This formula is an abbreviation for $W = Fd\cos\theta$. $F\cos\theta$ is the component of force in the direction parallel to displacement, so when you see $W = Fd$, $F$ is understood to be the force parallel to displacement.

---

**FIGURE 2.3** | Work

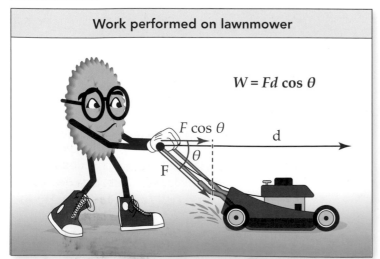

**Work performed on lawnmower**

$$W = Fd\cos\theta$$

$F\cos\theta$

$d$

$\theta$

$F$

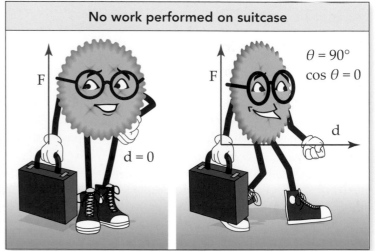

**No work performed on suitcase**

$F$

$d = 0$

$\theta = 90°$

$\cos\theta = 0$

$F$

$d$

The simplest way to understand work is to remember the first law of thermodynamics: energy is always conserved, or

$$\Delta E = W + q$$

where $q$ is heat and $\Delta E$ is the total change in energy of a closed system. There are only two ways that energy can leave or enter a system: work and heat.

If you want to know whether work is done, first define your system. If your system is the same temperature as its surroundings, there can be no heat. Any energy change to such a system must be accomplished through work. Add up the change in energy and you have the work done on the system. If your system is not the same temperature as its surroundings, heat must be considered and you have a thermodynamics problem. (Caveat: change in temperature is not the same thing as heat.)

## Sign Conventions for Work

Sign conventions for work provide a standardized way to show where energy is coming from and where it is going.

When deciding whether to assign a positive or negative value to work done on or by a system, first identify the system of interest. Is energy going into or out of this system? If energy is going in, assign it a positive value. If energy is going out, assign it a negative value. Energy goes into a system when work is done on the system. If 50 J of work are done on a system, $W$ for that system = +50 J. Energy goes out of a system when the system does work. If 50 J of work are done by a system, $W$ for that system is -50 J. This all makes sense given the First Law of Thermodynamics, $\Delta E_{total} = W + q$. When a system does work, it transfers energy to its surroundings, decreasing its own total energy. $\Delta E_{total} < 0$, so $W < 0$.

Once you've chosen a sign convention for force and energy, stick with it as you complete practice problems. The signs suggested here are the most common conventions. No need to confuse yourself on Test Day by changing it up at the last minute!

When deciding whether to assign a positive or negative value to work done by a force, consider the direction of the force. If the force acts in the direction of displacement, assign it a positive value. If the force acts in the opposite direction of displacement, assign it a negative value. The force of gravity does positive work on a skydiver falling towards the earth. The force of air resistance does negative work on that same skydiver.

## Power

The amount of work done by a force per unit time is described in terms of power:

$$P = \frac{W}{t}$$

More generally, **power (P)** is the rate of energy transfer:

$$P = \frac{\Delta E}{t}$$

where $t$ is the time during which energy is transferred and $\Delta E$ is the energy change of the system, which equals work plus heat.

The unit of power is the watt (W), which is defined as J/s. Do not confuse the unit W with the variable $W$, which represents work.

Manipulation of the power equation can produce the following equation that factors in the contribution of force:

$$P = \frac{W}{t}$$

$$P = \frac{Fd \cos \theta}{t}$$

$$P = Fv \cos \theta$$

Digesting a cracker releases five times as much energy per gram as exploding dynamite, but the dynamite releases energy over a much shorter time. That's why the power of the dynamite is greater and we don't make bombs out of crackers.

where $\theta$ is the angle between $F$ and $v$. The $\cos\theta$ indicates that the force is in the direction of the velocity. This equation is sometimes written as $P = Fv$, where it is understood that $F$ is the force in the direction of the velocity (so $\theta = 180°$ and $\cos\theta = 1$). This is the same shorthand often used for the equation for work. Note that power is a scalar quantity, not a vector; it does not have direction.

## Conservative and Non-conservative Forces

To determine whether a force is conservative or non-conservative, think like an accountant and check to see if the force has changed the total mechanical energy of the system on which it acts. Does mechanical energy before equal mechanical energy after? If so, the force is conservative. If not, the force is non-conservative.

When a conservative force does work on a system, the system experiences no change in mechanical energy. The total work done by a conservative force is equal to zero. Recall that in the absence of friction, $W = \Delta E_m$.

The **Law of Conservation of Mechanical Energy** states that when only conservative forces are acting, the sum of mechanical energies remains constant. Mechanical energy before equals mechanical energy after.

$$K_1 + U_1 = K_2 + U_2 \text{ (conservative forces only, no heat)}$$

Written another way:

$$0 = \Delta K + \Delta U \text{ (conservative forces only, no heat)}$$

Gravitational forces and Hooke's law forces are the conservative forces that are most likely to appear on the MCAT®. To be a conservative force, it is necessary but not sufficient that a force be a function of position only. The conservative force of gravity experienced by an object depends on its position within a gravitational field. The conservative Hooke's law force depends on the position of the spring or object creating it.

Conservative forces have associated potential energies. This makes sense since potential energy is the energy of position.

**Warning:** If a question asks, "How much work is done by gravity?" (or any other conservative force), the question implies that gravity is not part of the system. There are three methods to answer such a question: 1. use $Fd \cos\theta$; 2. calculate the change in $\Delta U_g$; or 3. use $W = \Delta K + \Delta U$ but do not include gravitational potential energy in your calculation of $\Delta U$. Technically speaking, a conservative force does not do work because energy is never lost or gained by the system.

When a non-conservative force does work on a system, the mechanical energy of the system changes. Mechanical energy before is not equal to mechanical energy after. Examples of non-conservative forces are kinetic frictional forces and the pushing and pulling forces applied by animals. For instance, if a human lifts an object from rest to height $h$, the total mechanical energy of the object has changed. If an object is propelled to height $h$ by its own kinetic energy, its total mechanical energy remains constant.

Non-conservative forces withdraw energy from a system. Conservative forces convert energy from one form to another without changing the total amount of energy in the system.

The pushing and pulling forces applied by animals are non-conservative. In this picture, the force applied to the cart by the horses is a non-conservative force.

Except for frictional forces, the work done by all non-conservative forces equals the change in the mechanical energy of the systems upon which they are applied. This result is described by the equation:

$$W = \Delta K + \Delta U$$

Notice that this equation was also given as one of the definitions of work. This is because non-conservative forces do work. Compare this equation to the equation for the change in mechanical energy when only conservative forces act.

The MCAT® might ask you to identify conservative and non-conservative forces, but the most important thing to understand is how they affect work. If you already understand work and can do most MCAT® problems involving work, don't worry too much about conservative and non-conservative forces.

When conservative forces are acting, the total mechanical energy, meaning the sum of the potential and kinetic energies, remains constant. A conservative force may convert energy from one form of mechanical energy to another while the total mechanical energy is unchanged.

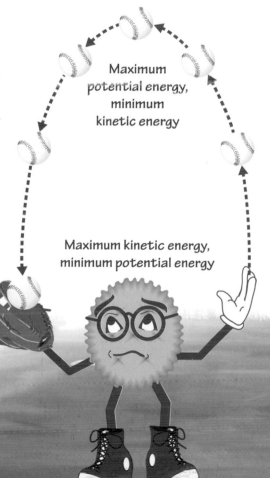

Maximum potential energy, minimum kinetic energy

Maximum kinetic energy, minimum potential energy

The work done against conservative forces is conserved in potential energy. The work done against non-conservative forces is not conserved.

## Examples of Work

Figure 2.4 shows a force acting at an angle to the direction of displacement.

**FIGURE 2.4** | A Force at a 60° Angle

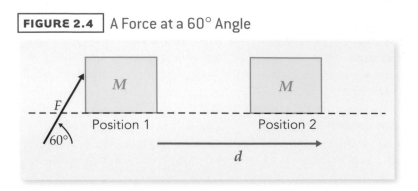

A force $F$ acts on mass $M$ along a frictionless surface, resulting in displacement $d$. The force is acting through the entire displacement of the mass from position 1 to position 2. This example demonstrates several concepts about work. First, since an applied force transfers energy from the applicator of the force to the mass, work is done. The vertical component of the force was apparently too small to move the mass off the horizontal line. The vertical displacement is zero, and the vertical component of force does no work. Gravity and the normal force are 90° to the displacement and also do no work. The horizontal component of the force moves the mass a displacement of $d$ and thus does work. We can use the equation $W = Fd \cos 60°$ to find the work done by the force. (Notice that $F \cos 60°$ is the horizontal component of the force.) The mass does not change height, so there is no change in potential energy. The work done on the mass goes completely into changing its kinetic energy. The change in kinetic energy is equal to the work.

Consider the physical manifestations of work in the example above. Since work is a transfer of energy, what physical changes to a mass result from this energy transfer? Imagine the same force acting on the box at an angle of 30°. How would the changed force affect the work done on the box? Would one force do more work than the other? What would be the physical manifestations of a change in the amount of work done?

When faced with a problem involving work, follow my 5 step system given at the beginning of Physics Lecture 1. Once you have defined your system, decide what energy transfers are taking place. If there is heat or pressure-volume change, you have a thermodynamics problem. See the Thermodynamics Lecture of the *Chemistry* manual for more on this type of problem. Otherwise, all energy transfer is work. The work done will be given by $W = Fd \cos\theta$ unless friction is acting, but can always be found by $W = \Delta K + \Delta U + \Delta E_i$ if information on internal energy change is available. Remember, you have three methods to calculate the work done by a conservative force:

1. $Fd \cos\theta$,

2. $\Delta U$,

3. everything but $\Delta U$.

**FIGURE 2.5** | A Force at a 30° Angle

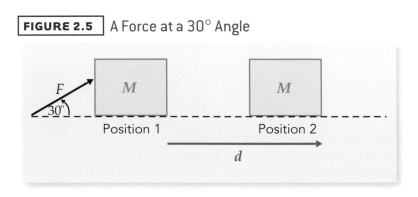

Since the force applied at 30° has a greater horizontal component, it does more work. This greater work would lead to a greater acceleration throughout the displacement, greater velocity at the end of the displacement, and less time required to achieve the displacement.

## Questions 33–40 are NOT related to a passage.

### Question 33

A meteor with a mass of 1 kg moving at 20 km/s collides with Jupiter's atmosphere. The meteor penetrates 100 km into the atmosphere and disintegrates. What is the average force on the meteor once it enters Jupiter's atmosphere? (Note: ignore gravity.)

- ○ **A.** $2 \times 10^3$ N
- ○ **B.** $4 \times 10^3$ N
- ○ **C.** $8 \times 10^3$ N
- ○ **D.** $2 \times 10^5$ N

### Question 34

If 1 kg blocks were stacked one upon the other starting at the surface of the earth and continuing forever into space, the blocks near the bottom of the stack would have:

- ○ **A.** less gravitational potential energy than blocks at the middle or blocks near the top of the stack.
- ○ **B.** less gravitational potential energy than blocks at the middle and the same gravitational energy as blocks near the top of the stack.
- ○ **C.** the same gravitational potential energy as all other blocks.
- ○ **D.** more gravitational potential energy than blocks at the middle or blocks near the top of the stack.

### Question 35

Objects A and B are placed on the spring as shown. Object A has twice as much mass as object B. If the spring is depressed and released, propelling the objects into the air, object A will:

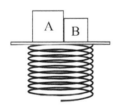

- ○ **A.** rise one fourth as high as object B.
- ○ **B.** rise half as high as object B.
- ○ **C.** rise to the same height as object B.
- ○ **D.** rise twice as high as object B.

### Question 36

A spring powered dart-gun fires a dart 1 m vertically into the air. In order for the dart to go 4 m, the spring would have to be depressed:

- ○ **A.** 2 times the distance.
- ○ **B.** 3 times the distance.
- ○ **C.** 4 times the distance.
- ○ **D.** 8 times the distance.

### Question 37

A 100 N force is applied as shown to a 10 kg object for 2 seconds. If the object is initially at rest, what is its final velocity? (Ignore friction: sin 30° = 0.5; cos 30° = 0.87)

- ○ **A.** 8.7 m/s
- ○ **B.** 1 m/s
- ○ **C.** 17.4 m/s
- ○ **D.** 34.8 m/s

### Question 38

A large rock is tied to a rubber band and dropped straight down. As the rock falls, the rubber band gradually stretches, eventually bringing the rock to a stop. Which of the following energy transfers is taking place in this process?

- ○ **A.** Kinetic to gravitational potential to elastic potential
- ○ **B.** Kinetic to elastic potential to gravitational potential
- ○ **C.** Gravitational potential to elastic potential to kinetic
- ○ **D.** Gravitational potential to kinetic to elastic potential

### Question 39

Energy consumption in the home is generally measured in units of kilowatt hours. A kilowatt hour is equal to:

- ○ **A.** 3,600 J.
- ○ **B.** 6,000 J.
- ○ **C.** 3,600,000 J.
- ○ **D.** 6,000,000 J.

### Question 40

A winch is used to lift heavy objects to the top of a building under construction. A winch with a power of 50 kW was replaced with a new winch with a power of 100 kW. Which of the following statements about the new winch is NOT true?

- ○ **A.** The new winch can do twice as much work in the same time as the old winch.
- ○ **B.** The new winch takes twice as much time to do the same work as the old winch.
- ○ **C.** The new winch can raise objects with twice as much mass at the same speed as the old winch.
- ○ **D.** The new winch can raise objects with the same mass at twice the speed of the old winch.

# Machines: Ramp, Lever and Pulley

Machines reduce the force required to do a given amount of work. This ability to reduce applied force is referred to as mechanical **advantage**. Machines are able to reduce force but do not change work. Remembering that machines do not change work can make otherwise difficult MCAT® problems fast and simple. This section will examine the ramp, lever, and pulley. The Fluids Lecture of this manual will present one more simple machine, a hydraulic lift.

These topics could appear on the MCAT® in the context of biomedical devices that assist in hospital operations. Ramps allow patients using wheelchairs to bypass stairs. Pulley systems can be used to support limbs that need to be elevated.

## The Ramp

A ramp is an inclined plane that reduces the force needed to do work by increasing the distance over which the force is applied. The work required to lift a mass $m$ to a tabletop of height $h$ is equal to the force $mg$ multiplied by the distance $h$, or $mgh$. A frictionless ramp makes it possible to achieve the same result with a reduced force. To push the mass up the inclined plane, we must only overcome the force that is pushing the mass down the plane, $mg \sin\theta$. Since the sine of any angle is a fraction, we know that this force is only a fraction of $mg$. Thus the force required to move the mass has been reduced by the machine. Multiplying the force by the distance shows that the work is still the same. From SOH CAH TOA, we know that the distance along the ramp is the opposite, or $h$, divided by $\sin\theta$. Therefore $W = mg \sin\theta \times h/\sin\theta$. This reduces to $W = mgh$, the same as the work that would be required without the machine. This example shows that in order to *reduce* the force by a certain fraction, we must *increase* the length of the ramp by the reciprocal of that fraction. To reduce the force to ½ $mg$, for example, we must make a ramp with length $2h$. This is the same as saying that force and distance are inversely proportional to each other when work is held constant, as shown by $W = Fd$.

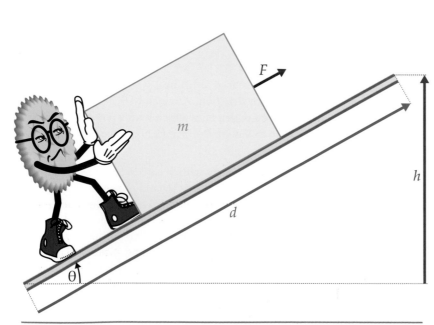

$$\sin\theta = \frac{h}{d} \qquad W = Fd$$

$$F = mg \sin\theta \qquad \therefore W = mg\frac{h}{d}d$$

$$\therefore F = mg\frac{h}{d} \qquad \therefore W = mgh$$

In the work equation, force and work are inversely related. To do some quantity of work W, machines can decrease F by increasing d. The total work done hasn't changed, but the force required is a lot less.

Work equation:

$$W = Fd$$

Work equation with machine:

$$W = F\boldsymbol{d}$$

## The Lever

A lever is a beam attached to a fulcrum (pivot point). A lever reduces the force needed to do a given amount of work by increasing the distance over which the force is applied, as does a ramp. The lever differs from a ramp in that it is based on the principle of torque. Again, consider the process of lifting a mass $m$ to a height $h$. Assume that the system is in dynamic equilibrium, meaning that the magnitudes of the clockwise and counter-clockwise torques are equal. Torque is force multiplied by lever arm. Doubling the length of the lever arm reduces the force required by a factor of two. We can do this by placing the fulcrum so that it is twice as far from the force as from the mass. The diagram below shows that the curve traveled by the mass to reach height $h_1$ is only half as long as the curve traveled by the force-bearing end of the lever. As with the ramp, the force is inversely proportional to the distance, and the work is the same with or without the machine.

Notice that as soon as the lever begins to move, the lever arm shortens. As long as both gravity and the force point downward, the lever arms remain in the same proportions.

Many bones in your body act as levers. Think about this as you lift something heavy! See more on levers in the body (Muscle, Bone and Skin Lecture, *Biology 2: Systems* manual).

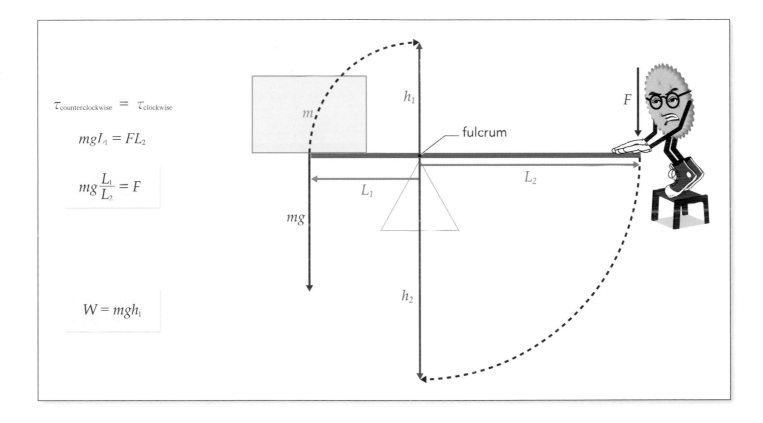

$$\tau_{counterclockwise} = \tau_{clockwise}$$

$$mgl_1 = FL_2$$

$$mg\frac{L_1}{L_2} = F$$

$$W = mgh_1$$

FIGURE 2.6

## The Pulley

A pulley acts by the same principle as the ramp and lever: it allows force to act over a greater distance so that the same amount of work can be done with less force. A pulley uses rope to increase the distance over which the force acts. The magnitude of the force acting throughout the length of a rope is called *tension*. Tension is a scalar quantity and has no direction. For the purposes of the MCAT®, assume that tension throughout a rope is constant. In the diagram below, the tension $T$ is the same at every point in the rope: $T = T_1 = T_2 = T_3$.

---

**If you see tension on the MCAT®, replace the rope through which it acts with a force vector acting on your system.**

---

Without a pulley, the force $F$ required to lift the mass $m$ would be equal to *mg*. With a pulley, the tension $T$ lifts the mass. In order to solve for $T$, select the system on which $T$ acts directly. This system is pulley number 1.

As usual, assume that the system is in dynamic equilibrium. This means that the magnitudes of the upward and downward forces are equal. The downward force is *mg*. The upward forces are the two tensions, $T_1$ and $T_2$, in the rope attached to the pulley. The tension throughout a rope in an ideal pulley is the same at every point, so the two tensions here must be equal: $T = T_1 = T_2 = T_3$. Setting upward forces equal to downward forces gives us mg = 2T, or $T = \frac{1}{2}$ mg.

### Mass Hanging by a Rope

Tension at the top of the rope is equal to mg. Tension at the bottom of the rope is also equal to mg. Overall, the tension in the rope is just mg. Remember that the tension throughout a rope is assumed to be constant. Do not add tension at one end of a rope to tension at the other end of the rope.

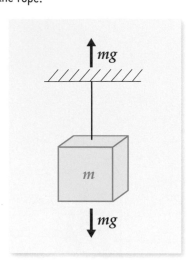

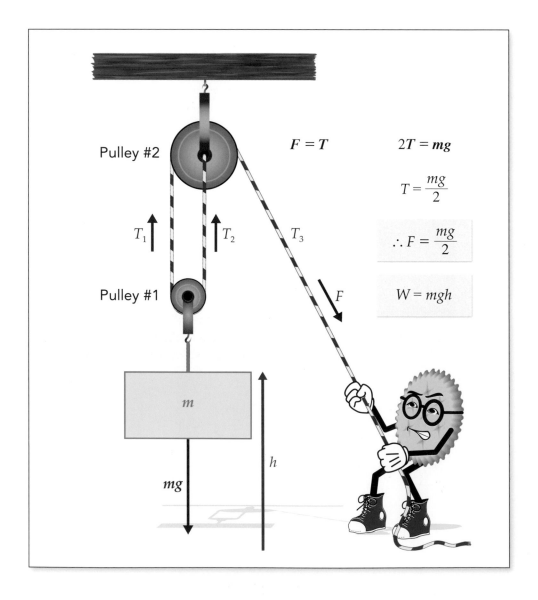

The work required to lift the mass to the table has not changed. Since the force is halved, the force must be applied over twice the distance. If we look closely at the pulley system and imagine that the mass is raised one meter, we see that in order for the rope to lift evenly, one meter must come off of both sides of the pulley rope. Since it is all one rope, this amounts to pulling the rope a distance of two meters when the force $F$ is applied. Thus we have reduced the force by a factor of two by increasing the distance over which it acts by a factor of two. Again, when work is held constant, force and distance are inversely proportional.

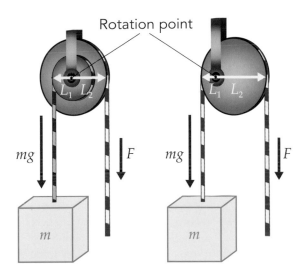

**FIGURE 2.7** | Modified Levers

These machines appear to be pulleys, but they are actually modified levers. They work on the principle of torque. In each, the lever arm acted on by force F is greater than the lever arm acted on by mg. Notice that $L_1 \neq L_2$, so the force required to lift mg is reduced. The work remains the same. Notice that the tension is not constant throughout these ropes as it is throughout the ropes of a true pulley.

## MCAT® THINK

The screw is an ingenious simple machine because it allows small inputs of force to do tremendous amounts of work. To which of the three classes of simple machines presented in this lecture does the screw belong, and why?

Answer: See page 59

## Question 41

The frictionless pulley system below reduces the force necessary to lift any mass by a factor of 3. How much power is required to lift a 30 kg object 2 meters in 60 seconds using this pulley system?

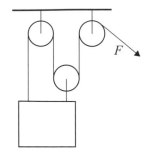

○ **A.** 4 W
○ **B.** 10 W
○ **C.** 24 W
○ **D.** 120 W

## Question 42

An eccentric pulley can be used on a compound bow to increase the velocity of an arrow. The pulleys pivot around the dots as shown. Below is a compound bow in two positions. The tension at point A compared to point B is most likely:

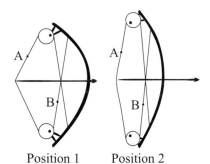

Position 1          Position 2

○ **A.** less in both position 1 and position 2.
○ **B.** less in position 1 and greater in position 2.
○ **C.** greater in both position 1 and position 2.
○ **D.** greater in position 1 and less in position 2.

## Question 43

A crate is to be lifted to a height of 3 meters with the assistance of an inclined plane. If the inclined plane is a non-ideal machine, which of the following statements is most likely true?

○ **A.** The non-ideal inclined plane increases the force required and decreases the work that has to be done.
○ **B.** The non-ideal inclined plane decreases the force required and increases the work.
○ **C.** The non-ideal inclined plane increases the force and the work required.
○ **D.** The non-ideal inclined plane decreases the force and the work required.

## Question 44

A girl riding her bicycle up a steep hill decides to save energy by zigzagging rather than riding straight up. Ignoring friction, her strategy will:

○ **A.** require the same amount of energy but less force on the pedals.
○ **B.** require the same amount of energy and the same amount of force on the pedals.
○ **C.** require less energy and less force on the pedals.
○ **D.** require less energy and more force on the pedals.

Next ▶

## Question 45

An inventor designs a machine that he claims will lift a 30 kg object with the application of only a 25 N force. If the inventor is correct, what is the shortest possible distance through which the force must be applied for each meter that the object is raised?

- ○ **A.** 5 m
- ○ **B.** 8 m
- ○ **C.** 12 m
- ○ **D.** 15 m

## Question 46

The pulley system shown below operates as a modified lever. Pulley A and pulley B turn together, so when a person pulls on rope A the mass attached to rope B will be lifted. Which of the following changes to the system will reduce the force needed to lift the mass?

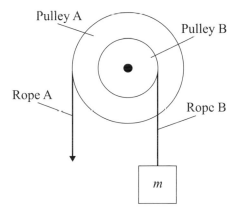

- ○ **A.** Increasing the length of rope A
- ○ **B.** Increasing the length of rope B
- ○ **C.** Increasing the diameter of pulley A
- ○ **D.** Increasing the diameter of pulley B

## Question 47

The mechanical advantage for a machine is defined as the output force divided by the input force. Since the output force is typically greater than the input force, this value is normally greater than one. For an ideal machine, what would be another way of representing the mechanical advantage?

- ○ **A.** (output distance)/(input distance)
- ○ **B.** (input distance)/(output distance)
- ○ **C.** (output distance) × (input distance)
- ○ **D.** (input distance) + (output distance)

## Question 48

A wheelchair access ramp is to be designed so that 1000 N can be lifted to a height of 1 meter through the application of 50 N of force. The length of the ramp must be at least:

- ○ **A.** 5 m.
- ○ **B.** 10 m.
- ○ **C.** 20 m.
- ○ **D.** 100 m.

### Equilibrium (no acceleration)

$$F_{\text{upward}} = F_{\text{downward}}$$

$$F_{\text{rightward}} = F_{\text{leftward}}$$

$$\tau_{\text{clockwise}} = \tau_{\text{counter-clockwise}}$$

### Non-equilibrium (acceleration)

$$F_{\text{upward}} = F_{\text{downward}} \pm ma$$

$$F_{\text{rightward}} = F_{\text{leftward}} \pm ma$$

Add $ma$ to the weaker side.

### Torque

$$\tau = Fl$$

### Energy

$$K = \tfrac{1}{2}mv^2$$

$$U_g = mgh$$

$$U_e = \tfrac{1}{2}k\Delta x^2$$

### Work

$$W = Fd\cos\theta \quad {\text{(for all forces except friction)}}$$

$$W = \Delta K + \Delta U + \Delta E_{i\,\text{(no heat)}}$$

### Power

$$P = \frac{\Delta E}{t}$$

$$P = Fv\cos\theta$$

---

## TERMS YOU NEED TO KNOW

Dynamic equilibrium

Elastic potential energy ($U_e$)

Energy

Equilibrium

First Law of Thermodynamics

Gravitational potential energy ($U_g$)

Heat ($q$)

Joule ($J$)

Kinetic energy ($K$)

Law of Conservation of Mechanical Energy

Lever

Lever arm ($l$)

Machines

Mechanical advantage

Mechanical energy ($\Delta E_m$)

Potential energy ($U$)

Power ($P$)

Pulley

Ramp

Sign conventions

Static equilibrium

Torque

Work ($W$)

Work-Kinetic Energy Theorem

Pg. 45: (a) Gravitational potential energy to kinetic energy and gravitational potential energy; (b) Kinetic energy and gravitational potential energy to spring potential energy. In part (a), because the ball still has distance to fall, its gravitational energy is not totally depleted once it touches the platform.

Pg. 47: Yes, Salty is responsible for the suitcase's movement, but that does not mean he is doing work on it. He accelerated the suitcase and keeps it in the air, but once it has achieved the constant velocity at which Salty is walking, there is no net force on it. Think back to Newton's First Law. The suitcase has inertia, and once it is moving, it will stay moving until a force acts to slow it down. So Salty is not constantly exerting a horizontal force on the suitcase; he's simply preventing the suitcase from contacting the ground.

Pg. 47: 1. The work being done is transferring energy into the surroundings, while the heat is transferring energy into me.

2. The sun beating down on me is transferring heat into me, but that does not make me feel more energized as this example suggests.

3. The change in energy should be final energy minus initial energy, so in this case, my final energy is greater than my initial energy; my energy has increased. It doesn't make much sense if my energy increases after doing work on the surroundings. So this example is wrong in at least three ways. We can fix all this by doing the following:

   1. Recognize that since I am doing work on the surroundings, the work is negative.

   2. I can sit on ice and heat the surroundings, so that heat is now negative.

   3. I reverse the energy pictures so that my initial high energy state is subtracted from my final low energy state where I am in bed, and the net energy change is negative. Now it is correct.

Pg. 55: The screw is a steel peg around which a small ramp is wrapped. The length of the screw is small compared to the length of the ramp, and when someone turns a screw one full turn, it moves very little distance. That increase in distance allows small forces to be applied across the length of the screw to perform an equivalent amount of work!

---

**THE 3 KEYS**

1. Equilibrium means no net force and no net torque, therefore no acceleration.

2. Energy is conserved but can change forms. Use accounting to build equations: energy before equals energy after, energy in equals energy out.

3. Assume that work in Physics means total change in energy, or force times displacement.

# Fluids

## 3.1 | Introduction

This lecture begins with an overview of fluids and the properties used to describe them. It then discusses fluids at rest and the forces experienced by an object in a fluid at rest. Next, it introduces fluids in motion and the energy associated with these fluids. The lecture closes with a discussion of non-ideal fluids and the forces that they experience due to drag.

The lecture will emphasize that forces can be used to make predictions about standing fluids and conservation of energy can be used to make predictions about moving fluids. Standing (non-moving) fluids contain a pressure gradient that results in an upward force called buoyant force, which acts counter to the downward force of gravity. Problems involving standing fluids should be thought of as problems about forces.

Recall that energy is never lost, but rather is converted from one form to another or transferred as work or heat. The law of conservation of energy can be restated in terms of density and pressure, properties commonly used to describe fluids. In a moving fluid, the sum of the kinetic energy per unit volume and potential energy per unit volume remains constant. Problems involving moving fluids should be thought of as problems about energy.

> **THE 3 KEYS**
>
> 1. Fluids are described by density, $\rho$. When you need the mass of a fluid, use $m = \rho V$.
>
> 2. When an object is floating, masses are equal – the mass of the object equals the mass of fluid displaced. When an object is fully submerged, volumes are equal – the volume of the object equals the volume of fluid displaced.
>
> 3. See standing fluids, think forces. See moving fluids, think energy.

**Molecules of a solid bond strongly and vibrate in a fixed position.**

**Molecules of a fluid bond weakly and rotate, spin, and move past each other.**

## 3.2 | Fluids

Most substances can be classified as either a solid or a fluid. Fluids can be understood by examining the characteristics that make fluids different from solids. The molecules of a solid are held in place by molecular bonds that can permanently resist a force from any direction. A **fluid** is a liquid or gas. Molecular bonds in a fluid, unlike those in a solid, are constantly breaking and reforming due to the high kinetic energy of the molecules.

The molecules of a fluid are not arranged with any order or structure. Instead they move about in random directions relative to each other. As a result, a fluid has only temporal (non-permanent) resistance to forces that are not perpendicular to its surface. However, since fluid molecules require room to move, collectively they can create a permanent force directed outward. This outward force allows a fluid to permanently withstand forces that are perpendicular to its surface. In other words, the only permanent force that a resting fluid can exert is one normal to its surface. A fluid is pushed and molded until its surface matches the shape of its container exactly. When the fluid comes to rest, it experiences only the normal force from the surface of its container and the force of gravity. A liquid takes on a flat upper surface so that the gravitational force is also perpendicular. In a gas, gravity has an insignificant effect on the path of an individual molecule due to the high average velocity of the molecules, so a gas will fill an enclosed container.

A fluid changes to take on the shape of its container. The ocean, a fluid, will withstand the weight of a motionless battleship forever by conforming its surface to that of the battleship so that all forces are normal to its surface. However, the ship can move through the water propelled by a much smaller force than its own weight. This is because the net force from the moving ship is not perpendicular to the surface of the water, so the water provides only temporal resistance.

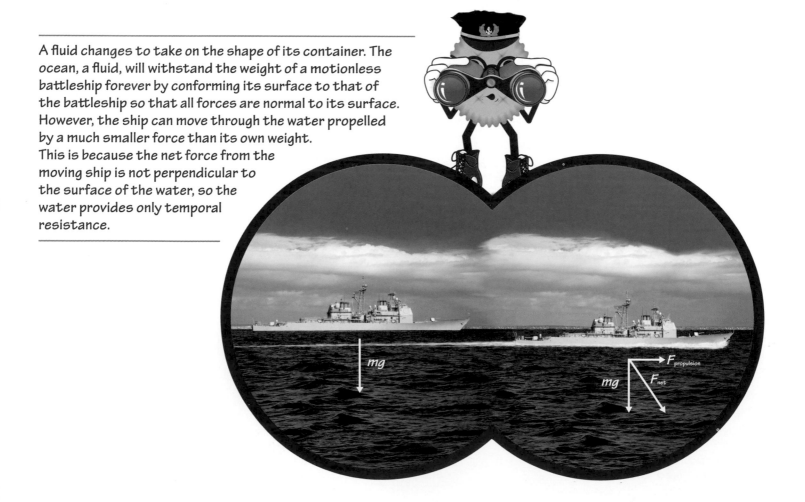

## 3.3 | Density

We often do not know how much of a given fluid is present, so mass and energy cannot be measured. In the two previous lectures, mass and energy were useful properties because the exact amount of substance could be known. The entire object could be viewed, and these properties could be measured. Properties that are concerned with quantity, like mass and energy, are called extensive properties. Extensive properties change with the quantity of a substance.

Because the exact amount of fluid usually cannot be determined, fluids are generally described in terms of intensive properties rather than extensive properties. Intensive properties are concerned with the intrinsic nature of a substance and do not change with the quantity of a substance. The two intensive properties that are analogous to mass and energy are density and pressure. Density ($\rho$) is the "heaviness" of a fluid, defined as how much mass the fluid contains in a specified volume ($V$). The formula for density is:

$$\rho = \frac{m}{v}$$

The S.I. units of density are kg/m$^3$. Changing the amount of a given substance does not change the density of that substance. Compressing a fluid changes its volume without changing its mass, changing the density of the fluid. Gases compress more easily than liquids, so the density of a gas is easily changed while that of a liquid is not. Unless otherwise indicated, assume that all liquids and solids are totally incompressible and for this reason have constant density. In reality, gases are far more compressible than liquids, and liquids are far more compressible than solids. Gases on the MCAT® change their volume (and therefore their density) as described by the ideal gas law: $PV = nRT$.

We have a strong intuition about the concept of mass because we use it every day, but few of us have a strong sense of density. It is easy to imagine how it feels to lift a 13 kg mass (about 29 pounds), but what would it be like to lift a bucket full of mercury, which has a density of about 13,600 kg/m$^3$? Most of us have no idea. We just do not know density well enough.

Specific gravity was created in order to make density a more intuitive concept. The **specific gravity (S.G.)** of a substance is the density of that substance ($\rho_{\text{substance}}$) compared to the density of water ($\rho_{\text{water}}$).

$$\text{S.G.} = \frac{\rho_{\text{substance}}}{\rho_{\text{water}}}$$

A specific gravity of less than one indicates a substance lighter than water; a specific gravity of one indicates a substance equally as heavy as water; and a specific gravity greater than one indicates a substance heavier than water. Since we all have an intuitive feel for the heaviness of water, we can relate this to a substance whose specific gravity is known. The specific gravity of mercury is 13.6, so lifting one bucket of mercury would be equivalent to lifting 13.6 buckets of water.

For the MCAT®, memorize the density of water in the following two forms:

$$\rho_{\text{water}} = 1000 \text{ kg/m}^3$$

$$\rho_{\text{water}} = 1 \text{ g/cm3}$$

Centrifugation is a lab technique that relies on the principles discussed in this lecture. To isolate cellular components, biological matter is spun in tubes at high speeds, resulting in a solid pellet beneath a liquid supernatant. Centrifuges operate by sedimentation, where denser components, like nuclei, will settle to the bottom of the tube while less dense components rise to the top of the tube.

Understand Key 1: You will almost certainly need this equation for problems on Test Day. Not only does it tease out properties of fluids from a physics perspective, but it is also a helpful tool for stoichiometry. If a fluid – or solid – is described in a question stem, the passage may also give its volume and density. To solve for the mass of the substance, rearrange the density equation as m = $\rho$V. Remember: the density equation is helpful for determining the mass of an object given that you know its composition.

**FIGURE 3.1** | Specific Gravity

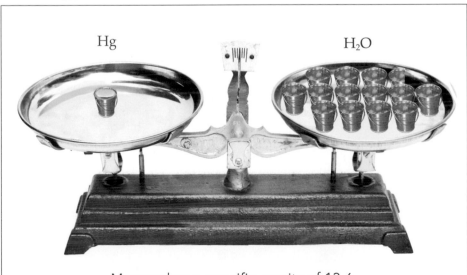

Mercury has a specific gravity of 13.6.
1 bucket of mercury has the same mass as 13.6 buckets of water.

## 3.4 | Pressure

The millions of molecules in a fluid move rapidly in random directions. As a result, some will collide with an object submerged in that fluid. In any given time $t$, a submerged object will experience millions of collisions. If we divide the magnitude of the impulse of each collision—that is, the force of the collision multiplied by the duration of the collision ($F\Delta t$)— by the time over which the collisions occur, we arrive at the average magnitude of force created by the collisions. Since the molecules are moving in random directions and at random speeds, no single direction or speed is more likely than any other. The force on one side of the object will be exactly countered by the force on its other side. (We will ignore gravity for the moment and assume that if the fluid is moving, the object is moving at the same velocity as the fluid.)

If we then divide the average magnitude of the force by the area over which the collisions are taking place (the surface area of the object), we arrive at the fluid pressure. The **fluid pressure** is the pressure experienced by the object as a result of the impulse of molecular collisions. It is the average of the magnitudes of the change in momentum of these collisions divided by the time duration of the collisions and the area over which these collisions occur. The pressure $P$ is defined as force $F$ per unit area $A$.

$$P = \frac{F}{A}$$

The S.I. unit of pressure is the Pascal (Pa). Pressure is a scalar; it has no direction. Pressure exists in a fluid whether or not an object is immersed in that fluid.

Fluid pressure can be thought of as a type of 'stored' energy per unit volume. The units of pressure are equivalent to energy per unit volume. According to this definition, pressure is a measure of the energy due to the random velocities of molecules within a fluid distributed over the volume of the fluid.

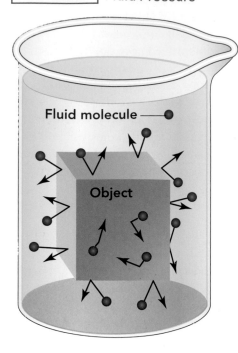

Excretory System
BIOLOGY 2

An important application of pressure in the body occurs in the kidneys. The kidneys are responsible for keeping blood pressure within a narrow range. To maintain this delicate balance, the kidneys modify glomerular filtration rate (GFR) through the renin-angiotensin-aldosterone system (RAAS). Released renin converts angiotensinogen to angiotensin I, and angiotensin converting enzyme (ACE) converts angiotensin I to angiotensin II. Angiotensin II signals the contraction of the efferent arterioles leading away from the glomerulus. When the efferent arterioles contract, blood pressure in the glomerular capillary increases because resistance in these vessels is increased.

## 3.5 | Fluids at Rest

A fluid at rest experiences only forces perpendicular to its surface. At any given depth, the pressure is equal to the weight of the fluid above a disk with area $A$ divided by the area of the disk. As shown in Figure 3.3, the pressure is the same regardless of what area is chosen.

For a fluid at rest with uniform density in a sealed container, pressure $P$ is given by:

$$P = \rho g y$$

where $\rho$ is the density of the fluid, $g$ is the gravitational constant, and $y$ is the depth of the fluid.

**FIGURE 3.2** | Fluid Pressure

Water in a glass is a fluid at rest. Blood travelling through the circulatory system is not.

## FIGURE 3.3 | The Weight of a Fluid Creates the Fluid Pressure

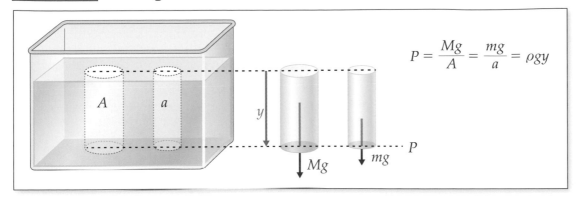

$$P = \frac{Mg}{A} = \frac{mg}{a} = \rho g y$$

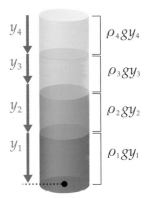

$$P_{total} = \rho_1 g y_1 + \rho_2 g y_2 + \rho_3 g y_3 + \rho_4 g y_4$$

Additional fluids on top of the first fluid increase the total pressure by adding their weight. The total pressure can be found by summing the pressures due to each fluid, as shown in Figure 3.3.

Air is a fluid. If we open the sealed container and expose it to the atmosphere, we must add atmospheric pressure to any point in the fluid. In any fluid open to the atmosphere, the pressure can be found from $P = \rho g y + P_{atm}$. When using meters and kilograms, measure the atmospheric pressure at sea level in pascals (Pa). Note that $P_{atmospheric} = 101,000$ Pa. Liquids boil when vapor pressure is equal to atmospheric pressure. Since atmospheric pressure is inversely proportional to altitude, it is easier for a solution boil at higher altitudes.

Since fluid pressure is a function of depth, the shape of the container does not affect it. The pressure everywhere at a given depth in the same resting fluid will be constant.

Just as each block in a stack of blocks must bear the weight of all the blocks above it, each point in an enclosed fluid must bear any increase in pressure. **Pascal's principle** states that pressure applied anywhere to an enclosed incompressible fluid will be distributed undiminished throughout that fluid. This is true because if a pressure gradient exists between two points with the same vertical distance from the surface, fluid flows in the direction that relieves the differential.

## FIGURE 3.4 | Pascal's Principle

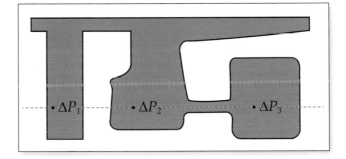

Think of the atmosphere as a sea of air. As you move closer to the top of this sea, your depth (y) decreases. Near the top, there are fewer molecules above you, which means less weight and lower pressure.

Air pressure up here is low, making it tough to breathe.

## Gauge Pressure

Sometimes problems refer to absolute pressures and gauge pressures. *Absolute pressure* is the pressure of a system relative to a vacuum. On the other hand, *gauge pressure* is the amount by which a system's pressure deviates from atmospheric pressure. To find absolute pressure from gauge pressure, simply add atmospheric pressure:

$$P_{abs} = P_{gauge} + P_{atm}$$

To better understand this relationship, consider the use of a tire pressure gauge. $P_{abs}$ reflects the tire's pressure. Before placing the gauge on the tire to check the tire pressure, the gauge is already subject to atmospheric pressure. If the inflated tire's pressure exceeds atmospheric pressure, the gauge will display a reading of the tire's pressure. The pressure in the gauge, after equilibrating, was raised from $P_{atm}$ to $P_{abs}$ by some amount equal to $P_{gauge}$. $P_{gauge}$ is the difference in pressure between the system being measured and the surroundings.

An analogue of gauge pressure in the human body is the intrapleural pressure in the thoracic cavity, which typically fluctuates between -5 and -8 mmHg during normal respiration. As with many topics in physics, the negative sign in this range of values is a statement about the qualitative nature of a system. Here, the negative sign indicates that the pressure of the thoracic cavity is less than the atmospheric pressure. Rearranging the equation above to:

$$P_{abs} - P_{atm} = P_{gauge}$$

demonstrates that the gauge pressure is the difference between absolute and atmospheric pressures. Maintaining a negative gauge pressure in the intrapleural space is critical to sustaining life. Without this pressure gradient, the elastic properties of the lungs would cause them to collapse. Following this, inspiration and expiration could not occur.

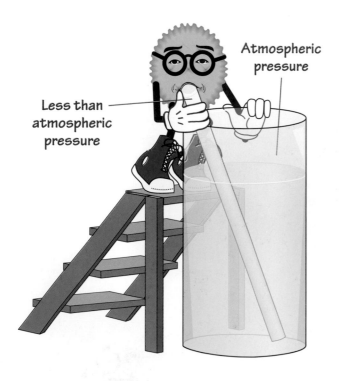

Biologists often talk about negative pressure created in your chest when you suck in air. According to the molecular collision model of pressure, it is impossible for pressure to be literally negative. This would indicate fewer than zero collisions, an absurdity. The negative pressure that biologists refer to in the chest cavity is gauge pressure. Gauge pressure is a measure of the pressure compared to local atmospheric pressure. In other words, local atmospheric pressure is arbitrarily assigned a value of zero. When a biologist says there is negative pressure inside your chest, there is still pressure in your chest - it is just lower than atmospheric pressure. The higher pressure of the atmosphere pushes air into your lungs. The same thing happens when you 'suck' fluid through a straw. You create a partial vacuum inside the straw. But a vacuum doesn't really 'suck' anything into it. The atmospheric pressure pushes down on the fluid outside the straw, pushing up the fluid inside the straw. Without atmospheric pressure, a straw would not work. Just remember, in real life, physics never sucks.

## Hydraulic Lift

The *hydraulic lift* is a simple machine that works via Pascal's principle. Two pistons and a container enclose a standing incompressible fluid. A force on piston 1 applies a pressure on the fluid. This pressure is transferred undiminished to piston 2. Since piston 2 has a greater area than piston 1, and force and area are directly proportional when pressure is constant, the force on piston 2 is proportionally greater than the force on piston 1, even though the pressure is the same. However, a machine does not change work. If piston 2 moved the same distance as piston 1 while also experiencing greater force, the work done by piston 2 would be greater than the work done by piston 1. Instead the force of piston 2 is applied through a proportionally smaller distance, keeping work the same.

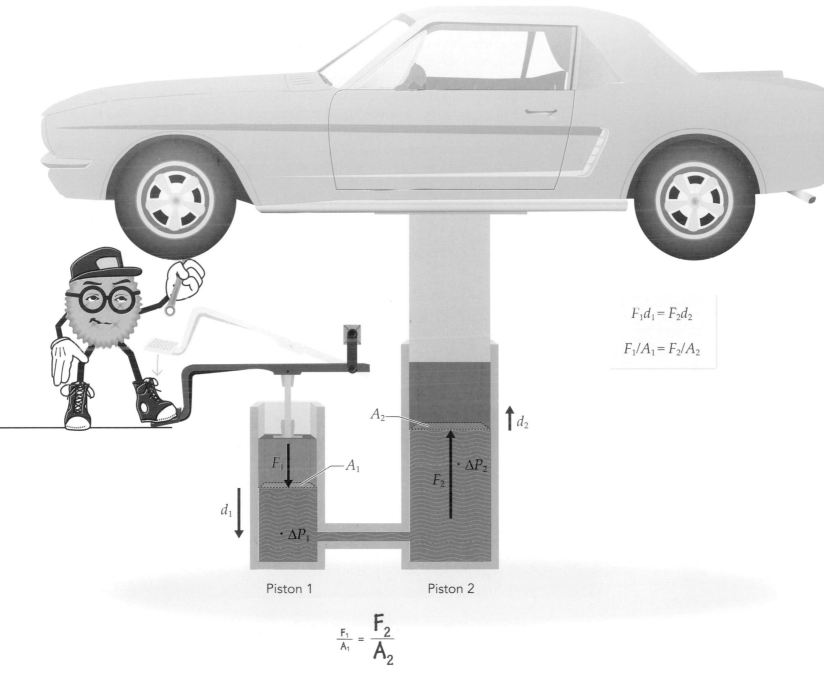

$$F_1 d_1 = F_2 d_2$$

$$F_1/A_1 = F_2/A_2$$

$A_2$  $d_2$

$F_1$  $A_1$  $\Delta P_2$  $F_2$

$d_1$

$\Delta P_1$

Piston 1    Piston 2

$$\frac{F_1}{A_1} = \frac{F_2}{A_2}$$

The pressure applied on a fluid must be the same throughout. Notice that piston 1 has a much smaller area than does piston 2. By Pascal's principle, both pistons must exert the same pressure at the point of contact with the liquid. Even if my pedal applies a relatively small force, it's being applied to a similarly small area. The ratio of force to area will stay the same for piston 2, which, with a larger area, must be subject to a larger force!

## The Forces Experienced by Objects in Fluids at Rest

Problems about fluids at rest can be thought of as problems about forces. A standing fluid exerts a force called the buoyant force on any object that is floating, submerged, or sunk in the fluid. Within a standing fluid, pressure increases as a function of depth, as shown by the equation $P = \rho g y$. Recall also that pressure is a measure of force per unit area, $P = F/A$. For a given cross-sectional area $A$, an increase in pressure must be associated with an increase in force. Within a fluid at rest, both pressure and force increase with depth, causing an object in the fluid to experience both greater pressure and greater force at points farther from the fluid's surface. As a result, the object experiences an upward force. This upward force is called the buoyant force because it has the potential to buoy the object—to cause it to float.

The difference in pressure (and therefore force) experienced by points closest to and farthest from the surface creates the upward buoyant force. Assuming that $A$ is constant, $\Delta P = \Delta F/A$, where $\Delta P$ is the difference in pressure experienced by two points at different depths on the object and $\Delta F$ is the difference in force experienced by those two points. $\Delta F$ increases with increasing $\Delta P$, and since $\Delta P = \rho g \Delta y$, $\Delta P$ increases with increasing $\Delta y$. The difference in the depths of points closest to and farthest from the fluid's surface, $\Delta y$, and the difference in pressure, $\Delta P$, both reach their maximum values when the object is fully submerged. Therefore, the buoyant force also reaches its maximum value when the object is fully submerged.

Buoyant force results from the pressure difference between the upper and lower surfaces of a submerged object. Since pressure increases with depth, the lower surface of an object experiences greater pressure than the upper surface. This pressure difference multiplied by the upper or lower surface area is equal to the buoyant force. A fully submerged object displaces its volume in fluid; a floating object displaces its weight in fluid. Since the buoyant force is due to the "difference" in pressure, the buoyant force does not change with depth once an object is submerged.

The magnitude of the buoyant force experienced by an object, whether floating, submerged, or sunk, is directly proportional to the volume of fluid it displaces.

$$F_B = \rho_{fluid} \, V_{fluid} \, g$$

where $\rho_{fluid}$ is the density of the fluid, $V_{fluid}$ is the volume of fluid displaced, and $g$ is acceleration due to gravity. The equation above can be rewritten as

$$F_B = (m_{fluid}/V_{fluid}) \, (V_{fluid})(g) = m_{fluid} g.$$

This equation shows that the upward buoyant force is equal in magnitude to the weight of the displaced fluid. This phenomenon is known as **Archimedes' Principle**.

To better appreciate the relationships among $\Delta y$, $\Delta P$, $V_{fluid}$, and $F_B$, imagine an object being slowly submerged beneath the surface of a fluid, as shown in Figure 3.6. At first the bottom of the object is relatively close to the surface of the fluid. The difference between the depths of the portions of the object closest to and farthest from the fluid's surface, $y_1$ and $y_2$, is relatively small. The volume of fluid displaced is also relatively small. Because $\Delta y$ is relatively small, so is $\Delta P$, and the buoyant force is also small. In other words, a relatively small volume of displaced fluid is associated with a relatively small buoyant force. As the object sinks deeper and deeper, $\Delta y$ increases, reaching its maximum value when the object is fully submerged. At this point, the buoyant force also reaches its maximum.

Three special cases involving buoyant force are commonly cited: the case of the floating object, the case of the submerged object, and the case of the sunk object.

**FIGURE 3.5** | The Buoyant Force Results from a Pressure Difference

Objects experience a buoyant force because of the difference in pressure experienced by their upper and lower surfaces. As depth increases, pressure $P$ increases according to the equation $P = \rho_{fluid} g \Delta y$, where $y$ is depth below the surface. Because pressure equals force $F$ per unit area $A$, the force exerted on the surface of the object—represented by the purple arrows—also increases as depth increases. Notice that the forces acting on the sides of the object are equal in magnitude and opposite in direction. This is not the case for the forces acting on the top and bottom of the object. The force acting on the bottom is greater than the force acting on the top. This means that the object experiences a net upward force called the buoyant force, represented by the orange arrow, that opposes the downward force of gravity, represented by the green arrow. In this example, the buoyant force is equal in magnitude to the force of gravity and the object experiences no net force.

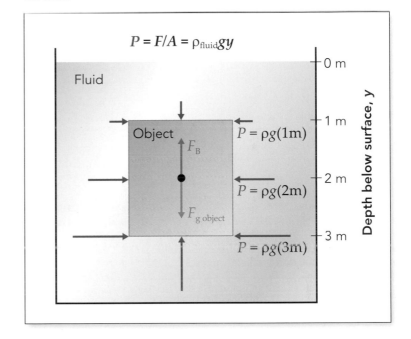

**FIGURE 3.6** | Relationships among $\Delta y$, Volume of Displaced Fluid, and Buoyant Force

As an object sinks deeper beneath the surface of a fluid, both the volume of fluid displaced by the object, $V_{displaced \, fluid}$, and the buoyant force experienced by the object, $F_B$, increase. Both $V_{displaced \, fluid}$ and $F_B$ reach their maximum values when the object is fully submerged. It is at this point that $\Delta y$, the difference between the depths of the points closest to and farthest from the surface of the liquid, reaches its maximum value.

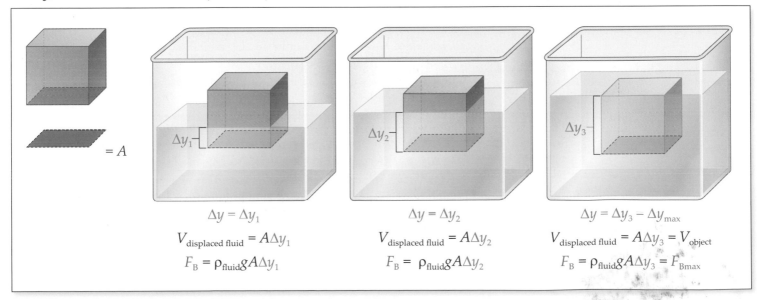

**FIGURE 3.7** A Floating Object

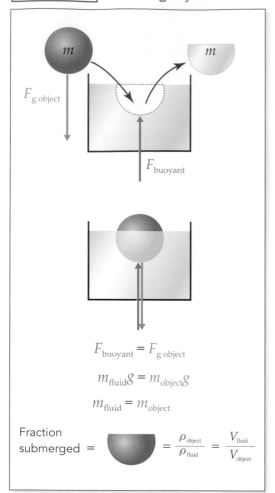

Note that in standing fluids, as in Figures 3.7, 3.8, and 3.9, $m_{fluid}$ refers only to the mass of the fluid displaced by the object. $V_{fluid}$ refers only to the volume of the fluid displaced by the object. Density of the fluid ($\rho_{fluid}$) is an intensive property and refers to the density of any part of the fluid.

Why is the upward buoyant force equal in magnitude to the weight of the displaced fluid? Before the object is submerged, the upward force on the fluid that it will displace must equal the weight of that fluid ($F_{buoyant} = m_{fluid}g$). Otherwise the downward force of gravity would cause the fluid to accelerate downward. The net upward force remains when the object is submerged, but the fluid is gone, replaced by the object. The remaining upward force acts on the submerged object.

*The Case of the Floating Object:* A floating object displaces a volume of fluid with mass equal to its own mass and experiences an upward buoyant force equal in magnitude to the downward gravitational force.

An object floats when the upward buoyant force is equal in magnitude to the downward force of gravity. Imagine an object slowly lowering into a fluid. At first, as the object just penetrates the surface of the fluid, the volume of fluid it displaces is relatively small and the buoyant force it experiences is therefore also relatively small. As the object sinks deeper and deeper, displacing greater and greater volumes of fluid, the buoyant force it experiences becomes relatively larger, reaching its maximum when the object is submerged. If the upward buoyant force becomes equal to the downward force of gravity at any point before the object is fully submerged, the object floats.

For a floating object:

$$F_B = \rho_{fluid}\, V_{fluid}\, g = m_{fluid}\, g = F_G = m_{object}\, g$$

Notice that this equation simplifies to $m_{fluid} = m_{object}$. Thus the equation demonstrates that a floating object displaces a volume of fluid with a mass equal to its own mass.

Because $m_{fluid} = m_{object}$,

$$\frac{\rho_{object}}{\rho_{fluid}} = \frac{\dfrac{m_{object}}{V_{object}}}{\dfrac{m_{fluid}}{V_{fluid}}} = \frac{V_{fluid}}{V_{object}} = \text{fraction of object submerged}$$

This equation shows that the ratio of the density of a floating object to the density of the fluid in which it floats is equal to the fraction of the object submerged. If the object is floating in water, this ratio equals the specific gravity of the floating object. To remember that the density of the floating object is in the numerator of the equation above, remember that the object is floating on top of the fluid. Note that for a floating object this ratio must always be equal to or less than one. Otherwise the fraction submerged would be greater than one, which is impossible. An object only floats when its density is less than the density of the fluid on which it floats.

Summary of Floating Objects: They experience a buoyant force that is equal in magnitude to their weight, and they displace a volume of water with the same mass. The fraction of the object submerged is exactly equal to its specific gravity.

*The Case of the Submerged Object:* A submerged object displaces a volume of fluid equal to its own volume and experiences an upward buoyant force equal in magnitude to the downward gravitational force.

If the upward buoyant force equals the downward force of gravity when $\Delta y$ (and therefore, $V_{fluid}$) are at their maximum values, the object is submerged. A submerged object is like a floating object in that it does not sink, but unlike a floating object, the entirety of a submerged object is within the fluid. Because $F_B = F_G$, a submerged object displaces a volume of fluid with mass equal to its own mass, just like a floating object. Because the object is submerged, the volume of displaced fluid is equal to the volume of the object. For a submerged object:

$$m_{fluid} = m_{object} \text{ and } V_{fluid} = V_{object}$$

In other words, an object remains submerged when its density is equal to the density of the fluid in which it is submerged. Recall that density equals mass divided by volume. This makes sense when considering that the fraction of the object submerged, which is equal to $\rho_{object}/\rho_{fluid}$, equals one.

A submerged object does not necessarily rest just below the surface. The buoyant force depends on $\Delta P$, which reaches its maximum value the moment the object is submerged. If the top and bottom of the object were moved from depths $y_1$ and $y_2$ to depths $y_3$ and $y_4$, the object would remain there and would not experience an upward or downward net force. The upward buoyant force would continue to equal the downward gravitational force.

*The Case of the Sunk Object:* A sunk object displaces a volume of fluid equal to its own volume and experiences an upward buoyant force of lesser magnitude than the downward gravitational force (Figure 3.9).

Recall that an object is submerged when it is completely under the surface of the fluid and experiences an upward buoyant force equal to the downward gravitational force. If the upward buoyant force never becomes as great as the downward gravitational force, then the object sinks. It experiences a net downward force that causes the object to accelerate downward until it contacts a surface able to provide enough upward normal force to counter the downward force of gravity. Because $F_B < F_G$, $m_{fluid} < m_{object}$. However, $V_{fluid} = V_{object}$; a sunk object displaces a volume of fluid with volume equal to its own. In other words, an object sinks when its density is greater than the density of the surrounding fluid.

For a sunk object,

$$F_B + F_N = F_G = m_{object}\, g.$$

Together, the buoyant force $F_B$ and normal force $F_N$ supply the upward force needed to counter the downward force of gravity. As a result, the apparent weight of the object, equal to $F_N$, is less than the weight of the object, $mg$. The apparent weight is equal to the difference between the downward force of gravity and the upward buoyant force.

A quick trick for finding the apparent weight loss makes use of the fact that a sunk object displaces a volume of fluid equal to its own volume.

Because $V_{fluid} = V_{object}$

$$\frac{\rho_{fluid}}{\rho_{object}} = \frac{\dfrac{m_{fluid}}{V_{fluid}}}{\dfrac{m_{object}}{V_{object}}} = \frac{m_{fluid}}{m_{object}} = \frac{m_{fluid}\, g}{m_{object}\, g}$$

$$\frac{\rho_{fluid}}{\rho_{object}} \times 100\% = \boxed{\text{apparent weight loss of the object.}}$$

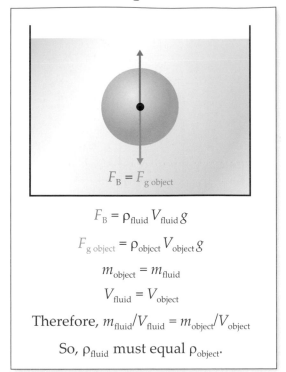

**FIGURE 3.8** | A Fully Submerged Object That Is Also Floating

$$F_B = F_{g\ object}$$

$$F_B = \rho_{fluid} V_{fluid}\, g$$

$$F_{g\ object} = \rho_{object} V_{object}\, g$$

$$m_{object} = m_{fluid}$$

$$V_{fluid} = V_{object}$$

Therefore, $m_{fluid}/V_{fluid} = m_{object}/V_{object}$

So, $\rho_{fluid}$ must equal $\rho_{object}$.

**Summary of Submerged Objects:** Like a floating object, the submerged object has a buoyant force equal and opposite to its gravitational force, but it also displaces a volume of water equal to its volume. In this case, the density of the object is equal to the density of the fluid.

**Summary of Sunk Objects:** A sunk object displaces a volume of fluid equivalent to its volume, but it experiences a buoyant force that is smaller than the gravitational force. Its apparent weight loss can be determined by $\frac{\rho_{fluid}}{\rho_{object}} \times 100\%$.

**Apply Key 2:** Remember the relationship between the object and the fluid it displaces. When an object is floating, the weight of the object is exactly canceled out by the weight of the water displaced. When an object is fully submerged, it displaces a volume of fluid equal to its own. In this case, the weight of the object could be higher than the weight of the fluid displaced, but the maximum buoyant force is the weight of the volume of fluid displaced by the object.

FIGURE 3.9 A Sunk Object is Fully Submerged

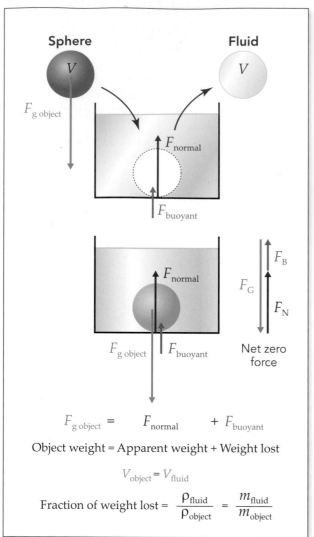

**Sphere**

$V$

**Fluid**

$V$

$F_{g\ object}$

$F_{normal}$

$F_{buoyant}$

$F_{normal}$

$F_{B}$

$F_{G}$

$F_{N}$

$F_{g\ object}$  $F_{buoyant}$

Net zero force

$$F_{g\ object} = F_{normal} + F_{buoyant}$$

Object weight = Apparent weight + Weight lost

$$V_{object} = V_{fluid}$$

$$\text{Fraction of weight lost} = \frac{\rho_{fluid}}{\rho_{object}} = \frac{m_{fluid}}{m_{object}}$$

On the MCAT®, skip the derivation. Divide the density of the fluid by the density of the object and multiply by 100% to find the object's percentage of weight apparently lost. An object with density twice that of the fluid in which it is sunk will appear to lose 50% of its weight. To remember that the density of the fluid is on top, remember that the fluid is on top of the sunk object.

TABLE 3.1 > **Summary of the Three Special Cases**

|  | Floating object | Submerged object | Sunk object |
|---|---|---|---|
| **Has $\rho_{object}$** | less than $\rho_{fluid}$ | equal to $\rho_{fluid}$ | greater than $\rho_{fluid}$ |
| **Displaces $V_{fluid}$** | with mass equal to its own mass | with mass equal to its own mass and equal to its own volume | equal to its own volume |
| **Experiences $F_b$** | equal to $F_G$ | equal to $F_G$ | less than $F_G$ |

## MCAT® THINK

Two marbles with the same dimensions are placed in a beaker of water. One marble has a specific gravity of 1.2 while the other has a specific gravity of 1.0. Which experiences the greater buoyant force?

Answer: See page 87

### Center of Buoyancy

The buoyant force acts at an object's *center of buoyancy*. The center of buoyancy is the point where the center of mass would be if the object had a uniform density. If the object is not uniformly dense, the center of mass and the center of buoyancy are not at the same place. This can result in a torque on the object that causes it to spin, as shown in Figure 3.10. Center of buoyancy explains why a fishing bobber always floats upright.

FIGURE 3.10 Center of Buoyancy

● Center of buoyancy
● Center of mass

$mg$  $F_B$

$F_B$

lead  foam

$mg$

## Question 49

Mercury has specific gravity of 13.6. The column of mercury in the barometer below has a height $h = 76$ cm. If a similar barometer were made with water, what would be the approximate height $h$ of the column of water?

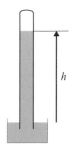

- ○ **A.** 5.6 cm
- ○ **B.** 76 cm
- ○ **C.** 154 cm
- ○ **D.** 1034 cm

## Question 50

Two identical discs sit at the bottom of a 3 m pool of water whose surface is exposed to atmospheric pressure. The first disc acts as a plug to seal the drain as shown. The second disc covers a container containing nearly a perfect vacuum. If each disc has an area of 1 m², what is the approximate difference in the force necessary to open the containers? (Note: 1 atm = 101,300 Pa)

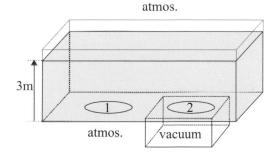

- ○ **A.** There is no difference.
- ○ **B.** 3000 N
- ○ **C.** 101,300 N
- ○ **D.** 104,300 N

## Question 51

A brick with a density of $1.4 \times 10^3$ kg/m³ is placed on top of a piece of Styrofoam floating on water. If one half the volume of the Styrofoam sinks below the water, what is the ratio of the volume of the Styrofoam compared to the volume of the brick? Assume that the Styrofoam is massless.

- ○ **A.** 0.7
- ○ **B.** 1.4
- ○ **C.** 2.8
- ○ **D.** 5.6

## Question 52

A helium balloon will rise into the atmosphere until:

- ○ **A.** The temperature of the helium inside the balloon is equal to the temperature of the air outside the balloon.
- ○ **B.** The mass of the helium inside the balloon is equal to the mass of the air outside the balloon.
- ○ **C.** The volume of the helium is equal to the volume of the air it displaces.
- ○ **D.** The density of the helium in the balloon is equal to the density of the air surrounding the balloon.

## Question 53

A child's bathtub toy has a density of 0.45 g/cm³. What fraction of the toy floats above the water?

- ○ **A.** 5%
- ○ **B.** 45%
- ○ **C.** 55%
- ○ **D.** 95%

## Question 54

The diagram below shows a hydraulic lift. A force is applied at side 1 and an output force is generated at side 2. Which of the following is true?

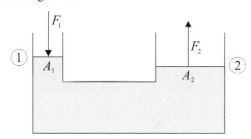

- ○ **A.** The force at side 1 is greater than the force at side 2.
- ○ **B.** The force at side 1 is less than the force at side 2.
- ○ **C.** The pressure at side 1 is greater than the force at side 2.
- ○ **D.** The pressure at side 1 is less than the pressure at side 2.

## Question 55

The pressure at the bottom of a cylindrical tube filled with water was measured to be 5000 Pa. If the water in the tube were replaced with ethyl alcohol, what would be the new pressure at the bottom of the tube? (The density of ethyl alcohol is 0.8 g/cm³.)

- ○ **A.** 4000 Pa
- ○ **B.** 4800 Pa
- ○ **C.** 5000 Pa
- ○ **D.** 6250 Pa

## Question 56

Three containers are filled with water to a depth of 1 meter. At the bottom of which container is the pressure the greatest?

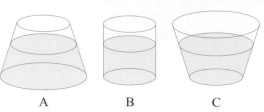

A       B       C

- ○ **A.** Container A
- ○ **B.** Container B
- ○ **C.** Container C
- ○ **D.** The pressure is the same at the bottom of all the containers.

STOP

## 3.6 | Fluids in Motion

Fluids in motion play a significant role in biological systems, particularly the circulatory and respiratory systems. The study of moving fluids is necessary in order to understand the circulation of blood, the inspiration and expiration of air, and the diffusion of gases into and out of the blood. Questions about fluids in motion are very likely to appear in the Chemical and Physical Foundations of Biological Systems Section. Try to integrate the information presented in this lecture with topics presented in *Biology 2: Systems*.

The molecules of a moving fluid have two types of motion:
1. the **random translational motion** that contributes to fluid pressure as in a fluid at rest, and
2. a **uniform translational motion** shared equally by all the molecules at a given location in a fluid.

The uniform translational motion is the motion of the fluid as a whole. This motion does not contribute to fluid pressure. According to the molecular model of fluid pressure, an object moving along with the fluid will not experience additional collisions due to this uniform translational motion. Therefore, it will not experience any additional pressure. The energy from the two types of motion can be converted back and forth. Some of the random translational motion can be converted to uniform translational motion and vice versa. If we remove a portion of the wall of a container holding a fluid at rest, the fluid will move through the opening. This occurs because the molecules moving in the direction of the opening do not collide with anything and can continue moving in the same direction. In this example, some of the random motion has changed to uniform motion. Since there are fewer collisions in the fluid moving through the opening, there is less pressure.

Circulatory and Respiratory Systems
≡ BIOLOGY 2

The motion of molecules is the basis of chemical reactions in the body. Our bodies consist mostly of water because it acts as an excellent buffer and provides an environment in which chemical reactions can occur via random and uniform translational motion. Water works so well as a solvent for the chemical reactions of living systems that efforts to look for life on other planets usually begin with the search for liquid $H_2O$.

**FIGURE 3.11** | Molecular Motion Inside a Fluid

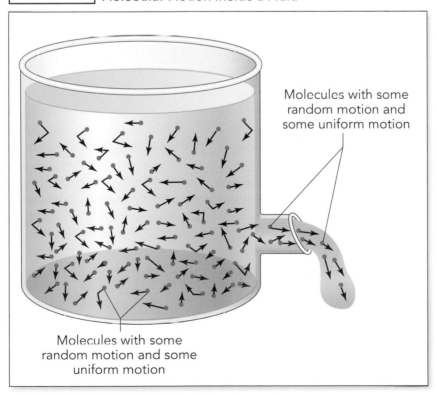

Molecules with some random motion and some uniform motion

Molecules with some random motion and some uniform motion

## Ideal Fluids

The characteristics of moving fluids are complex, so it is useful to create a hypothetical fluid that lacks certain characteristics of real fluids. This hypothetical fluid is called an ideal fluid. Ideal fluids differ from real fluids in the following ways:

1. Ideal fluids have no viscosity. Viscosity is a measure of a fluid's temporal resistance to forces that are not perpendicular to its surface. Think of a fluid's viscosity as its tendency to resist flow. Syrup has greater viscosity than water. A closely related concept to viscosity is drag. Drag is a force, similar to friction, created by viscosity and pressure due to motion. Drag always opposes the motion of an object through a fluid.

2. Ideal fluids are incompressible, with uniform density. This can be assumed for any liquid on the MCAT® unless otherwise indicated, but not for gases.

3. Ideal fluids lack turbulence; they experience steady (or *laminar*) flow. Steady flow means that all fluid flowing through any fixed point has the same velocity. Recall that velocity specifies magnitude and direction. Turbulence means that the velocity at any fixed point in the fluid may vary with time.

4. Ideal fluids experience *irrotational flow*. Any object moving with an ideal fluid will not rotate about its axis as it flows, but will continue to point in one direction regardless of the direction of flow. The MCAT® is not likely to require knowledge of irrotational flow.

No ideal fluid actually exists, but ideal fluids can be used to make rough predictions about real fluids. This is done by imagining how an ideal fluid would behave in a given situation and then considering how the characteristics of a real fluid would alter this behavior. On the MCAT®, assume that all fluids are ideal unless otherwise indicated.

**FIGURE 3.12** Ideal Fluid Flow

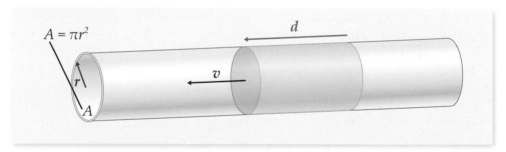

Blood flow throughout the circulatory system is usually laminar. When blood encounters irregular surfaces or experiences high flow rates or sudden changes in vessel diameter, its flow may become turbulent. Since turbulent flow generates sound waves, this phenomenon can be used to determine systolic and diastolic blood pressures. A blood pressure cuff is inflated to a pressure higher than the systolic pressure, preventing blood flow. As the pressure on the cuff decreases below the systolic pressure, blood flow resumes but is turbulent rather than laminar. The pressure at which the sounds associated with turbulence are first heard is recorded as the systolic pressure. As pressure on the cuff decreases below the diastolic pressure, laminar flow resumes. The pressure at which the sounds of turbulence cease is recorded as the diastolic pressure.

## The Continuity Equation

Since ideal fluids are incompressible, their volume remains constant. The volume of a fluid moving through a section of pipe is given by the cross-sectional area $A$ of the pipe multiplied by the distance $d$ of the pipe section. If this same volume of fluid moves completely through the pipe section in a given time $t$, the rate $Q$ at which volume passes through the pipe is $Ad/t$. Since the fluid moves a distance $d$ in time $t$, its velocity is $v = d/t$. These two equations can be combined to give the continuity equation:

$$Q = Av$$

where $Q$ is called the volume flow rate. Flow can also be expressed in terms of mass. To calculate the mass flow rate $I$, multiply the volume flow rate by density:

$$I = \rho Q = \rho Av$$

In an ideal fluid, flow rate is constant. These equations show that area is inversely proportional to velocity; the narrower the pipe, the greater the velocity.

When I put my thumb over the opening of a running hose, I decrease the area of the opening. According to the principles of continuity, the volume of water coming from the spout at any time must remain constant. To maintain the volume flow rate, the velocity of the water must increase. Velocity, acceleration, and other aspects of translational motion were examined in Lecture 1.

## Visualizing an Ideal Fluid

The concept of *streamlines* was created to allow visualization of an ideal fluid. A streamline is a path followed by a hypothetical fluid particle. This particle follows only the uniform translational motion of the moving fluid. The magnitude and direction can change from one point to the next, but its velocity at any fixed point will remain the same. The velocity of the particle at any point along a streamline is tangent to the curve made by the streamline. The magnitude of the velocity is inversely related to the distance between streamlines; the closer the streamlines, the greater the velocity. Streamlines can never intersect, since this would indicate two possible velocities for the same fixed point. A group of streamlines makes up a three-dimensional *tube of flow*.

**FIGURE 3.13** Streamlines

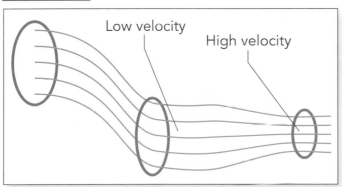

Low velocity

High velocity

The continuity equation can be used to make predictions about the velocity of blood as it travels through the blood vessels.

## MCAT® THINK

(a) Suppose that a hole was drilled in the sides of container shown in Figure 3.14 at a height above the spigot. How would the velocity of the water pouring out of the hole compare to the velocity of the water in the spigot? Would drilling the holes affect the velocity of the water pouring from the spigot? (b) If a very strong wind were blowing across the top of this container, how would the velocity of the water pouring from the spigot change?

Answer: See page 87

## The Energy of Fluids in Motion

Conservation of energy can be applied to ideal fluids to predict how a change in the pressure, velocity, or height of an ideal fluid will affect its behavior. Just as energy can be converted from one form to another but not destroyed, properties that describe fluid flow sum to a constant.

Bernoulli's equation restates conservation of energy in terms of densities and pressures, the intensive properties used to describe fluids. It states that the sum of the pressure, kinetic energy per unit volume, and potential energy per unit volume of a fluid remain constant throughout that fluid:

$$P_1 + \tfrac{1}{2}\rho v_1^2 + \rho g h_1 = P_2 + \tfrac{1}{2}\rho v_2^2 + \rho g h_2$$

where $P$ is the pressure of the fluid, $v$ is its velocity, and $h$ is its height. **Warning:** $h$ is not the same as $y$ in $P = \rho g y$. $h$ is the distance above some arbitrary point. $y$ is the distance beneath the surface.

Multiplying any of the terms in Bernoulli's equation by volume gives units of energy. The second term gives the gravitational potential energy per unit volume, $mgh/V$. The third term gives the kinetic energy from the uniform translational motion of the molecules per unit volume, $(\tfrac{1}{2}mv^2)/V$. The first term, pressure, is the energy per unit volume from the random motion of the molecules. Energy is conserved in ideal fluid flow, so the total energy must remain constant: the sum of the three terms is constant throughout the fluid.

Thinking of Bernoulli's equation as a restatement of conservation of energy makes understanding the terms easier. The $h$ in the second term is related to the $h$ in gravitational potential energy. Like the $h$ term in gravitational potential energy, the zero value can be chosen arbitrarily, and it is measured from bottom to top. Notice that this is the opposite direction of measurement from the $y$ term in hydrostatic pressure. Also, recall the equation that predicts the velocity of a body in free fall when all of its potential energy is converted to kinetic energy. Bernoulli's equation predicts the same result for a fluid. If a spigot attached to a tank of fluid is opened and $h = 0$ is assigned to the height of the spigot, the velocity of the fluid coming from the spigot can be derived from Bernoulli's equation as:

$$v = \sqrt{2gh}$$

**FIGURE 3.14**   Lost Pressure Becomes Increased Velocity

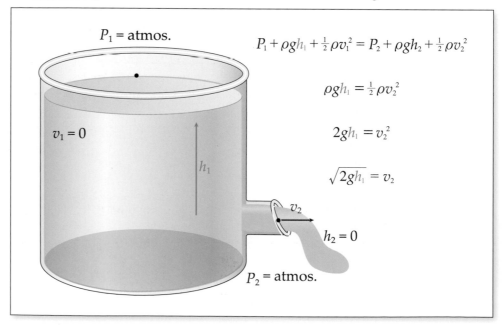

We can use Bernoulli's equation to understand the important (and possibly counter-intuitive) relationship between pressure and velocity in ideal fluid flow. Assuming constant height, as velocity increases, pressure decreases. This makes sense when we consider that an increase in velocity corresponds to an increase in kinetic energy. An ideal fluid conserves energy, so an increase in kinetic energy density must correspond to a decrease in either potential energy density or pressure. Assuming that the height of the fluid does not change, the pressure must change.

The Bernoulli equation establishes relationships between fluid pressure, height, and velocity that can be used to calculate an unknown pressure, height, or velocity from measurements of the other properties. Two tubes, the pitot tube and the Venturi tube, are commonly used to obtain pressure measurements in order to calculate fluid velocities.

A **pitot tube** is a horizontal tube that contains a U-shaped tube. The surface of the pitot tube has at least two openings, one of which faces directly into the fluid flow. This first opening encounters fluid with a velocity of zero. The pressure at this opening is equal to the static pressure exerted by the fluid. The second opening encounters moving fluid. The pressure at this opening is equal to the total pressure exerted by the fluid. Each end of the U-tube is exposed to the pressure at just one of these openings, so the difference in fluid heights within the U-tube can be used to calculate the difference in pressures according to $\Delta P = \rho g \Delta h$, where $\rho$ is the density of the liquid. Because $h_1 = h_2$ and $v_1 = 0$ m/s, Bernoulli's equation can be simplified to:

$$P_2 + \tfrac{1}{2}\rho v_2^2 = P_1 \quad or \quad \tfrac{1}{2}\rho v_2^2 = P_1 - P_2 = \Delta P$$

If the density of the fluid is known, the difference in pressure measured by the U-tube can be used to determine the velocity of the fluid flowing past the pitot tube:

$$v_2 = \sqrt{\frac{2\Delta P}{\rho_{\text{fluid}}}}$$

---

**Don't worry about memorizing these equations. If you know Bernoulli's equation and you understand how a pitot tube works, you can derive them if needed.**

---

A *Venturi tube* is a horizontal tube with a constricted region — a region with decreased cross-sectional area — in its middle. A Venturi tube can be used to determine the velocity of a fluid that is flowing within it. This is in contrast to the pitot tube, which is used to determine the velocity of a fluid flowing past it. The continuity equation states that for a fluid with constant flow rate $Q$, a decrease in cross sectional area $A$ is associated with an increase in velocity $v$. Recall that $Q = Av$. Bernoulli's equation states that for a fluid at a constant height, an increase in velocity is associated with a decrease in pressure.

The decrease in pressure that occurs when a fluid flows into a constricted region of a pipe is known as the **Venturi effect**. A *venturi meter* can be used to determine the velocity of a fluid in a pipe.

---

**The pitot tube measures the velocity of a fluid moving around it. The venturi meter measures the velocity of a fluid moving through it.**

---

Consider Key 3: Bernoulli's equation looks a lot like the energy accounting equations from the last lecture. When fluids are moving, they possess a certain energy. Assemble the variables in the same way as in energy equations. The first half of this lecture looked at standing fluids and talked about their properties in terms of forces and equilibrium. If a fluid is not moving in a problem, apply the logic of accounting to solve it.

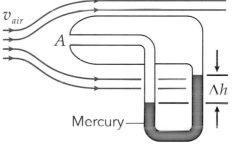

A pitot tube provides pressure measurements that can be used to calculate the velocity of a fluid flowing *past* it.

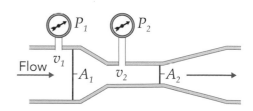

A venturi meter provides pressure measurements that can be used to calculate the velocity of a fluid flowing *within* it.

## Questions 57–64 are NOT related to a passage.

### Question 57

An ideal fluid with pressure $P$ flows through a horizontal pipe with radius $r$. If the radius of the pipe is increased by a factor of 2, which of the following most likely gives the new pressure?

- ○ **A.** $P$
- ○ **B.** $4P$
- ○ **C.** $16P$
- ○ **D.** The new pressure cannot be determined without more information.

### Question 58

If the container pictured below is filled with an ideal fluid, which point in the fluid most likely has the greatest pressure?

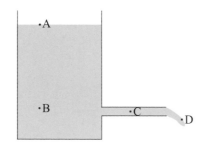

- ○ **A.** A
- ○ **B.** B
- ○ **C.** C
- ○ **D.** D

### Question 59

A spigot is to be placed on a water tank below the surface of the water. Which of the following gives the distance of the spigot below the surface, $h$, compared to the velocity with which the water will run through the spigot?

○ **A.**
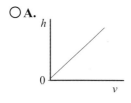

○ **C.**
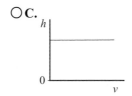

○ **B.**
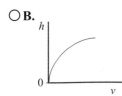

○ **D.**
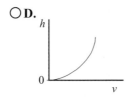

### Question 60

A pipe with varying cross sectional areas $A_1$ and $A_2$ is carrying an ideal fluid, where $A_1 > A_2$. Suppose one point is chosen at each area, both at the same height. How do the velocities and static pressures at these two points compare?

- ○ **A.** $V_1 > V_2$, $P_1 > P_2$
- ○ **B.** $V_1 > V_2$, $P_1 < P_2$
- ○ **C.** $V_1 < V_2$, $P_1 < P_2$
- ○ **D.** $V_1 < V_2$, $P_1 > P_2$

### Question 61

Circular tanks with narrow dispensers are set up with each of the following sets of characteristics. Which tank will dispense water at the quickest rate?

- ○ **A.** Diameter of surface is 100 m, fluid level is 10 m above dispenser
- ○ **B.** Diameter of surface is 50 m, fluid level is 10 m above dispenser
- ○ **C.** Diameter of surface is 100 m, fluid level is 15 m above dispenser
- ○ **D.** Diameter of surface is 50 m, fluid level is 5 m above dispenser

### Question 62

Which of the following is true of blood pressure measurements taken in a person standing upright? Assume the blood vessels in the arms and legs have the same radius.

- ○ **A.** Blood pressure is greater in the arms.
- ○ **B.** Blood pressure is greater in the legs.
- ○ **C.** Blood pressure is the same in the arms and legs.
- ○ **D.** The answer cannot be determined from the information given.

### Question 63

How much work is done by pressure to force 1 cm$^3$ of blood across a vessel with a pressure drop of $10^{-3}$ atm?

- ○ **A.** $10^{-9}$ J
- ○ **B.** $10^{-6}$ J
- ○ **C.** $10^{-4}$ J
- ○ **D.** $10^{-3}$ J

### Question 64

Atherosclerosis is a vascular disease associated with the development of plaques, which are fatty masses of tissue. Assume that blood flows through a healthy artery at a speed of 0.5 m/s. If a plaque were to decrease the radius of that artery by 40%, at what speed would blood flow through it?

- ○ **A.** 0.5 m/s
- ○ **B.** 1.0 m/s
- ○ **C.** 1.4 m/s
- ○ **D.** 2.0 m/s

STOP

## Non-ideal Fluids (Real Fluids)

All real fluids are non-ideal. The MCAT® only requires a qualitative understanding of non-ideal fluids. This means predicting the general deviation to ideal fluid when we add the first three of the four characteristics that an ideal fluid lacks. (Irrotational flow will not be tested on the MCAT®.)

Drag and viscosity are like friction and always act to impede flow. Increasing viscosity increases drag. Drag occurs at the fluid-object interface and is a force working against flow. As we move away from the fluid-object interface, the effect of drag lessens. In a real fluid flowing through a pipe, the greatest velocity would be at the center of the pipe, the spot furthest from the fluid-object interface. This model can be used to describe blood flow in the circulatory system.

Remember the general rule about drag by thinking of the dusty blades of a well-used fan. The dust on the fan blade stays put despite the high speed of the fan. This is because the air immediately adjacent to the fan moves extremely slowly or not at all due to drag.

The resistance to flow increases as the length of a pipe increases, since the amount of fluid-object interface increases with length. Further, the effect of drag increases as the pipe narrows: if the radius of a pipe is reduced by a factor of 2, the fluid volume $(V = \pi r^2 d)$ is reduced by a factor of 4, but the surface area is only cut in half $(A = 2\pi r d)$.

Fluid does not necessarily move from high pressure to low pressure. Pressure is a scalar quantity with no direction. The driving force behind the direction of fluid flow is the fluid's tendency to move such that its entropy increases. For the MCAT®, use intuition to predict the direction of fluid flow. Fluid moves from high pressure to low pressure under normal conditions. In a horizontal pipe of constant cross-sectional area, fluid will flow from high pressure to low pressure according to the following equation:

$$\Delta P = QR$$

where $R$ is the resistance to flow. The Electricity Lecture will discuss the similarity of this equation to Ohm's law for voltage and the analogy of pressure to voltage. The volume flow rate for real fluid in a horizontal pipe with constant cross-sectional area can also be given in terms of pressure, viscosity $\eta$, pipe length $L$, and pipe radius $r$:

$$Q = \Delta P \frac{\pi r^4}{8\eta L}$$

This equation is known as Poiseuille's Law. Poiseuille's Law is commonly used to predict the flow rate of real fluids, including blood in the circulatory system. Try to become familiar with the relationships between variables in this equation. A small increase in radius can result in a large increase in flow rate. Notice that as the viscosity of a fluid increases, the flow rate of that fluid decreases.

> **Warning:** a non-ideal fluid does NOT behave in an opposite manner to an ideal fluid. Narrowing a pipe increases the velocity of an ideal fluid, and it will probably increase the velocity of a non-ideal fluid as well. But with a non-ideal fluid you have to also consider drag, which impedes flow. If you narrow the pipe in a non-ideal fluid, velocity will probably increase, but not as much as it would if there were no drag.

---

**Blood is a non-ideal fluid, which has stark implications on its movement through the vasculature of the body. Consider the case of a blood clot. As the area of a vessel decreases, the continuity equation predicts that the velocity of an ideal fluid must increase. However, obstructions in the blood vessel and the interaction of various components of blood result in drag forces that are not present in ideal fluids. The result is oxygen-deficiency and decreased blood flow to tissues supplied by the partially blocked vessel.**

**Don't confuse the terms in the continuity equation with those in Poiseuille's Law. When a vessel narrows, the continuity equation predicts an increased velocity while Poiseuille's Law predicts a decreased volume flow rate.**

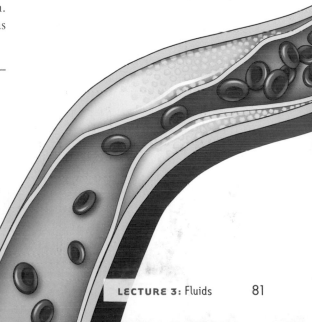

## A Method for Greater Understanding of Fluid Flow

This section illustrates how the components of Bernoulli's equation can change while their sum remains constant. Puzzling out how changes in one component relate to changes in one or both of the other two components facilitates understanding of fluids in motion. Focus on the relationships between components rather than memorizing the terms introduced in this section. They are unlikely to appear on the MCAT®.

As stated previously, Bernoulli's equation describes conservation of energy within an ideal fluid. If each term in Bernoulli's equation is divided by the specific weight $\rho g$ of the fluid, each new term has units of meters and is referred to as a 'head'. $\rho gh$ becomes $h$ and is called the elevation head. $\frac{1}{2}\rho v^2$ becomes $\frac{1}{2}v^2/g$ and is called the velocity head. $P$ becomes $P/(\rho g)$ and is called the pressure head. This section will refer to the original terms by the heads but, for simplicity, will not divide by the specific weight.

In the figure below, a hypothetical fluid particle at the top of the tank is stationary. Its energy is completely contained as gravitational potential energy. The height of the fluid at this point is its elevation head. The zero point is arbitrary, so we will choose the floor. The velocity and pressure heads are zero because the particle is at zero velocity and zero gauge pressure. Since energy is conserved in ideal fluid flow, the sum of the three heads, the piezometric head, always equals this same value. An energy line *(EL)* can be drawn horizontally at this level. The piezometer tube measures the piezometric head. A static pressure tap measures the pressure head and the elevation head, but not the velocity head. The hydraulic gradient line *(HGL)* can be drawn along the top of the static pressure taps.

With these terms in mind, use the continuity equation, $Q = Av$, to better understand fluid flow. The difference between the piezometric tube and the static pressure tap is the velocity head. The top of the elevation head is at the center of mass of the moving fluid. The displacement from where the elevation head ends to where the velocity head begins is the pressure head. If that displacement is downward, there is negative gauge pressure. If a static pressure tap were placed at a position where there is negative gauge pressure, atmospheric pressure would push air into the fluid.

In a real fluid, the energy line drops as the fluid progresses.

**FIGURE 3.15** Analysis of Ideal Fluid Flow

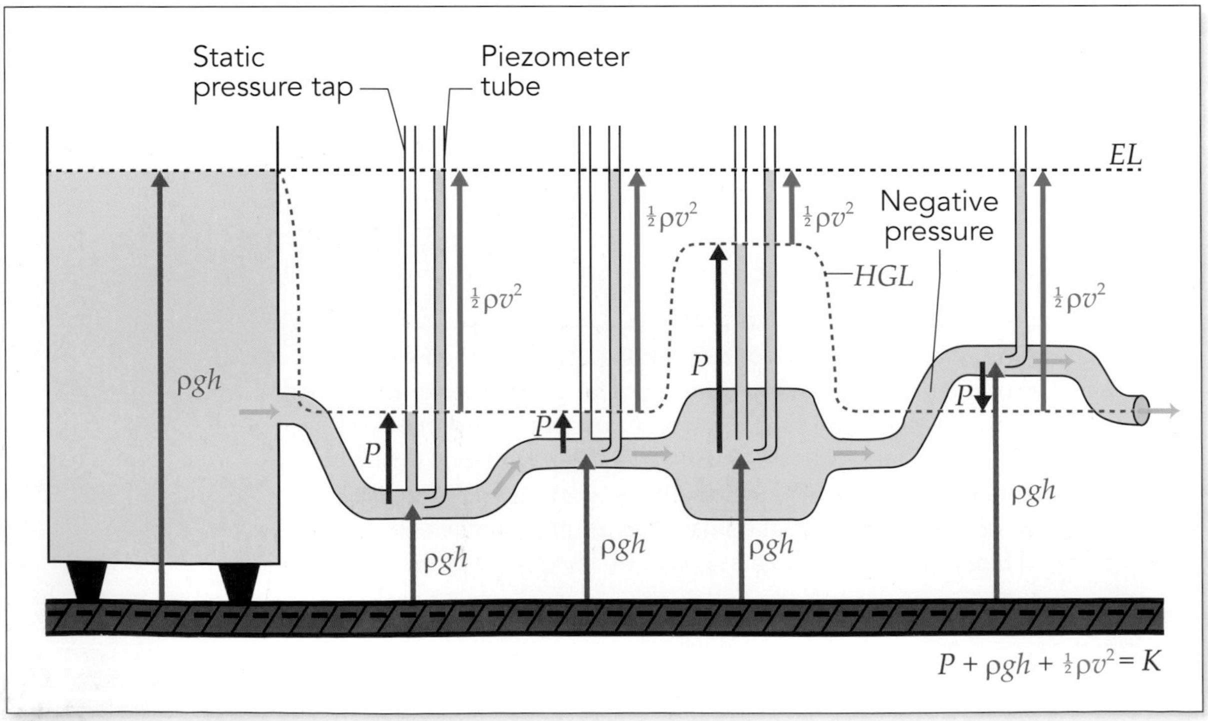

## 3.7 | Surface Tension and Capillary Action

**Surface tension** describes the intensity of the intermolecular forces of a fluid per unit length. A tiny needle can be made to float on the surface of water, even though it is denser than the water. The force supporting the needle is not the buoyant force; no water is displaced. Instead, the force supporting the needle is created by surface tension. Much like a spring, when the molecules at the surface of the water are pushed downward by the weight of the needle, the intermolecular bonds of the water are stretched and pull upward.

Surface tension is also responsible for the formation of water droplets. The **intermolecular forces** pull inward, minimizing the surface area by creating a more spherical shape. (A sphere has the least surface area per volume of any shape.) Since surface tension is a function of intermolecular forces, it is affected by the temperature of the fluid (higher temperature leads to weaker surface tension) and by the properties of the fluid. A qualitative understanding of surface tension is necessary for the MCAT®, but any equations would be given if needed.

Related to surface tension is the phenomenon of *capillary action*, where a fluid is pulled up a thin tube. Recognize that there are two types of forces acting in capillary action: the intermolecular forces responsible for surface tension (*cohesive forces*) and the forces between the molecules of the tube and the fluid molecules (*adhesive forces*). If the cohesive forces are stronger, a convex surface is formed as the fluid is pulled downward by the vertical component of the surface tension. If the adhesive forces are stronger, a concave surface is formed as the fluid is pulled upward by the vertical component of the surface tension. In Figure 3.16, the adhesive forces between water and glass are stronger than the cohesive forces between water molecules, so the water is pulled upward. In the other tube, the adhesive forces between mercury and glass are weaker than the cohesive forces between mercury molecules, so the mercury is pulled downward.

The surface tension in this water droplet is determined by the strength of its intermolecular forces, such as hydrogen bonds. These forces pull inward, minimizing the surface area and creating a spherical shape.

---

Surface tension plays a critical role in our lungs. The alveoli in our lungs are under constant pressure to collapse because of the surface tension in the alveolar wall. Our bodies prevent alveolar collapse by producing a substance called surfactant, which reduces the intermolecular forces in the alveolar wall. This maintenance of open alveoli allows for gas exchange. Since surfactant is necessary for breathing, it is necessary to sustain life. Infants born prematurely usually have not yet begun producing surfactant and often require a ventilator to survive their early weeks of life.

---

**FIGURE 3.16** Capillary Action

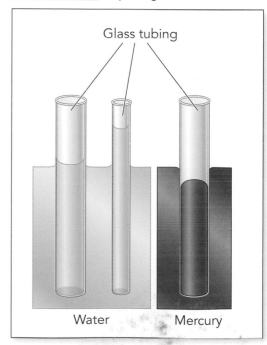

Glass tubing

Water          Mercury

## Question 65

Water in moist soil rises through capillary action. The intermolecular forces between water molecules are:

- ○ **A.** weaker than the intermolecular forces between water and soil molecules.
- ○ **B.** equal to the intermolecular forces between water and soil molecules.
- ○ **C.** stronger than the intermolecular forces between water and soil molecules.
- ○ **D.** The comparative strength between the intermolecular forces cannot be determined with the information given.

## Question 66

All of the following would increase the volume flow rate of a real fluid being pumped through a pipe EXCEPT:

- ○ **A.** increasing the pressure difference between the ends of the pipe.
- ○ **B.** decreasing the fluid viscosity.
- ○ **C.** increasing the pipe radius.
- ○ **D.** increasing the length of the pipe.

## Question 67

Two drops of equal volume of different substances were placed on the same flat surface. A side view of drop A and drop B is shown below.

Compared to drop B, drop A has:

Drop A          Drop B

- ○ **A.** stronger intermolecular forces and lesser surface tension.
- ○ **B.** stronger intermolecular forces and greater surface tension.
- ○ **C.** weaker intermolecular forces and lesser surface tension.
- ○ **D.** weaker intermolecular forces and greater surface tension.

## Question 68

Oxygen and carbon dioxide are exchanged at the interface between the alveolar wall and the pulmonary artery. Most of the carbon dioxide in the blood is carried in the form of bicarbonate ions:

$$CO_2 + H_2O \rightleftharpoons HCO_3^- + H^+$$

As carbon dioxide gas diffuses out of the blood and into the alveoli, the equilibrium shifts according to Le Châtelier's Principle. Which of the following best describes the partial pressure of $CO_2$ in the pulmonary artery relative to that in the alveoli?

- ○ **A.** The partial pressure of $CO_2$ is lower in the pulmonary artery than in the alveoli.
- ○ **B.** The partial pressure of $CO_2$ is the same in the pulmonary artery and the alveoli.
- ○ **C.** The partial pressure of $CO_2$ is higher in the pulmonary artery than in the alveoli.
- ○ **D.** The relative partial pressures of $CO_2$ cannot be determined from the information given.

## Question 69

An aneurysm is a localized bulge in the wall of a blood vessel. Is the pressure in the aneurysm higher of lower than the pressure in the normal vessel?

- ○ **A.** The pressure is higher in the aneurysm because it has a greater cross-sectional area than the normal blood vessel.
- ○ **B.** The pressure is lower in the aneurysm because it has a greater cross-sectional area than the normal blood vessel.
- ○ **C.** The pressure is higher in the aneurysm because flow speed is lower in the normal blood vessel.
- ○ **D.** The pressure is lower in the aneurysm because flow speed is lower in the normal blood vessel.

## Question 70

If a selection of tubes differing in length and radius were subject to the same driving pressure, fluid in the tube with which combination of length, $L$, and radius, $r$, would flow at the greatest rate?

- ○ **A.** $L = 4$ cm and $r = 1$ cm
- ○ **B.** $L = 2$ cm and $r = 1$ cm
- ○ **C.** $L = 4$ cm and $r = 2$ cm
- ○ **D.** $L = 2$ cm and $r = 2$ cm

## Question 71

Doubling which of the following parameters will increase the volume flow rate, $Q$, between points A and B in a pipe by the greatest amount? Assume laminar flow.

- ○ **A.** The distance between points A and B
- ○ **B.** The difference in pressure between points A and B
- ○ **C.** The viscosity of the fluid
- ○ **D.** The radius of the pipe

## Question 72

In order for white blood cells to leave the circulation and enter tissues, they must roll along the wall of the blood vessel. Which of the following is true regarding white blood cell rolling?

- ○ **A.** Blood is a non-ideal fluid so the velocity of the blood is less at the wall of the vessel than in the center of the vessel.
- ○ **B.** Blood is an ideal fluid so the velocity of the blood is less at the wall of the vessel than in the center of the vessel.
- ○ **C.** Blood is an ideal fluid so the velocity of the blood is greater at the wall of the vessel than in the center of the vessel.
- ○ **D.** Blood is a non-ideal fluid so the velocity of the blood is greater at the wall of the vessel than in the center of the vessel.

### Fluids at Rest

$$\rho = \frac{m}{v}$$

$$S.G. = \frac{\rho_{substance}}{\rho_{water}}$$

$$P = \rho g y$$

$$P = \frac{F}{A}$$

### Fluids in Motion

$$Q = Av$$

$$K = P + \frac{1}{2}\rho v^2 + \rho g h$$

$$v = \sqrt{2gh}$$

$$\Delta P = QR$$

### Buoyant Force

$$F_B = \rho_{fluid} V g$$

## TERMS YOU NEED TO KNOW

| | | |
|---|---|---|
| Archimedes' Principle | Incompressible | Random translational motion |
| Bernoulli's equation | Intermolecular forces | Specific gravity (S.G.) |
| Buoyant force ($F_B$) | No viscosity | Surface tension |
| Continuity equation | Non-ideal | Turbulence |
| Density ($\rho$) | Pascal (Pa) | Uniform translational motion |
| Fluid | Pascal's principle | Venturi effect |
| Fluid pressure | $P_{atmospheric} = 101{,}000$ Pa | Volume flow rate |
| Ideal fluid | Poiseuille's Law | |

# MCAT® THINK Answers

Pg. 72:  The first marble will sink because it has a greater density compared to that of water. Meanwhile, the second marble will be fully submerged. The buoyant forces on the two marbles are equivalent because they both displace the same volume of water.

Pg. 78:  (a) If a hole were drilled above the spigot, the stream of water leaving at the new hole would have less velocity than that of water leaving at the spigot. Examine the derivation of Bernoulli's equation for spigots. As the distance from the water's surface (h) decreases, the velocity decreases. Notice that although water would empty from the container faster with two openings to exit from, the velocity of the water from the spigot would not be affected for any particular height because the additional hole does not change the height difference from to the spigot to the top of the container. This is the only variable in determining velocity of water leaving a spigot based on the equation. (b) A strong wind across the top of the container would lower the pressure at the surface of the water. Initially, the pressures at the top of the container and at the spigot opening are both atmospheric. When the pressure at the top decreases, the pressure is now relatively higher at the spigot. Remember that fluids tend to move from areas of high to low pressure. If the spigot has higher pressure than the top of the container, the velocity of the stream will decrease.

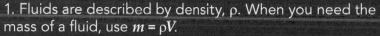

**THE 3 KEYS**

1. Fluids are described by density, $\rho$. When you need the mass of a fluid, use $m = \rho V$.

2. When an object is floating, masses are equal – the mass of object equals the mass of fluid displaced. When an object is fully submerged, volumes are equal – the volume of the object equals the volume of fluid displaced.

3. See standing fluids, think forces. See moving fluids, think energy.

# Electricity

## 4.1 | Introduction

This lecture covers electricity and magnetism as these topics are tested on the MCAT®. It begins by introducing electric force and the characteristics of static electric charge. Electric force can be either attractive or repulsive. It exists between any two charges and is inversely proportional to the square of the distance between them. Recall gravitational force while learning about electricity. Gravitational force is always attractive and exists between any two masses, electrical force between two charges. Both are inversely proportional to the square of distance. Electric force acts through fields that exert a given force per unit charge, much as gravitational force acts through fields that exert a given force per unit mass.

A static charge in a field can possess more or less potential energy depending on its position. Like fluids that flow from higher pressures to lower pressures, charges move from areas of higher potential to areas of lower potential. For this reason, moving charge, or current, is analogous to fluid flow. A difference in potential can produce a flow of charge that continues as long as the potential difference is present.

After discussing the features of static and moving charge, the lecture will cover electrical circuits and their components. In electric circuits, batteries maintain potential difference that cause electrons to flow through wires from areas of higher potential to areas of lower potential. Other circuit elements can change the current or act as energy stores, as will be described.

Finally, the lecture will close with a brief discussion of magnetism and electro-magnetic induction.

**THE 3 KEYS**

1. Electric field ($E$) is a general expression of force – force per unit charge – and voltage ($V$) is a general expression of energy – energy per unit charge.

2. Static electricity de-scribes point charge and is like gravity. Current describes moving charge and is like fluid flow.

3. $R \propto L/A$, $C \propto A/D$. Think of resistors and capacitors in parallel as having increased width (more capacitance, less resistance) and resistors or capacitors in series as having increased length or distance (more resistance, less capacitance).

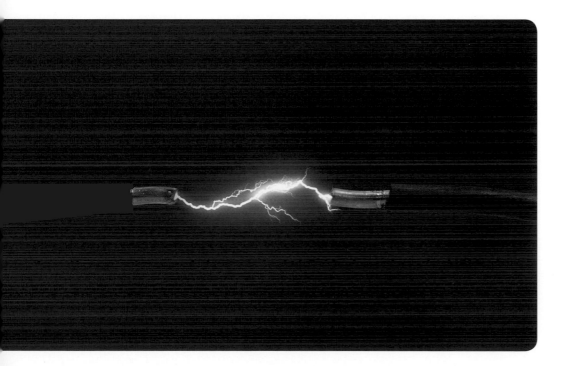

Questions about electricity are much more likely to appear on the MCAT® than are questions on gravity. Don't focus on adding to your knowledge of gravity. Instead, use any pre-existing knowledge of gravity to understand electricity.

## 4.2 Static Electric Charge

A force, called the electric force, exists between charges. If the charges are of the same type, the force is repulsive, and if the charges are of different types, the force is attractive. The magnitude of the force depends not only on the magnitudes of the charges but also the square of the distance between them. Surrounding a charge or group of charges is a field, and at any given position, the field has a particular strength called its potential. The potential at a given position is the potential energy per unit charge that a point charge would have at that position. Think of electric force as analogous to gravitational force, which is helpful for understanding electric potential. Gravitational potential is the gravitational potential energy per unit mass; the greater an object's mass, the more potential energy it possesses. The equations for electric force, field, potential energy and potential are very similar to those for gravitational force, field, potential energy and potential. The key difference is that gravitational force is always attractive, whereas electric force can be either attractive or repulsive.

**FIGURE 4.1** Like Charges Repel, Opposite Charges Attract

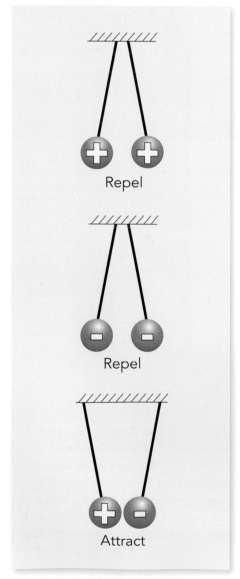

### Charge

Like energy, **charge** is an entity that defies definition. Yet, all of us have an intuitive idea about what it is; we've all experienced a shock from static electricity, for instance. Charge is intrinsic to the nature of some subatomic particles; it is part of their identity. Most of us are aware that there is positive charge and negative charge. The 'positive' and 'negative' signify nothing more than these charges being opposite to each other. Instead of positive and negative, they could have been called up and down, black and white, or even had their names reversed to 'negative' and 'positive'. It is due to this arbitrary convention that electrons were labeled negative and not positive, and as a result, current runs in the opposite direction of electrons. Charge ($q$) is given in units of **coulombs (C)**.

**Opposite charges** attract each other; **like charges** repel each other. The formula describing the magnitude of the force of the repulsion or attraction between two charged objects is called *Coulomb's law* and is analogous to the formula for gravitational force:

$$F = k\frac{q_1 q_2}{r^2}$$

where $k$ is Coulomb's constant ($k = 8.988 \times 10^9$ N $\cdot$ m$^2$/C$^2$), $q$ represents the respective charges, and $r$ is the distance between the centers of charge.

*Some transmembrane proteins like aquaporins use electrostatic repulsion to prevent charged molecules from passing through. Aquaporins allow water to enter the cell, but a positively charged arginine residue in the protein prevents protons from entering.*

### Conservation of Charge

Just as there is a universal law of conservation of energy, there is a **Universal Law of Conservation of Charge**. The universe has no net charge. In the majority of situations (and for the MCAT®), net charge is created by separating electrons from protons. If we were to put all the positive and negative charges in the universe together, they would cancel each other out, right down to the last electron and proton. Anytime a negative charge is isolated, a positive charge is also isolated, and vice versa. Charge is quantized. This means that any charge must be at least as large as a certain smallest possible unit. The smallest possible unit of charge is one electron unit ($e = 1.6 \times 10^{-19}$ C), the charge on one electron or one proton.

**FIGURE 4.2** | Electric Force

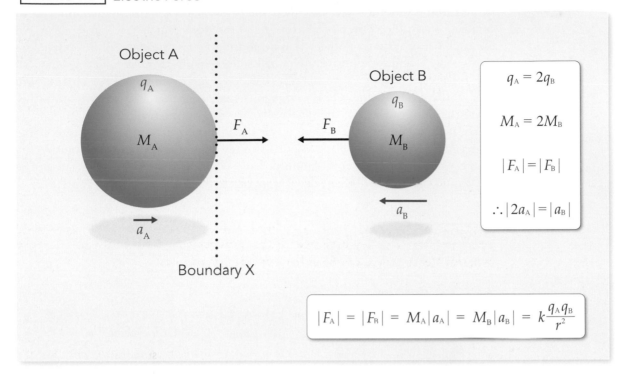

Figure 4.2 assumes that the gravity force is negligible compared to the force due to charge. This is often a safe assumption when dealing with particles of this size.

Two point charges, $q_A$ and $q_B$, experience attractive electric forces $F_A$ and $F_B$, which are equal in magnitude and opposite in direction. Because the point charges have masses $M_A$ and $M_B$, they also experience attractive gravitational forces likewise equal in magnitude and opposite in direction. However, the magnitude of the gravitational forces is negligible in comparison to the magnitude of the electric forces.

Notice that the diagram above is the same as that used for gravity in Lecture 1. Use the similarities between these forces to better understand the electric force. Both types of forces change inversely with the square of the distance between the centers of mass or charge. One major difference is that gravitational forces are always attractive while electrical forces may be either attractive or repulsive.

Also notice that the force due to gravity in the diagram above is ignored. Coulomb forces are usually of a far greater magnitude than gravitational forces, and, unless the masses are very large, gravitational forces are negligible.

---

**To compare electrical forces with gravitational forces, imagine the following. Place two tiny grains of sand 30 meters apart. Not much gravitational force between them, right? What if all the charged parts of one grain were negatively charged and all the charged parts of the other grain were positively charged so that the electric forces were entirely attractive rather than balanced? The resulting electric force pulling the two grains of sand together would be about three million tons.**

---

## Center of Charge

In defining Coulomb's law, we used the phrase "center of charge." Similar to center of mass, the center of charge is a point from which the charge generated by an object or system of objects can be considered to originate. For example, the charges on a hollow, positively charged sphere made from conducting material will repel each other so as to maximize the average distance of each charge from each of the other charges. This results in the positive charge spreading uniformly along the outer surface of the sphere. Due to the symmetry, the center of charge exists at the center of the sphere, even though there is no actual charge at the center of the sphere. The electrostatic force on a charged object placed outside the sphere can be found using Coulomb's Law, where $r$ is the distance between the object and the center of the sphere. Note that the same is true for gravity.

---

**FIGURE 4.3** Center of Charge

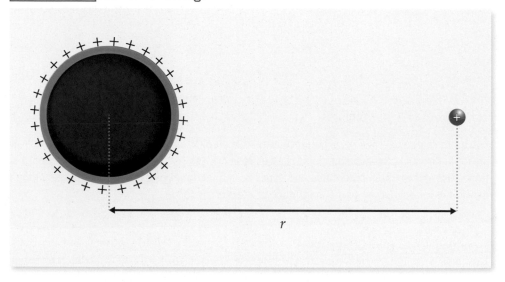

---

The similarities between gravity and electricity stem from the fact that both mass and charge create fields. A field is some type of distortion or condition in space that creates a force on a charge (or mass, if it is a gravitational field; or magnet, if it is a magnetic field [A magnetic field and an electric field are really the same field]). Recall that on the MCAT®, any force that acts on your system must be physically in contact with it, except for the forces of gravity, electricity, or magnetism. This is because these forces are created by fields and can act at a distance.

Any field can be represented by lines of force. Lines of force point in the direction of the field (positive to negative for electric fields, towards the mass creating the field for gravitational fields). The relative distance between lines indicates the strength of the field; the closer the lines, the stronger the field. Lines of force can never intersect, as this would indicate a field pointing in two opposite directions from the same location, an impossibility. The lines of force for a single positive point charge are shown in Figure 4.4.

Examine the lines of force for the field created by the positively charged, hollow sphere in Figure 4.5. Notice that the inside of the sphere has no electric field. A negatively charged sphere would produce the same result. This is because the lines of force must begin on a positive charge and end on a negative charge. This is impossible for lines entering the sphere, so there can be no lines of force inside a uniformly charged sphere. Again, the same is true for a gravitational field.

**FIGURE 4.4** | Electric Field

**FIGURE 4.5** | No Lines of Force Inside a Uniformly Charged Sphere

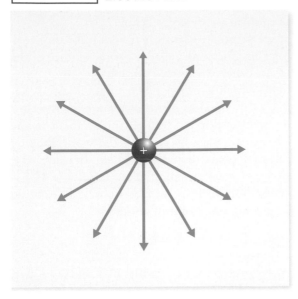

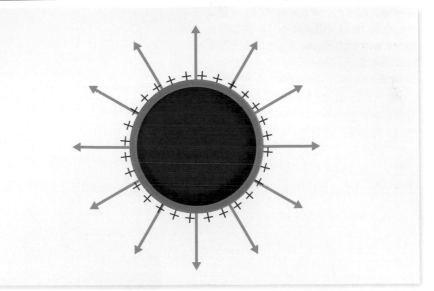

An electric field is defined as the electrostatic force per unit charge. The symbol for any **electric field** is $E$. $E$ is a vector pointing in the direction of the field and has units of N/C or V/m. For a point charge, the electric field is found by dividing Coulomb's law by $q$, giving:

$$E = k\frac{q_1}{r^2}$$

The electric field for a system of point charges is found by summing the fields due to each charge. Remember that $E$ is a vector and vector addition is required when summing fields.

The symbol for the gravitational field near the surface of the earth is the familiar $g$. When we want to discuss the gravitational force on any object at the surface of the earth, we normally use "$mg$" and not "$F = Gm_1m_2/r^2$". We are very familiar with the gravitational field near the surface of the earth, so we have created a shorthand method for describing the gravitational force for any mass. That method is the mass multiplied by the field, $mg$. Similarly, the force on a charge ($q$) in an electric field ($E$) is

$$F = qE$$

## Electric Potential Energy and Potential

To find the potential energy of a mass in the earth's gravitational field relative to some other position, we multiply this force by the displacement in the direction opposite the field, $mgh$. Similarly, the **potential energy** ($U$) of a charge in an electric field is the force multiplied by the displacement ($d$):

$$U = qEd$$

where $d$ is measured from a zero point of our own choosing, similar to the variable $h$ in gravitational potential energy. Notice that this equation was derived from the work equation and the electric force equation. If $W = Fd$, and $F = qE$, then $U = qEd$. In this case, potential energy changes when electric work is done on a charge.

Like any type of potential energy, the electrical potential energy of a charge depends on the position of the charge in the field. If the electric field is created by a point charge, we can derive the electric potential energy from Coulomb's law:

$$U = k\frac{q_1q_2}{r}$$

Because I am inside the car, a hollow conductor, there is no electric field and I am safe from the lighting strike.

According to this formula, electric potential is zero for particles separated by an infinite distance. Since energy is a state function, its value can be arbitrarily assigned, and it is given a zero value in this case by convention.

Recalling our study of gravity, if we wanted to create a function for the work required to move any given mass along any frictionless path near the surface of the earth, what would this function be? In other words, we are looking for a function intrinsic to the gravitational field, which is independent of any mass. What function would give us the 'potential' of the field in terms of work gained or lost per unit mass? The answer is $gh$, the field multiplied by the displacement in the direction opposite the field. Multiplying any mass by $gh$ gives the work done by the field in moving that mass. This is called the potential of the field. In electricity, potential has a special name, voltage. **Voltage ($V$)** is the potential for work by an electric field in moving any charge from one point to another.

$$V = Ed$$

Voltage is given in units of **volts (V)**, and is a scalar. Also recognize voltage in units of J/C.

The voltage due to a point charge is:

$$V = k\frac{q_1}{r}$$

Since voltage is a scalar, when finding the voltage due to a group of point charges, the voltages due to each individual charge can be summed directly.

Notice from Figure 4.6 that, like the work done by gravity, the work done by an electrostatic field is independent of the path. This is because both fields are conservative; they both conserve mechanical energy. As we will see when we discuss magnetism, this is not true of all electric fields.

**FIGURE 4.6** | Work Done by a Field is Path Independent

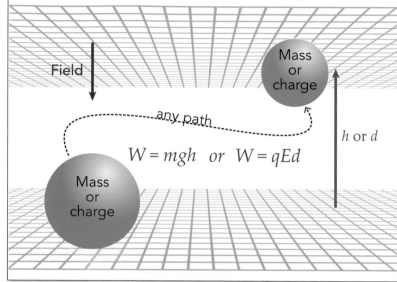

TABLE 4.1 > **Related Concepts: Electricity and Gravity**

| Concept | GRAVITY | | ELECTRICITY | | |
| --- | --- | --- | --- | --- | --- |
| | Analogy | Name | | Formula | Units |
| Force | $F = \frac{GMm}{r^2} = mg$ | Force | | $F = \frac{kq_1q_2}{r^2} = qE$ | N |
| | $g = \frac{F}{m}$ | Field | | $E = \frac{F}{q}$ | N/C or V/m |
| Energy | $PE = Fd = mgh$ | Potential Energy | | $PE = Fd = qEd$ | J |
| | $\frac{PE}{m} = gh$ | Potential (gravitational/ electric) | | $V = \frac{PE}{q} = Ed$ | J/C or V |

Use the similarities between electricity and gravity to help you learn and remember electricity. There are two concepts to consider: force and energy. Electric field is a general way to talk about force, i.e. force per unit charge. Voltage is a general way to talk about energy, i.e. potential energy per unit charge. Electric field and voltage are generalizations that describe the effects of a single charge, while force and potential energy are specific to two particular masses or charges. Use the analogy of buying potatoes: force and potential energy are the cost of a specific bag of potatoes where field and voltage are the cost in general of potatoes per pound.

Within an electric field, movement perpendicular to the field does not result in a change in potential, just as a mass moving along the surface of the earth does not experience a change in its gravitational potential. In any electric field we can define a surface normal to the field that describes a set of points all with the same potential. Examples of such surfaces are shown as dashed lines in Figure 4.7. They are called *equipotential surfaces*. All points on an equipotential surface are at the same voltage. An equipotential surface can be drawn at any point in the field.

Also shown in the diagram are the field lines of an *electric dipole*. An electric dipole is created by two opposite charges with equal magnitude. An electric *dipole moment* ($p = qd$) is a vector whose magnitude is the charge $q$ on one of the charges multiplied by the distance $d$ between the charges. In physics, this vector points in the opposite direction to the electric field, from the negative charge to the positive charge.

In chemistry the vector points from positive to negative. At large distances the electric field of a dipole varies by $1/r^3$.

If an electrostatics problem appears on Test Day, you'll need to observe proper sign conventions. When dealing with force (the first two rows in Table 4.1), don't use signs even if a negative charge is present. You don't use signs because drawing out the force and electric field vectors will give you the correct direction rather than the sign. If you're dealing with energy (the last two rows in Table 4.1), be sure to use the signs associated with the charges. Energy and electric potential are scalar quantities – they don't have direction – so the appropriate signs will be necessary.

**FIGURE 4.7** | Electric Dipole Field Lines and Equipotential Surfaces

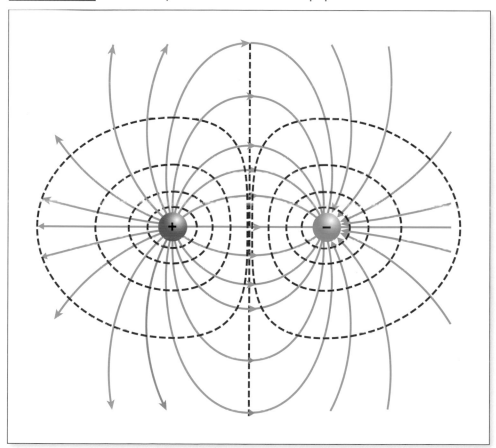

When solving electricity problems, be sure to know what type of electric field you're working with. Point charges create electric fields that, unlike constant electric fields, change with $r$. Use only those formulas that apply to the field.

A potential difference, or voltage, exists across neuronal membranes because of differences in the concentration of $K^+$ ions in the intracellular and extracellular fluids. This voltage creates an electric field that draws sodium into the cell when voltage-gated ion channels open.

Nervous System
BIOLOGY 2

A dipole placed in an electric field will tend to align itself along the field in the opposite orientation to the field.

FIGURE 4.8 A Dipole in an Electric Field

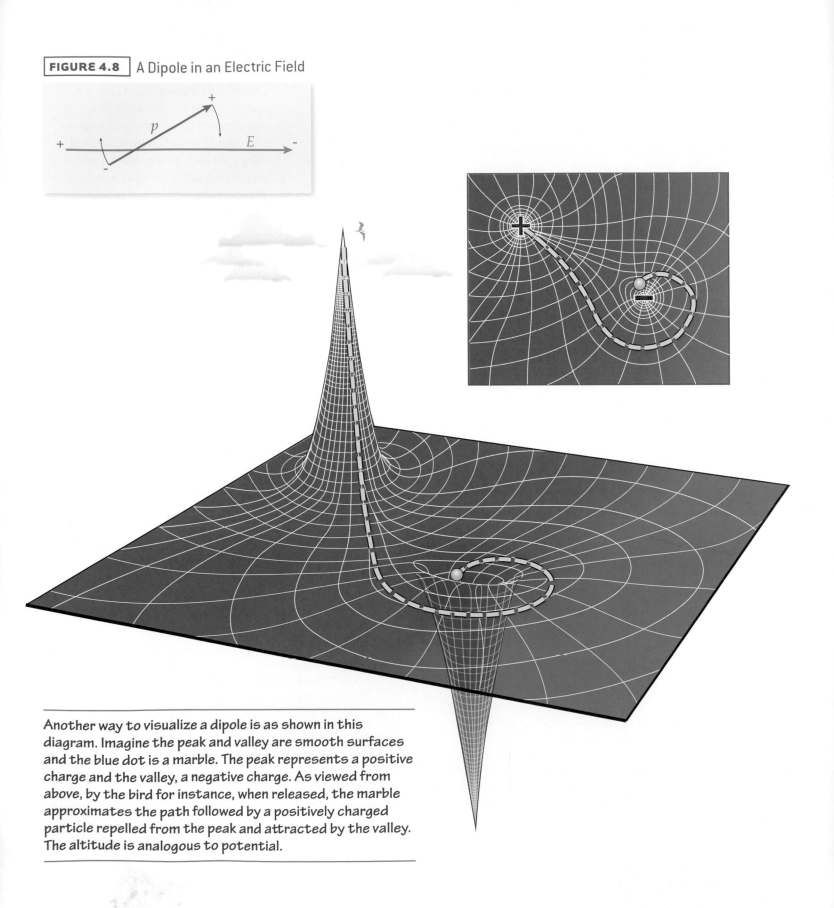

Another way to visualize a dipole is as shown in this diagram. Imagine the peak and valley are smooth surfaces and the blue dot is a marble. The peak represents a positive charge and the valley, a negative charge. As viewed from above, by the bird for instance, when released, the marble approximates the path followed by a positively charged particle repelled from the peak and attracted by the valley. The altitude is analogous to potential.

## Question 73

Two charged metal plates are placed one meter apart creating a constant electric field between them. A one coulomb charged particle is placed in the space between them. The particle experiences a force of 100 Newtons due to the electric field. What is the potential difference between the plates?

○ **A.** 1 V
○ **B.** 10 V
○ **C.** 100 V
○ **D.** 1000 V

## Question 74

How much work is required to move a positively charged particle along the 15 cm path shown if the electric field E is 10 N/C and the charge on the particle is 8 C? (Note: Ignore gravity.)

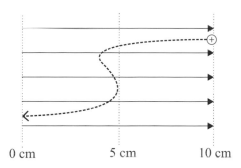

○ **A.** 0.8 J
○ **B.** 8 J
○ **C.** 12 J
○ **D.** 1200 J

## Question 75

If the distance between two point charges is increased by a factor of 3, the new force on either charge will:

○ **A.** decrease by a factor of 9.
○ **B.** decrease by a factor of 3.
○ **C.** remain the same.
○ **D.** increase by a factor of 3.

## Question 76

A positively charged particle starts at rest 25 cm from a second positively charged particle that is held stationary throughout the experiment. The first particle is released and accelerates away from the second particle. When the first particle has moved 25 cm, it has reached a velocity of 10 m/s. What is the maximum velocity the first particle will reach?

○ **A.** 10 m/s
○ **B.** 14 m/s
○ **C.** 20 m/s
○ **D.** The first particle will never stop accelerating and will reach an infinite velocity.

## Question 77

If the distance between a point charge and an infinitely large charged plate is increased by a factor of 2, the new force on the point charge will:

○ **A.** decrease by a factor of 4.
○ **B.** decrease by a factor of 2.
○ **C.** remain the same.
○ **D.** increase by a factor of 2.

## Question 78

The electric field for the two point charges A and B is shown below. Which of the following is true?

○ **A.** Both charges are positive.
○ **B.** Both charges are negative.
○ **C.** The charges have opposite signs.
○ **D.** The signs of the charges cannot be determined.

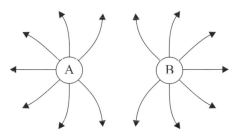

## Question 79

Electroporation transiently exposes cells to powerful electrical fields that form pores in the membrane. If the distance between a cell and an electric field source doubles, charged particles within the cell:

○ **A.** will experience a two-fold increase in the magnitude of their acceleration.
○ **B.** will experience a two-fold decrease in the magnitude of their acceleration.
○ **C.** will experience a four-fold increase in the magnitude of their acceleration.
○ **D.** will experience a four-fold decrease in the magnitude of their acceleration.

## Question 80

When –10 C of charge are moved from point A to point B in the diagram below, 90 J of work is done. The voltage between point A and point B is:

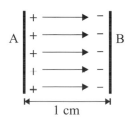

○ **A.** 0.9 V.
○ **B.** 9 V.
○ **C.** 90 V.
○ **D.** 900 V.

**FIGURE 4.9** Excess Charge is Held on the Surface

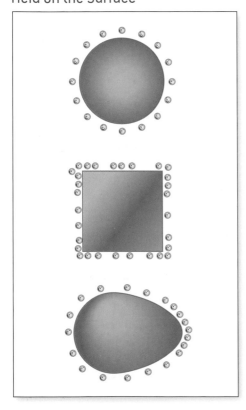

## 4.3 | Moving Electricity

A force, called the electric force, exists between charges. If the charges are experiencing a potential difference, charges move from areas of higher potential to areas of lower potential. A potential difference, or voltage, is said to produce a flow of charge, or current. Think of charge flow as analogous to fluid flow.

### Conductivity

When charge moves along an object (usually in the form of electrons), that object is said to be conducting electricity. At the same time that it is conducting electricity, the object also resists the movement of charge. All substances conduct electricity to some extent, and all substances resist movement of charge to some extent (superconductors excluded). Substances resist and conduct charge to varying degrees, but the vast majority of substances either conduct charge very well or very poorly. We can safely classify most substances as conductors or resistors. Good **conductors**, such as metals, allow electrons to flow relatively freely. Poor conductors (good **resistors**) hold electrons tightly in place. Poor conductors are represented by network solids such as diamond and glass, among other substances.

There are two classes of conductors. *Metallic conductors* conduct charge through the transfer of electrons, and no chemical change occurs as the result of that flow. The electrons in metals are delocalized, forming a "sea of electrons" that is conducive to electron flow. *Electrolytic conductors* are characterized by a flow of ions in a membrane, which entails a transfer of matter. Both types of conductors are present in the galvanic and electrolytic cells studied in chemistry. Electrons move through the wire, which acts as a metallic conductor, while the salt bridge functions as an electrolytic conductor, exchanging ions to maintain neutral charge in the half cells. This lecture examines circuits of which metallic and electrolytic conductors are a part.

### Current

Moving charge is called **current**. Current is given in **amps (A)**, or C/s. Current is a scalar, but we describe its flow to be in the direction of the movement of positive charge. Ben Franklin arbitrarily designated electrons to be negative. Because of this designation, current, which is usually created by flowing electrons, is in the opposite direction to the flow of electrons.

The flow of electrons resembles the flow of a fluid. Like molecules in a moving fluid, electrons move very fast in random directions, while there is a much slower uniform translational movement (called *drift speed*) opposite the direction of the current.

When I rub electrons off of my socks, I become positively charged. My positively charged finger pulls electrons from the doorknob.

When considering resistance in a conductor, think of electrons waltzing through a wire as current flows. If the dance floor gets wider with an increase in area, the electrons have more room and feel lower resistance as they dance. If the dance floor gets longer, the electrons need to travel farther to get to the other end of the floor, making it take longer to complete the dance. Increasing the length of a wire increases the resistance, while increasing the cross sectional area of a wire through increasing radius (or width) decreases resistance.

## 4.4 | Circuit Elements

Just as fluid will only flow in the presence of a pressure difference, charges will only flow in the presence of a potential difference. In a **circuit**, a cyclical pathway for moving charge, a battery provides the potential difference needed to maintain charge flow. Like flowing fluids, flowing charges encounter resistance.

As we learned earlier, all substances resist the flow of charge. The quantitative measure of this property is called **resistivity** ($\rho$). The quantitative measure of an object of a particular shape and size to resist the flow of charge is called its **resistance** ($R$) and is measured in **ohms** ($\Omega$). If an object is made from a homogeneous conductor, the resistance of the object when a voltage is applied uniformly to its ends is related to the resistivity of the material that it is made from by:

$$R = \rho \frac{L}{A}$$

This formula demonstrates that if the length of a wire is doubled or its cross-sectional area is cut in half, its resistance is also doubled. This is similar to what we would expect for fluid flowing through a pipe. Many useful analogies can be made between electron flow and fluid flow.

Note that the resistance of a material can also vary with temperature according to the equation:

$$R = R_o[1 + \alpha (T - T_o)]$$

where $R_o$ and $T_o$ are resistance and temperature at some reference value and $\alpha$ is a constant specific to the material in the substance. The important takeaway of this equation is that an increase in the temperature of a material increases its resistance. When electrons in the material have more kinetic energy, they are more likely to come in proximity to one another, producing more repulsive interactions. More repulsive interactions between electrons impedes their flow, resulting in greater resistance in the material.

> Notice that the definition of a circuit includes the word 'cyclical' as in 'making a circle.' A circuit requires a complete circle for the current to flow around. No current will flow unless it can flow in a circle.

**FIGURE 4.10** Properties of the Flow of Charge

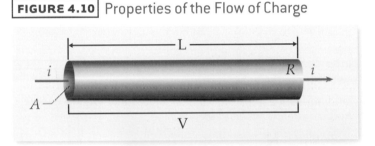

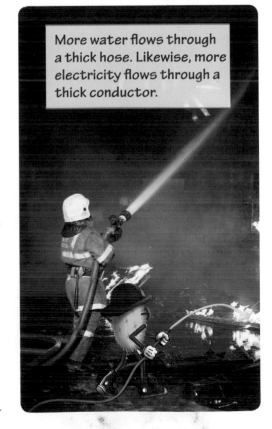

> More water flows through a thick hose. Likewise, more electricity flows through a thick conductor.

You've probably observed that light bulbs tend to burn out when they are first turned on. A thin filament in the bulb conducts charge, and when the filament breaks, the bulb is dead. When a bulb is burning, its temperature is very high and so is the resistance in the wire. A bulb that has been off for a while and is no longer hot has slightly lower resistance. The filament conducts more current when resistance is lower, and it is more likely to break. You can use that observation to remember how the resistance of a metallic conductor varies with temperature. Note that the reverse is true for electrolytic conductors. This is because an increase in temperature gives ions more kinetic energy, increasing their mobility and propensity to flow.

Electric current (i) is equal to potential difference, or voltage, divided by resistance.

$$i = \frac{V}{R}$$

This is known as **Ohm's law**. Note that the $V$ in this equation stands not for potential but for potential difference, or voltage.

Ohm's law is useful for analyzing circuits. Recall that the flow rate of a real fluid moving through a horizontal pipe with constant diameter is equal to change in pressure divided by resistance ($Q = \Delta P/R$). Think of current as flow through a constant diameter pipe, and voltage as the difference in height between two points in the pipe.

A **battery** adds energy to a circuit. In our analogy to fluids, a battery pumps the fluid to a greater height. Batteries are rated by **electromotive force (EMF)**, which is a fancy word for voltage.

While real batteries have internal resistance, it can be ignored unless indicated. To account for internal resistance, simply redraw the battery and place a resistor with a resistance equal to the internal resistance directly behind or in front of the battery.

| **FIGURE 4.11** | Batteries as Galvanic Cells |

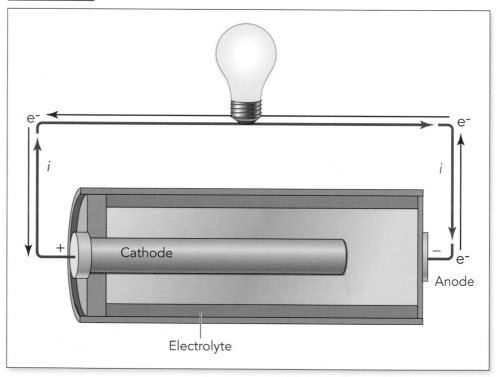

Note that rechargeable batteries behave as *both* galvanic and electrolytic cells. When rechargeable batteries discharge, they function as galvanic cells. An external power source such as the running engine of a car can force current in the opposite direction when the battery recharges. That means a recharging battery can be considered an electrolytic cell.

## MCAT® THINK

When you see a battery in a circuit, picture the inside of the battery. A battery generates the flow of energy in a circuit from its built-in potential difference. Charges flow "downhill" from higher potential to lower potential.

Batteries consist of one or more galvanic cells in which oxidation occurs at the anode and reduction at the cathode; when a wire connects the two electrodes, electrons flow from the anode to the cathode. Ionization energy, how easily an electron can be removed from an atom, determines the potential, or voltage, of a material. In physics current is defined as the flow of positive charge, not the flow of electrons. The direction of current in the wire is from the cathode to the anode, opposite the flow of electrons. Remember that current flows from high potential to low potential. In a battery, the electrode with the higher potential is the cathode and the electrode with the lower potential is the anode. The difference between the potentials of the cathode and anode is the voltage of the battery.

The wire from the cathode to the anode is not part of the battery. The wire connecting the electrodes in an electrochemical cell is the wire of the circuit driven by the battery. Connecting the cathode of the battery to the anode with a wire discharges the battery's energy.

Voltage, also called potential, is a way of expressing potential energy. The greater the potential difference between the two electrodes, the more energy the battery can put into the system. This energy is determined by the difference between the reduction potentials of the specific pair of reduction-oxidation (redox) reactions that occur inside the battery. A battery's energy is calculated using the equation $\Delta G = -nFE$, where $E$ is the maximum potential of the redox reactions and $\Delta G$ is the energy generated by the redox reaction, which becomes electrical energy.

In order for a circuit to draw current from a battery, a circuit element is required (resistor, capacitor, or inductor). When a resistor, such as a light bulb, is attached to the wire connecting the positive and negative nodes, some of the energy generated by the battery leaves the circuit through the resistor. When a capacitor is added to a circuit, some of the energy generated by the battery can be stored. The capacitor can later discharge that energy at a faster rate than the battery supplied it. In these ways, batteries provide the energy needed to operate many devices. The chemical energy is turned into electric energy which is then converted to the energy released by the device (i.e. light, sound, heat, kinetic energy of motion, etc...).

Here is an example of my analogous fluid circuit. Each spinning wheel represents resistance as it resists the movement of the fluid. Technically, voltage should only drop across resistance as per Ohm's law, so in my fluid circuit, the height of the fluid should only change when the fluid goes through a resistor. Notice that the resistors spin, using up energy. Anything attached to a circuit that uses energy also provides resistance, and anything that provides resistance uses energy.

A battery works to put energy back into the circuit. To analyze this circuit, we add the voltage drop across each resistor, and set it equal to the voltage of the battery. This is analogous to the work done per unit mass on each wheel set equal to the work done per unit mass.

A **capacitor** is used to temporarily store energy in a circuit. It stores it in the form of separated charge. In a **parallel plate capacitor**, two plates made from conductive material are separated by a very small distance. On a charged capacitor, one plate holds positive charge, and the other plate holds the exact same amount of negative charge. This separation of charge creates an electric field that is constant everywhere between the plates. The electric field is given by:

$$E = \frac{1}{\kappa} \frac{Q}{A\varepsilon_o}$$

This $\kappa$ is not Coulomb's constant. This is the dielectric $\kappa$, which we will discuss below. $Q$ is the charge on either plate. The $\varepsilon_o$ term is derived from Coulomb's constant $k$. It is related to $k$ by:

$$k = \frac{1}{4\pi\varepsilon_o}$$

Note that in the electric field equation, $E$ and $Q$ are directly proportional, which means that $V$ and $Q$ are also directly proportional. As the applied voltage increases, so too does the amount of stored charge. By definition, capacitance is the ability to store charge per unit voltage. In other words, something with a high capacity can store a lot of charge at low voltage.

$$C = \frac{Q}{V}$$

In a parallel plate capacitor, the amount of charge that can be stored is directly proportional to the area of each plate. This is because the charge sits on the surface of the plates. Recall that charge sits on the surface of a charged conductor. In a charged capacitor, the charge sits on only the inside face of each plate. As a result, increasing the thickness of the plates of a capacitor will not increase its ability to store charge. Recall also that voltage is defined by distance ($V = Ed$). The farther the plates are separated, the greater the voltage, and the lower the capacitance. The physical makeup of a parallel plate capacitor in terms of plate area ($A$) and separation distance ($d$) is given by:

$$C = \kappa \frac{A\varepsilon_o}{d}$$

Understand Key 3: Use what makes sense about resistors and capacitors to learn and remember the rules for series and parallel circuit elements on the following pages, rather than memorizing equations. Notice that resistance increases with length of the wire while capacitance increases with cross-sectional area. Use this to reason through the effects of putting circuit elements in series or in parallel. Putting circuit elements in series is like increasing the length of that circuit element. Putting circuit elements in parallel is like increasing the width, or area. Resistors in parallel are like one wider resistor, which would have less resistance. The net capacitance for capacitors in parallel is greater because they are like one capacitor with a wider surface area.

There is an intuitive explanation for the relationship between plate separation and capacitance. Remember that positive charge collects on one plate while electrons build on the opposing plate, generating an increasingly negative charge. These plates bear opposite charges, so an attractive force exists between them. The strong attractive force between the plates makes it difficult for the separation of charge to be maintained at longer distances. It is easier to maintain charge separation and storage when the plates are closer, which is why capacitance is inversely related to distance.

A capacitor's job is to store energy (generally for quick use in the future). The energy ($U$) stored in any shape capacitor is given by:

$$U = \frac{1}{2}QV \quad \text{or} \quad U = \frac{1}{2}CV^2 \quad \text{or} \quad U = \frac{1}{2}\frac{Q^2}{C}$$

Using any one of these equations, the others can be derived from $Q = CV$.

When you see an energy problem, think like an accountant. Use these equations to "balance the books."

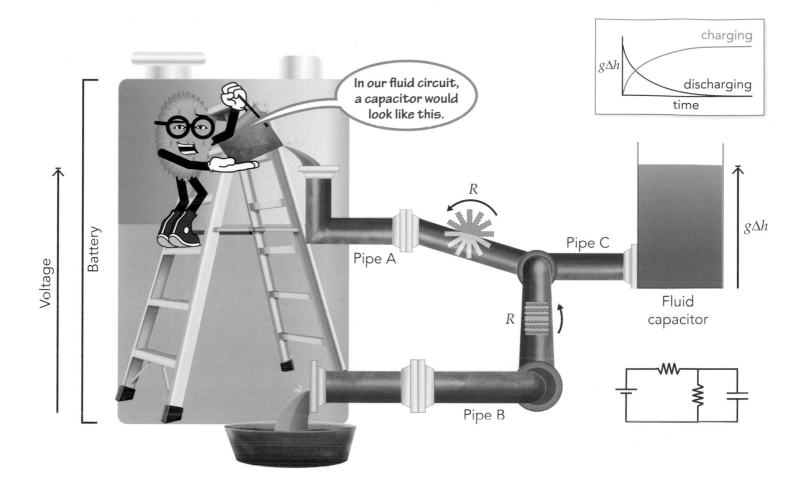

As the fluid comes to the fork at pipe B and C, some fluid would move in each direction. As the fluid capacitor fills, the fluid flow through pipe C would eventually come to a stop and all the fluid would move through pipe B. In order to maintain the fluid capacitor at height h, fluid flow through pipe A would have to have kinetic energy equal to the gravitational potential of the fluid capacitor. This results in the equation $v = \sqrt{2gh}$ . The fluid capacitor now stores energy for the circuit. If flow through pipe A is suddenly blocked, the capacitor would empty with an initial velocity of $v = \sqrt{2gh}$ . With this reasoning you can infer the shape of the voltage vs. time graphs for charging and discharging a capacitor. Since $g\Delta h$ is analogous to voltage, $\Delta V$, the $g\Delta h$ vs. time graph is the same shape as the $\Delta V$ vs. time graph.

The **dielectric constant**, κ, refers to the substance between the plates of a capacitor. The substance between the plates must be an insulator, or it would conduct electrons from one plate to the other and charge could not be built up. A dielectric acts to resist the creation of an electric field, allowing the capacitor to store more charge (to have greater capacitance). Usually a dielectric contains dipoles oriented in random directions. Recall that a dipole in an external electric field has potential energy depending upon its orientation. When the electric field begins to build up between the plates of a capacitor, the dipoles are rotated to point in the direction of the electric field. This rotation requires energy in the form of work done on the dielectric. The reoriented dipoles create a small electric field in

## FIGURE 4.12 Charge Building on Capacitor Plates

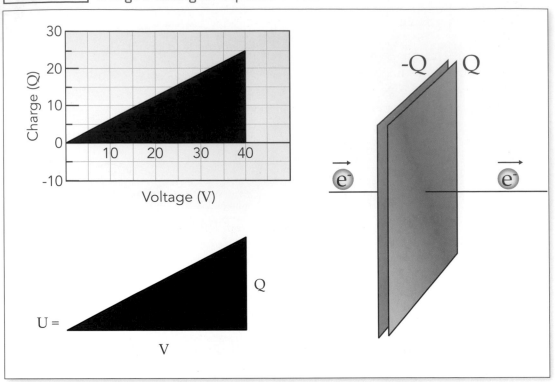

It's easy to see where the formula for energy stored by a capacitor comes from. If we imagine a capacitor with no charge on it, the voltage across this capacitor must be zero. For each unit of charge that we add, the voltage increases proportionally ($Q = CV$). If we graph this, we get a straight line. The area under this line is the product of charge times voltage, or energy. The area is a triangle, which is 1/2 base times height or 1/2QV.

the opposite direction of the plates. If the capacitor is in a closed circuit with a battery, the voltage across the dielectric remains constant. To counteract the reduced electric field in the presence of the dielectric, the plates retain more charge and maintain their original electric field strength. The result is that a dielectric allows a capacitor to store more energy. The dielectric constant of a vacuum is defined to be unity (one). Air is very close to one, and all other dielectric constants increase from there.

**Work is done on the dielectric and energy is stored in the dielectric.**

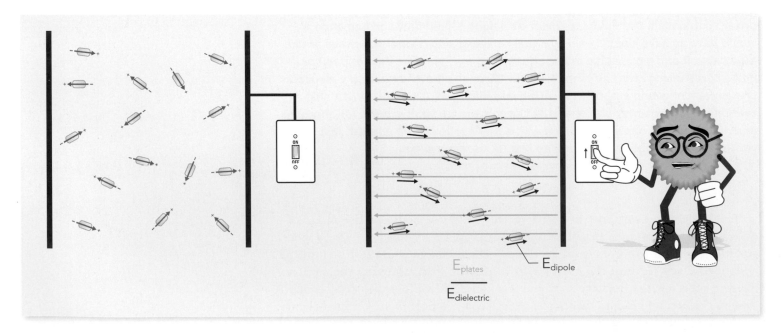

One other effect of a dielectric is to limit the value of the possible voltage across the plates. At some maximum voltage, the dielectric will break down and conduct electricity. This value of a dielectric is called the *dielectric strength*. If dielectric strength appears on the MCAT®, it will be explained in a passage.

In order to analyze a circuit, it is important to recognize the symbols for a resistor, a capacitor and a battery.

Lines connecting components should be considered completely non-resistive wires.

It is important to recognize when these components are in parallel and when they are in series. This has nothing to do with their orientation in space; parallel components are not always pointing in the same direction. Components lined up in a row, like train cars, are in series. More precisely, any two components not separated by a node are in series. Single components in alternate paths connecting the same nodes are in parallel.

Anytime current passes through a resistor, the voltage of the flowing charges is said to "drop." Just as gravitational potential of an object decreases as it falls and loses potential energy, the electrical potential also drops once a charge has passed through a resistor, which dissipates energy.

When resistors are in series, their total resistance (effective resistance, $R$) is the sum of their resistances.

$$R_{eff} = R_1 + R_2 + ... \qquad \text{(Resistors in series)}$$

Resistors in series can be thought of as a single resistor with length equal to the sum of the lengths of the individual resistors. Increasing the length of a resistor increases its resistance. $R \propto L$.

Think of resistors as toll booths. The flow of traffic that passes through three toll booths that are in series with one another will be impeded relative to the flow of traffic that passes through just one toll booth. The voltage will drop across each of the resistors in the series, just as drivers will have to pay three different tolls as they travel the road.

When resistors are in parallel, their effective resistance can be arrived at through the following equation:

$$\frac{1}{R_{eff}} = \frac{1}{R_1} + \frac{1}{R_2} + ... \qquad \text{(Resistors in parallel)}$$

Resistors in parallel can be through of as a single resistor with cross-sectional area equal to the sum of the cross-sectional areas of the resistors connected in parallel. Increasing the cross-sectional area of a resistor decreases resistance. $R \propto 1/A$. Again, think of resistors as toll booths. The flow of traffic that has the option to pass through one of four toll-booths in parallel with one another will be faster relative to the flow of traffic that must pass through a single toll booth. The voltage drop across each branch of the parallel wiring will also be the same. On a toll road with multiple booths, the road forks out to allow traffic to pass through many booths, lowering resistance, but then the road converges after the booth. All of the cars will have paid the same toll once their roads have rejoined, and charges passing through parallel branches will have paid the same energetic cost in each branch.

If we were to open a second bridge parallel to the first bridge, we would improve traffic flow, allowing for a greater 'current' of traffic.

**FIGURE 4.13** Important Symbols in Circuits and in Parallel

Resistor    Capacitor    Battery

**FIGURE 4.14** Resistors in Series and in Parallel

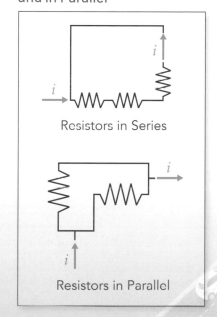

Resistors in Series

Resistors in Parallel

In physics class, you likely used Kirchhoff's rules to determine the unspecified voltages, currents and resistances of complex circuits. The MCAT® is very unlikely to test your knowledge of Kirchhoff's rules. Questions requiring knowledge beyond what is presented in this lecture would be accompanied by explanatory passages.

The analogy of the tollbooths is also helpful for understanding the movement of blood through the vasculature. The circulatory system is like a circuit, and the heart is the "battery" that creates flow. Blood leaves the heart and flows into arteries, arterioles, and finally capillaries. Capillaries are only wide enough to allow one cell to pass through at a time. Because it is a non-ideal fluid, blood flow is impeded by drag forces, but the parallel arrangement of capillaries still reduces the resistance throughout the vasculature and facilitates proper flow of blood.

Capacitors are exactly opposite to resistors. When capacitors are arranged in series, effective capacitance is calculated using the equation below:

$$\frac{1}{C_{eff}} = \frac{1}{C_1} + \frac{1}{C_2} + \dots \qquad \textbf{(Capacitors in series)}$$

Capacitors in series can be thought of as a single capacitor with a distance between plates equal to the distance between the first plate of the first capacitor and the second plate of the last capacitor. Increasing the distance between the plates of a capacitor decreases its capacitance.

In parallel, the capacitances of individual capacitors sum directly to give an effective capacitance:

$$C_{eff} = C_1 + C_2 + \dots \qquad \textbf{(Capacitors in parallel)}$$

Capacitors in parallel can be thought of as a single capacitor with plate area equal to the sum of the areas of the capacitors. Increasing the area of a capacitor's plates increases its capacitance because the charges gathering on the plate have more distance to spread out and therefore experience smaller repulsive forces.

To determine unspecified voltages, currents, and resistances, simplify circuits as shown in Figures 4.15 and 4.16. We begin by replacing components in parallel and series with their corresponding effective components. We continue this process until we have our simplified circuit; one of each element. Next we use Ohm's law to find the missing quantity.

**FIGURE 4.15** Simplifying Circuits That Have Multiple Resistors

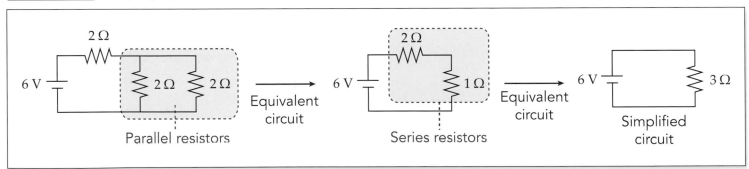

**FIGURE 4.16** Simplifying Circuits That Have Resistors and Capacitors

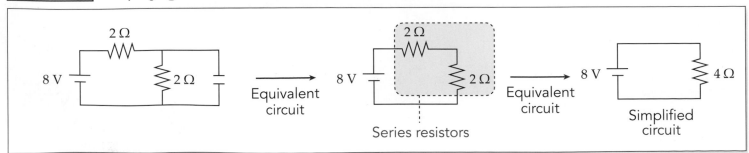

## Solution for Figure 4.15

Solution for
Current

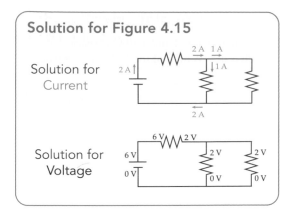

Solution for
Voltage

## Solution for Figure 4.16

Solution for
Current

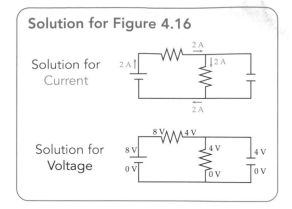

Solution for
Voltage

The solution for Figure 4.16 is for when the circuit has been on for a long time.

If the circuit contains a capacitor, initially, for the first tiny fraction of a second, the capacitor behaves like a bare wire with no resistance. Once the capacitor is fully charged (likely to be a fraction of a second later), the capacitor behaves like a break in the circuit. It is most likely that you would be asked to solve the circuit after it has been on for a while.

## Meters

Meters can be attached to a circuit in order to measure the voltage or flow of current at any point in the circuit.

An **ammeter** is an instrument that measures the current flowing through a circuit. An ammeter is connected in series with a circuit so that all current $i$ flowing through the circuit also flows through the meter. Since the ammeter measures the current, it should not affect the current. To maximize current, the resistance within the ammeter, $R_A$, is almost zero.

A **voltmeter** is an instrument that measures the potential difference between any two points on a circuit. In order to measure a voltage drop, the voltmeter is attached to two separate points on a circuit, often on either side of a circuit element. A voltmeter is always attached in parallel to the circuit, so the voltmeter does not affect the voltage of the circuit. In order to prevent the voltmeter from changing the potential difference between two points, it should not draw a current. To achieve this, the resistance within the voltmeter is functionally infinite. Maximizing the resistance of the voltmeter minimizes the amount of current that passes through it.

A device called a **multimeter** can serve as both an ammeter and a voltmeter. A switch determines whether current or voltage is measured. Multimeters may also serve as *ohmmeters*, which measure the resistance of circuit elements.

**FIGURE 4.17** Circuit Meters

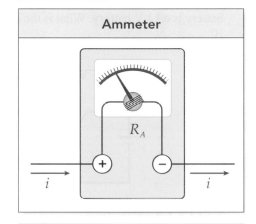

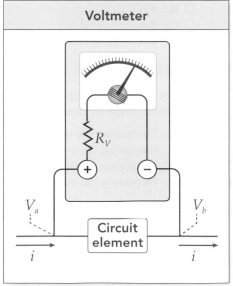

These turbines at the Hoover Dam change the gravitational potential energy of water into electrical energy. This energy is used to provide power to people across three states.

## 4.5 | Magnetism

A magnet creates a **magnetic field**. Magnetic field strength is measured in units of tesla, T. A magnetic field is concurrent with an electric field. It is easier to understand and deal with this single entity (the electromagnetic field) if we treat magnetic fields and electric fields as distinct yet linked. All charges, static and moving, create an electric field around them. Only moving charges produce magnetic fields. A static electric field produces no force on a magnet, and a magnetic field produces no force on a static electric charge.

Like the positive and negative of electric charges, a magnet comes with a north and south pole, where like poles repel and opposite poles attract. Unlike electric charges, magnetic poles have never been found to exist in isolation; one pole always accompanies the other. Similar to the electric field, the magnetic field can be represented by lines of force. The lines of force in a magnetic field point from the north pole to the south pole of the magnet that created the field. Magnets placed within a magnetic field experience a force pulling their south pole opposite to the direction of the lines of force while pushing their north pole in the same direction as the lines of force. Earth itself is a magnet. Interestingly, the geographic North Pole is the south pole of Earth's magnetic dipole. The Earth's geographic poles are named for the direction that the magnetic arrow of the compass points, and not for the poles on the actual magnet of the Earth. Because the north pole of the compass magnet is attracted to the Earth's magnetic south pole, this was named our geographic North Pole. For this reason, the lines of force made by Earth's magnetic field point from the geographic South Pole to the geographic North Pole. (The actual magnetic poles are also 11.5° away from the geographic poles and constantly shifting very slowly.)

Charges can be separated, but magnetic poles have never been found individually. If you try to separate magnetic poles by breaking a magnet, you just get more magnets with more poles.

**FIGURE 4.18** The Earth as a Magnet

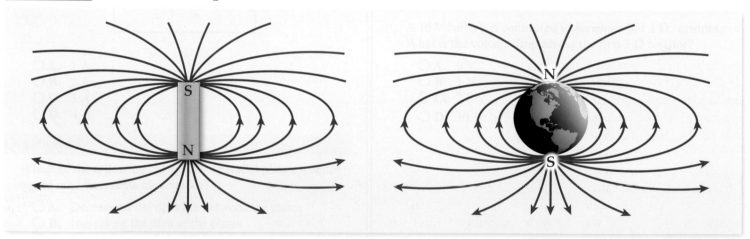

A stationary charge induces an electric field, but does not induce a magnetic field, while a moving charge induces both an electric and a magnetic field. Changing an electric field induces a magnetic field, and, vice versa: changing a magnetic field induces an electric field. This phenomenon is the basis for electromagnetic waves, which will be discussed in the context of light waves in Lecture 5 of this manual.

By 'induce' we mean 'create'. A changing electric field creates a magnetic field and a changing magnetic field creates an electric field.

Current is moving charge. Any and all current creates a magnetic field.

A small magnet out pulls the entire Earth: magnetic force is stronger than gravitational force.

A charge moving through a magnetic field experiences a force directed perpendicularly to both the velocity and the magnetic field. The magnitude of the force ($F$) on a charge ($q$) moving with velocity ($v$) through a magnetic field ($B$) is:

$$F = qvB \sin\theta$$

where $\theta$ is the angle between the magnetic field and the velocity of the charge.

Although we don't normally think about the body as creating magnetic fields, note that any movement of charge will generate a magnetic field. A physician could determine the velocity of blood by injecting particles of known charge into the bloodstream and measuring the strength of the magnetic field.

**FIGURE 4.19** The Magnetic Field Exerts a Centripetal Force on the Charged Particle

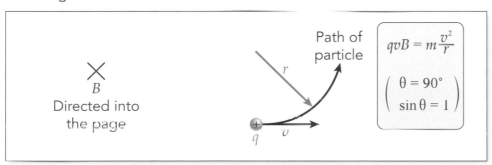

A changing magnetic field creates an electric field, but unlike the electric field created by a stationary charge, a magnetic field is non-conservative. The mechanical energy creating the electric field is not conserved, but is dissipated as heat in the charged object. Electric potential has no meaning for electric fields induced by changing magnetic fields.

Imagine a loop of wire pulled out of a magnetic field. As the magnetic field around the wire changes, an electric field is created and a current develops in the wire. The current created in the wire as it moves out of the external magnetic field creates its own magnetic field. A force is required to remove the loop at a constant velocity. The work done by this force is not conserved, but, instead, creates thermal energy in the loop.

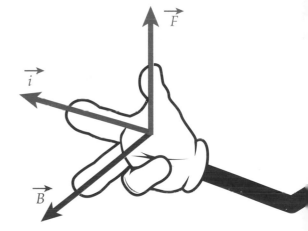

**FIGURE 4.20** Changing Magnetic Fields Induce a Current

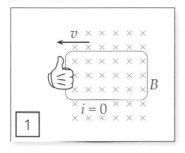

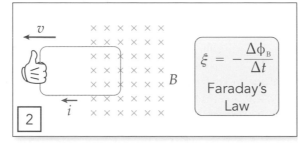

A charged particle moving through a magnetic field will be forced into a curved path. Recall that $W = Fd \cos\theta$. The magnetic force is always applied at 90° to the velocity of the particle and $\cos 90° = 0$, so no work can ever be done by this force. It cannot transfer energy to the particle, so it cannot change the speed of the particle.

## Question 89

Two ions in the blood, $-q_1$ and $+q_2$, carrying equal and opposite charges approach a uniform magnetic field at the same speed. Which of the following conditions is sufficient to guarantee a force on $-q_1$ within the field that has a greater magnitude than that on $+q_2$?

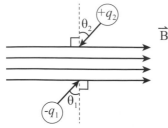

I. $-q_1$ accelerates before entering the magnetic field such that its speed exceeds that of $+q_2$
II. $\theta_1 < \theta_2$
III. $\theta_1 > \theta_2$

- **A.** II only
- **B.** III only
- **C.** I and II
- **D.** I and III

## Question 90

All of the following expressions are equal to an Ohm EXCEPT (Power = IV = $I^2R$ = $V^2/R$):

- **A.** $V \cdot s/C$
- **B.** $W/A^2$
- **C.** $A/V$
- **D.** $V^2/W$

## Question 91

Voltage sources for alternating current are characterized by their average voltage, $V_{rms}$. ($V_{rms} = V_{max}/\sqrt{2}$). If the AC current delivered to a home by the electric company is delivered at 120 $V_{rms}$, what is the maximum voltage across an outlet?

- **A.** 86 V
- **B.** 120 V
- **C.** 170 V
- **D.** 220 V

## Question 92

Neurons send messages via electrical impulses along their axons. The impulse, called an action potential, is propagated when ions enter or exit the cell. Approximately $5.5 \times 10^{11}$ $Na^+$ ions per meter cross the cell membrane during a second of the propagation of an action potential. What is the current caused by the flow of $Na^+$ across 1 cm of the axon? (elementary charge = $1.6 \times 10^{-19}$ C)

- **A.** $5.5 \times 10^9$ C/s
- **B.** $8.8 \times 10^{-10}$ C/s
- **C.** $5.5 \times 10^{-9}$ C/s
- **D.** $8.8 \times 10^{-9}$ C/s

## Question 93

The resting voltage across the membrane of a neuron is measured at -70 mV. In multiple sclerosis, the axons of neurons lose their myelin sheath. This results in 30% decrease in the resistance of the membrane. What is the current flow across one cm of an axon in a patient with multiple sclerosis? Assume that the resistance of a healthy axon is 250 MΩ/cm.

- **A.** $2 \times 10^{-10}$ μA
- **B.** $4 \times 10^{-10}$ μA
- **C.** $2 \times 10^{-4}$ μA
- **D.** $4 \times 10^{-4}$ μA

## Question 94

An MRI has a magnetic field of 1.5 T. What force does the MRI have on a hydrogen ion at rest in the human brain?

- **A.** 0 N
- **B.** 1.5 N
- **C.** 15 N
- **D.** 150 N

## Question 95

Consider a uniform magnetic field coming out of the page. There is a wire loop in the plane of the page. Which of the following would induce an electromotive force in the wire loop?

I. Increasing the magnitude of the magnetic field
II. Rotating the wire loop to the right
III. Moving the wire loop vertically out of the page

- **A.** I and III
- **B.** I, II, and III
- **C.** I and II
- **D.** III only

## Question 96

Electrophoresis is used to separate proteins according to their mass. Proteins are placed into a gel matrix, and an electric field is applied. Which of the following will increase the speed at which the proteins move through the gel?

- **A.** Increasing the size of the pores in the gel
- **B.** Increasing the strength of the electric field
- **C.** Increasing the charge on the protein
- **D.** All of the above

## Electric Fields due to a point charge

$$F = k\frac{q_1 q_2}{r^2} \qquad U = k\frac{q_1 q_2}{r} \qquad E = k\frac{q_1}{r^2} \qquad V = k\frac{q_1}{r}$$

## Constant electric fields

$$F = Eq \qquad U = Vq \qquad U = qEd \qquad V = Ed$$

## Resistors

$$V = iR$$

$$R_{\text{eff}} = R_1 + R_2 + \dots \qquad \text{(Resistors in series)}$$

$$\frac{1}{R_{\text{eff}}} = \frac{1}{R_1} + \frac{1}{R_2} + \dots \qquad \text{(Resistors in parallel)}$$

## Capacitors

$$C = \frac{Q}{V}$$

$$\frac{1}{C_{\text{eff}}} = \frac{1}{C_1} + \frac{1}{C_2} + \dots \qquad \text{(Capacitors in series)}$$

$$C_{\text{eff}} = C_1 + C_2 + \dots \qquad \text{(Capacitors in parallel)}$$

$$U = \frac{1}{2}QV$$

$$U = \frac{1}{2}\frac{Q^2}{C}$$

$$U = \frac{1}{2}CV^2$$

## Magnetism

$$F = qvB\sin\theta$$

Ammeter

Amps (A)

Battery

Capacitor

Center of charge

Charge

Circuit

Conductors

Coulombs (C)

Coulomb's Law

Current

Dielectric constant, κ

Electric field

Electromotive force (EMF)

Field

Like charges

Lines of force

Magnetic field

Multimeter

Ohm's law

Ohms (Ω)

Opposite charges

Parallel

Parallel plate capacitor

Positive to negative

Potential energy (U)

Resistance (R)

Resistivity (ρ)

Resistors

Series

Universal Law of Conservation of Charge

Voltage (V)

Voltmeter

Volts (V)

### THE 3 KEYS

1. Electric field ($E$) is a general expression of force – force per unit charge – and voltage (V) is a general expression of energy – energy per unit charge.

2. Static electricity describes point charge and is like gravity. Current describes moving charge and is like fluid flow.

3. $R \propto L/A$, $C \propto A/D$. Think of resistors and capacitors in parallel as having increased width (more capacitance, less resistance) and resistors or capacitors in series as having increased length or distance (more resistance, less capacitance).

# Waves: Sound and Light

## 5.1 | Introduction

This lecture will discuss the general features of waves and the particular types of waves that are involved in hearing and vision. Waves are disturbances that transfer energy from one point to another, through vibration, for instance, or pressure variations. Sound is the transfer of energy as oscillations between high and low pressure through a medium such as air. Light is the transfer of energy through alternating electric and magnetic fields and does not require a medium.

The lecture begins by introducing the properties that are used to describe waves. Processes related to sound and light are covered next. How wave characteristics are determined and how they change will be described throughout the lecture. Some of the characteristics of a wave are constant and determined by the wave source. Others change as a wave passes from one medium to another. As waves propagate through media, reflection, refraction, diffraction or dispersion may occur. The reflection and refraction of light allow mirrors and lenses to create images, as will be described in the final sections of this lecture.

### THE 3 KEYS

1. To solve for the Doppler Effect: when a wave source and observer move towards one another, *frequency increases*—add $\Delta f$ to $f_s$ to get $f_o$. When a wave source and observer move away from each other, frequency decreases—subtract $\Delta f$ from $f_s$ to get $f_o$.

2. Determine whether a wave is undisturbed, reflected, refracted, diffracted, or dispersed.

3. Lenses and mirrors follow the three optics rules: the focal point rule, the object rule, and the image rule.

The awning of this building resembles a transverse wave.

## 5.2 | Wave Features

The source of a wave is a vibration on the atomic, microscopic or macroscopic level. For instance, the **production of sound** occurs via the vibration of a source such as the vocal cords. A **wave** is the propagation of that vibration from one point to another. As the vocal cords vibrate, they create sound waves that travel from point to point as **oscillations**, or regular variations, between high and low pressure. Waves are often said to be a transfers of energy from one point to another. Energy is transferred from the source, the vocal cords, through the air to the ear. As sound reaches the inner ear, energy is transferred to the sensory elements of the ear, causing them to vibrate and creating the sensation of sound.

Some waves, called **mechanical waves**, obey the laws of classical mechanics and **require a medium**, or substance, through which to travel. Sound waves and waves on a string are mechanical waves that displace the media through which they travel. Other waves, called **electromagnetic waves**, do not require a medium through which to travel; they can propagate **in vacuo**, or in a vacuum. Light is an electromagnetic wave.

Waves that travel through a medium can be further categorized according to the direction in which the medium is displaced. A *transverse wave*, such as a wave on a string, is one in which the medium is displaced perpendicularly to the direction of wave propagation. A *longitudinal wave*, such as a sound wave, is one in which the medium is displaced parallel to the direction of wave propagation.

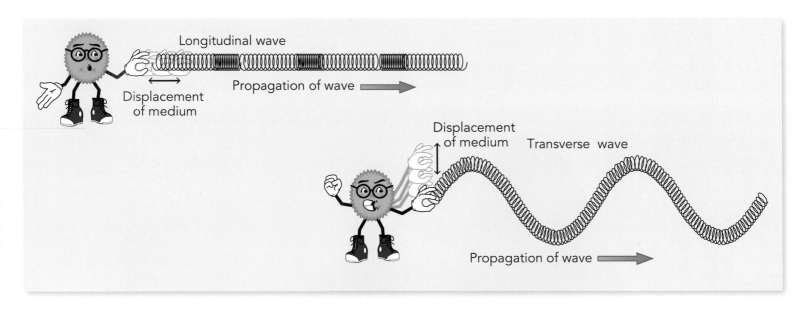

If a medium is perfectly elastic, it is momentarily displaced by a wave and then returned to its original position. Such a medium is *nondispersive* because the wave maintains its shape and does not disperse as it travels. Waves that travel through nondispersive media are considered *ideal waves*. On the MCAT® assume that all waves are ideal unless told otherwise.

Sometimes we mistakenly think of waves as the movement of matter. Watching surfers may be to blame for that. We see a surfer riding a wave, and because the surfer travels with the wave, it's convenient to think of the wave as a ball of matter that moves atop the water. Waves are fundamentally disturbances in a medium, and although the particles in the medium are displaced, they do not travel with the wave.

## Wavelength, Frequency and Period

Waves are also described in terms of their velocity, wavelength, frequency, and period. The **velocity** of a wave describes the distance over which the wave travels per unit time, and is determined by the medium through which the wave travels. Wave velocity is commonly expressed as $v = f\lambda$. This equation is similar to the familiar form of velocity in translational motion, $v = d/t$. In both cases, the relevant variables are distance and time: wavelength is a measurement of distance, usually expressed in meters or nanometers, and frequency is the inverse of time, expressed in $s^{-1}$ or hertz (Hz).

The **wavelength** ($\lambda$) of a wave is the distance from any point in the wave to the point where the wave begins to repeat itself.

The **frequency** ($f$) of a wave is the number of wavelengths that pass a fixed point in one second. It describes how often a vibration occurs. The frequency of a wave is determined by the frequency with which the wave source vibrates. It does not change as a wave moves from one medium to another.

The *period* ($T$) is the time it takes the wave to travel the distance of one wavelength and is the reciprocal of frequency. In other words, it is the number of seconds required for one wavelength to pass a fixed point. The period of a wave describes the length of time the wave source requires to complete one vibratory cycle. Just as frequency does not change when a wave moves from one medium to another, neither does the period.

$$T = \frac{1}{f}$$

Over the period, $T$, a wave travels a distance of the wavelength, $\lambda$. Therefore, the velocity of a wave is equal to $\lambda/T$ (just as $v = d/t$ in linear motion equations). The equation for velocity given above is derived from this relationship: because $T = 1/f$, the equation can be rewritten as $v = f\lambda$.

> Remember, frequency is determined by the source of the wave. Velocity is determined by the medium.

## 5.3 | Waves: Within and Between Media

The velocity of a wave is dictated by the medium through which it travels. As a wave travels within a medium, it has a fixed velocity determined by the characteristics of the medium; when a wave travels from one medium to another, its velocity changes according to the features of the new medium. Electromagnetic waves such as light are able to travel in the absence of a medium. When they do travel through a medium, they are affected just like other types of waves. The velocity of light in different media will be discussed in detail later in this lecture in the context of refraction.

> Imagine that I am knocking on the wall of a fish tank and a fish is listening on the other side. The fish will hear an altered version of the wave due to changes in the wavelength, velocity, and loudness as the wave passes through the glass and the water on the other side. But if I knock once per second, the fish will hear one knock per second! This is a good way to remember that frequency is set by the source and does not change as a wave passes from one medium to another.

The velocity of a wave traveling through a single medium is constant, assuming that the temperature of the medium does not change. Two characteristics of a given medium determine the velocity of waves traveling through it:

1. the medium's elasticity, or resistance to change in shape; and

2. the medium's inertia, or resistance to change in motion.

As an example, the velocity of a sound wave is given by $v = \sqrt{\dfrac{B}{\rho}}$ where $B$, bulk modulus of a medium is a measure of elasticity and $\rho$, the density of the medium, is a measure of inertia. Notice that this equation does not reference frequency or wavelength, demonstrating that the velocity of a wave within a medium depends only on the characteristics of the medium, not the characteristics of the wave. Sound waves of different frequencies, set by the wave source, will still have the same velocity within a given medium. This is possible because the two waves have distinct wavelengths.

In general, it is safe to assume that the temperature of the medium is constant unless told otherwise. However, if temperature does change, it can affect the velocity of a sound wave travelling through the medium. Within a gas, the velocity increases with temperature and is calculated as $v = \sqrt{\dfrac{\gamma R T}{M}}$ where $\gamma$ is the constant for a specific gas that compensates for temperature changes during contractions, $R$ is the universal gas constant, and $M$ is the molecular mass. The influence of temperature indicates that the random velocity of the gas molecules is a limiting factor for the velocity of a sound wave. The greater the temperature, the greater the random velocity, and the greater the sound wave velocity. In fact, the velocity of a sound wave through a gas is on the order of magnitude of (but slightly less than) the random velocity of its molecules.

The frequency of a wave that moves from one medium to another does not change, but the velocity does change according to the characteristics of the new medium. It is important to be able to predict how a change in medium might affect wave velocity. For a given measure of inertia, an increase in elasticity will increase the velocity of a wave. Conversely, for a given measure of elasticity, an increase in inertia will decrease the velocity of a wave. Know that elasticity increases as intermolecular attraction between molecules increases and inertia increases as mass and density increase. Assuming other variables are held constant, an increase in strength of intermolecular forces or a decrease in mass (or density) causes the velocity of the wave to increase.

---

The bulk modulus of solids is far higher than for gases because there are more and stronger intermolecular bonds between their molecules. A disturbance in one molecule will quickly be propagated and disturb other molecules. For a gas, which has far weaker and fewer intermolecular interactions, a disturbance will not be propagated as easily.

**Phases**
CHEMISTRY

The velocity of sound waves in a gas is limited by the average speed of the molecules within that gas. Sound waves move more quickly through hot gases than through cold gases.

---

Elasticity is a measure of how quickly disrupted molecules will spring back into their original shape, like a stretched rubber band. Intermolecular forces are what cause the molecules to spring back, so it makes sense that increasing intermolecular forces cause increased elasticity. The greater the elasticity of the medium, the faster it snaps back to position, moving the wave along.

Recall from the Motion and Force Lecture that mass is a measure of inertia, so inertia increases when mass and density (mass per volume) increase. Since a wave must move the medium in order to pass through it, the inertia of the medium (its resistance to motion) tends to slow it down.

The take home message: heavier mediums tend to slow waves down, while stiffer mediums tend to speed waves up.

---

TABLE 5.1 > Wave Velocity as a Function of Changing Mediums

| Type of Change | Wave Comes from... | Wave Enters... | Change in Wave Properties |
|---|---|---|---|
| Elastic | Less elastic medium | More elastic medium | $v, \lambda \uparrow$ |
| | More elastic medium | Less elastic medium | $v, \lambda \downarrow$ |
| Inertial (mass and density) | Less dense medium | Denser medium | $v, \lambda \downarrow$ |
| | Denser medium | Less dense medium | $v, \lambda \uparrow$ |

Without actual values, we cannot predict relative velocities in media differing in both elasticity and inertia. To illustrate, consider sound waves traveling from air to water. Since water is denser than air, one might think it should slow sound waves. Water more than makes up for its higher density, though, with a much greater bulk modulus, and sound waves travel significantly faster in water. In general:

$$v_{\text{sound in solid}} > v_{\text{sound in liquid}} > v_{\text{sound in gas}}$$

In summary, a wave can be described in terms of wavelength, frequency, period and velocity. Frequency and period are determined by the wave source and do not change as a wave passes from one medium to another. Velocity is determined by the medium through which the wave travels, and velocity changes as a wave moves through a boundary between media. Because $v = f\lambda$, for a given frequency, an increase in velocity is associated with an increase in wavelength. Likewise, a decrease in velocity is associated with a decrease in wavelength.

> Frequency is fixed by the source, while changes in velocity and wavelength are directly proportional.

TABLE 5.2 > Wave Characteristics

| Wave Characteristics | Symbol | Unit | Definition | Determined by |
|---|---|---|---|---|
| Frequency | $f$ | Hz | Number of wavelengths that pass a fixed point in one second | Wave source |
| Period | $T$ | s | Number of seconds required for one wavelength to pass a fixed point | Wave source |
| Velocity | $v$ | m/s | Distance a wave travels per unit time | Medium |
| Wavelength | $\lambda$ | m | Distance from any point on a wave to the point where the wave begins to repeat | Medium |

# 5.4 Representing Waves as Sine Functions

Because sine graphs, like simple transverse and longitudinal waves, consist of regularly repeating oscillations around an equilibrium position, it is convenient to represent waves as sine functions. Figure 5.1 shows a sine graph depicting displacement, either parallel or perpendicular to the direction of propagation, as a function of position at time $t$.

Be aware that sine graphs can also be used to depict displacement of a given point in the medium as a function of time. Figure 5.2 shows a sine graph depicting displacement at a given position as a function of time.

**FIGURE 5.1** | Displacement as a Function of Position

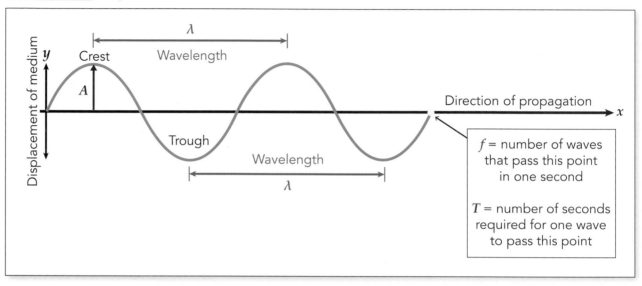

This graph shows displacement of the medium, whether perpendicular to or parallel to the direction in which that wave propagates, as a function of position.

**FIGURE 5.2** | Displacement at a Given Position as a Function of Time

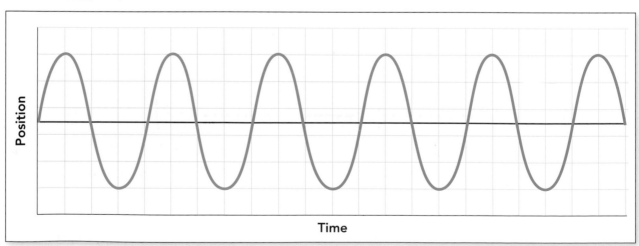

This graph shows displacement at a given point in the medium as a function of time.

On a sine graph, it is convenient to measure wavelength from either trough to trough or peak to peak. Some waves cannot be represented as sine functions because their oscillations are more complex. For these waves, wavelength is measured from any point to the next point where the function begins to repeat itself.

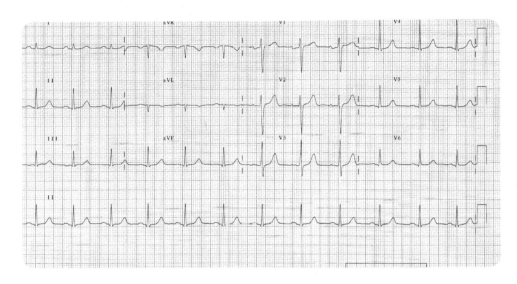

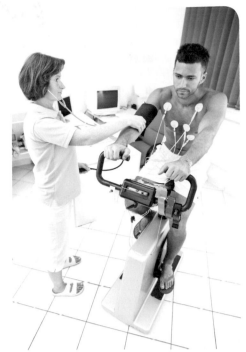

The **amplitude (A)** of a wave represented by a sine function can be measured as the distance between the x-axis and either the top of a crest or the bottom of a trough. Amplitude is always positive. Amplitude is another property commonly used to describe a wave, just like wavelength, frequency, period, velocity, and intensity. Like velocity and wavelength, amplitude can change as a wave moves from one medium to another.

---

For transverse waves, displacement refers to displacement of the medium perpendicular to the direction of propagation. For longitudinal waves, it refers to displacement of the medium parallel to the direction of propagation.

---

**FIGURE 5.3** | Sine and Cosine Functions

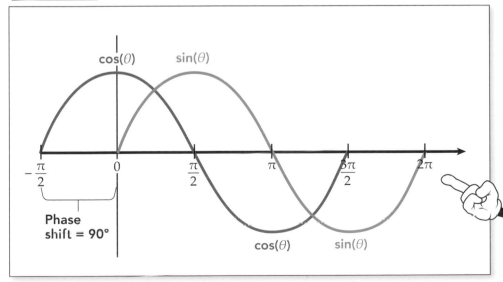

---

Waves are easy to depict with sine curves, but we could just as easily represent them with cosine curves. Cosine curves are sine curves shifted by 90°, or $\frac{\pi}{2}$ radians.

Modern noise-canceling headphones harness the power of wave interference to help us eliminate distractions. These devices contain a microphone that reads ambient noise patterns. The headphones then produce a wave that is exactly 180°, or half a wavelength, out of phase with the noise. A limitation of this technology is that it cannot cancel sudden disruptions like shouting or music because, unlike background noise, those sounds do not emit predictable wave patterns. The headphones cannot sufficiently predict the waves they would need to project.

## 5.5 | Wave Interference: Constructive and Destructive

The behavior of waves when they superimpose, or occupy the same space, is relevant to both sound and light waves. When two or more transverse waves are superimposed, their displacements add at each point along the wave to form a new wave. This superposition of waves is called interference. Interference can be constructive or destructive. **Constructive interference** occurs when the sum of the displacements results in a greater displacement. **Destructive interference** occurs when the sum of the displacements results in a smaller displacement. After passing through each other, waves that interfere will revert to their original shape, unaffected by the interference. Any waveform can be created by superposition of a sufficient number of sine waves with the correct amplitudes and wavelengths.

Whether interference is constructive or destructive depends on the **phase** of the wave, which relates to its wavelength, frequency, and place and time of origin. It is sufficient for the MCAT® to think of phase as a horizontal shift of a wave on a Cartesian graph as shown in Figure 5.4. Each wavelength represents 360°, so half of a wavelength represents 180°. Two waves that have the same wavelength and begin at the same point and time are said to be in phase. Two waves that have the same wavelength but travel different distances to arrive at the same point will be out of phase unless that distance is some multiple of the wavelength.

**FIGURE 5.4** | Constructive and Destructive Interference

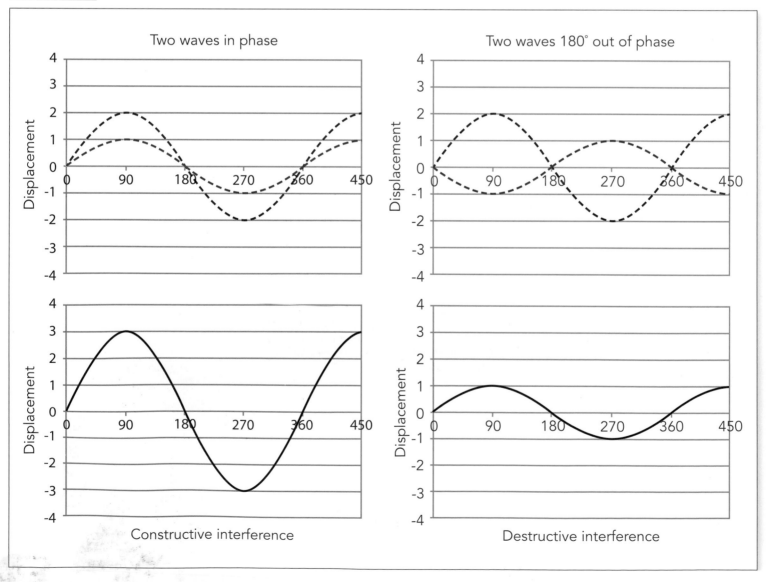

# 5.6 | Sound and Intensity

**Sound** is the transfer of energy through oscillations between high and low pressure. As a sound source vibrates back and forth, it does work on its surroundings, creating regions of high and low density. Sound becomes audible when oscillations in pressure within a certain frequency range cause the sensory elements of the ear to vibrate, triggering the transmission of electrical impulses to the brain.

Nervous System
BIOLOGY 2

**FIGURE 5.5** | Tuning Fork

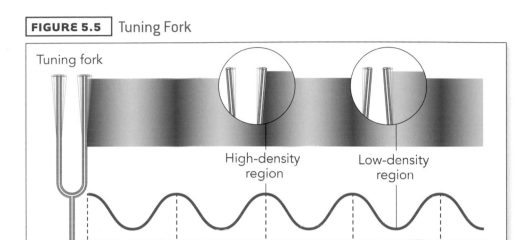

Tuning fork

High-density region

Low-density region

**FIGURE 5.6** | Inner Ear

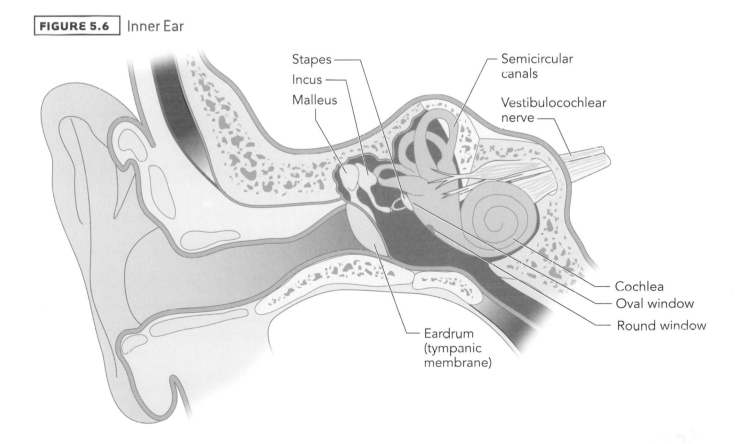

Stapes

Incus

Malleus

Semicircular canals

Vestibulocochlear nerve

Cochlea

Oval window

Round window

Eardrum (tympanic membrane)

Nobody can hear you scream in space!

Sound waves are commonly described in terms of pitch and intensity. **Pitch**, a measure of how "high" or "low" a note sounds, correlates with frequency; a high note has high pitch and high frequency.

As for intensity, recall that a wave is a transfer of energy from point to point. The rate at which a wave transfers energy is described in terms of power ($P = \Delta E/t$). The power of a wave is typically discussed in terms of *intensity*, or average rate of energy transfer per unit area. The intensity of a wave depends on the density of the medium, the wave frequency, and the wave velocity. Features intrinsic to the wave and those that are determined by the medium both contribute to intensity. Remember that frequency depends upon the wave source, while density is a property of the medium. Both amplitude and velocity can be changed by the medium. Since intensity is directly proportional to the squares of frequency and amplitude, these characteristics have the greatest effect on intensity.

Intensity is a useful way to discuss the rate of energy transfer of waves because a wave may travel in several directions at once. For instance, if you snap your fingers in the air, some of the energy is transferred away from your fingers in the form of a sound wave moving in all directions. The total energy of the wave is constant but is spread out over the surface area of an ever enlarging sphere. This increase in area is associated with a decrease in intensity.

---

Intensity (*I*) of a sound wave is given by: $I = 2\pi^2 \rho f^2 A^2 v$ where $\rho$ is the density of the medium, *f* is the wave frequency, *A* is the amplitude, and *v* is the wave velocity. Intensity, measured in W/m², can be used to describe any type of wave, but on the MCAT® it will likely be tested in the context of sound waves. There is no need to memorize the intensity equation.

---

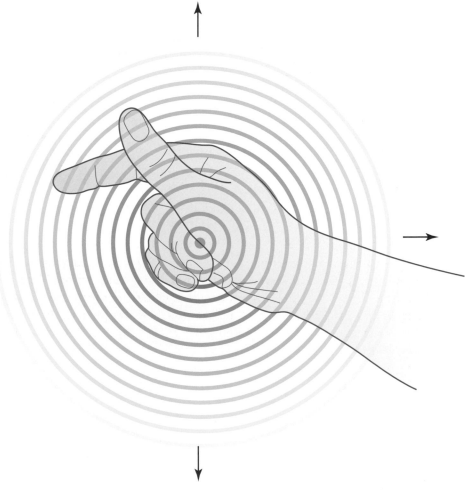

Although intensity is measured on a linear scale, humans do not perceive it that way. For instance, the sound waves created by the rustling of leaves are about 10 times more intense than those created by normal breathing, but we do not experience them as 10 times louder. **Intensity level**, a measure of loudness, describes how intense a sound seems to be. An artificial scale for intensity level (β) has been created based upon a **logarithmic scale** of intensities. The units of this scale are **decibels (dB)**. The relationship between β and *I* is given by:

$$\beta = 10 \log \frac{I}{I_0}$$

where $I_0$ is the threshold intensity of human hearing (the lowest intensity audible by the typical human).

The decibel system was created to provide an intuitive system that reflects how our human brain perceives the varying intensity of sound.

The decibel system was created to provide an intuitive system that reflects how our human brain perceives the varying intensity of sound.

All you need to understand about decibels on the MCAT® is that, if the intensity increases by a factor of 10, the decibels increase by the addition of 10 decibels. In other words, an increase in intensity from 30 W/m² to 3000 W/m² is equivalent to an increase of 20 decibels; I added 2 zeros to intensity, so I add 20 decibels to the decibel level. If I had added 3 zeros to the intensity, I would have added 30 decibels to the decibel level, and so on.

| $\Delta I$ | $\Delta \beta$ |
|---|---|
| $\times 10 = +10$ | |
| $\times 10^2 = +20$ | |
| $\times 10^3 = +30$ | |
| $\times 10^4 = +40$ | |

Humans have a *threshold of hearing* that represents the minimum sound intensity that can be perceived. For individuals with normal hearing, this value is about $10^{-12}$ W/m². Remember that what we can and cannot hear can depend on both frequency and intensity. Frequency is one of the factors that contributes to intensity, and its square is directly related to the intensity of a sound.

Biological Correlates
PSYCH & SOC

Based on their frequency, sound waves are categorized as audible, infrasonic, or ultrasonic. The sensory receptors in the human ear vibrate in response to waves with frequencies between 20 and 20,000 Hz. Waves with frequencies in this range are called audible waves. Waves with frequencies above this range are called ultrasonic waves. The reflections of high-frequency, ultrasonic waves are used in a medical imaging technology known as sonography, or ultrasonic imaging. An ultrasound machine creates images by first producing high-frequency sound waves and then receiving and processing their echoes. The probe of an ultrasound machine contains a crystal that vibrates and generates high-frequency, ultrasonic sound waves when subject to a high-frequency, alternating current. Waves reflected off of boundaries within the body return to the ultrasound probe. The returning waves cause the crystal to vibrate, generating a current that can be processed by the ultrasound machine.

Based on the time it takes reflected waves to return to the probe, an ultrasound machine determines the distance of the boundary from the probe. Based on the intensity of the reflected waves, the machine infers the relative densities of the media on either side of the boundary. The greater the difference in density, the greater the intensity of reflected sound. In this way, information provided by reflected sound waves can be used to generate sonographic images. The usefulness of ultrasonic waves for medical imaging is one of the reasons that sound waves are tested on the MCAT®.

Both pitch and intensity level are ways of relating the physical characteristics of sound to the way that we perceive it. Frequency (a physical property) is perceived as pitch; intensity (a physical property) is perceived as intensity level or "loudness."

## 5.7 | Resonance: Pipes and Strings

Waves can have any frequency, as set by their source. However, a structure such as a string or pipe will undergo a particular type of vibration (resonance) at only certain frequencies, determined by the length of the structure. To understand how this phenomenon occurs, first consider the reflection of a wave on a string. When a wave reaches an interface between two media, some or all of the energy will reflect back into the first medium (as described in detail later in this lecture). The orientation of a reflected wave depends upon the relative density of the two media. When a wave reflects off a medium that is denser, it is inverted. When a wave reflects off a medium that is less dense, it is reflected upright. An inverted wave is said to have experienced a phase shift. Both light and sound waves exhibit similar behavior and are likewise inverted when reflected off media that are denser.

Imagine sending a *wave pulse*, a single wavelength, down a string attached to a thread, a comparatively less dense medium, and observing its reflection. Some of the energy would continue into the thread as an upright wave pulse, and the rest of the energy would reflect back into the string as an upright wave pulse. Both the wave pulse and its reflection would be upright. By contrast, if the same string were instead attached to a heavy rope, a comparatively denser medium, the reflected wave would be inverted.

Now consider two sine waves with the same wavelength traveling in opposite directions on the same perfectly elastic string. As shown in the figure below, when they pass through each other and experience interference, something interesting happens. The point where they collide is never displaced. It does not move at all. This point, created by maximum destructive interference, is represented by

**FIGURE 5.7** | Node Formation

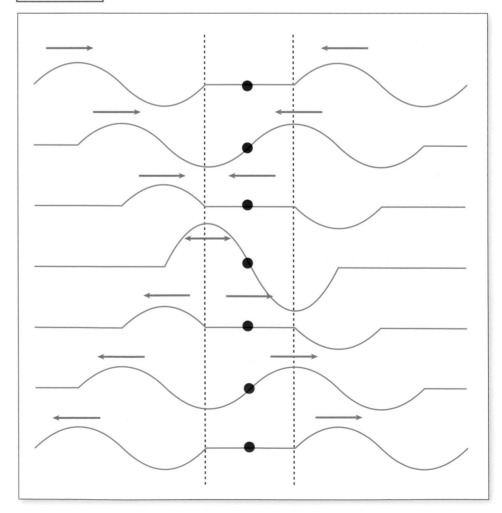

The strings on a guitar create standing waves when plucked. Changing the length and thickness of the string will alter the pitch.

the black dot in the diagram and is called a *node*. Notice also that only the points intersected by the two vertical lines experience maximum constructive interference. These points are called *antinodes*. Now imagine two endless rows of sine waves traveling in opposite directions on the same string. The string would hold perfectly still at the nodes and move violently up and down at the antinodes. This condition is known as a *standing wave*.

What would happen if a row of sine waves were generated on a string with both ends tied to a wall and fixed in place? At the string-wall interface, the entire wave is reflected back to the string and no energy passes into the wall. In this situation, two nodes are specified, one at each wall. The result is that only certain wavelengths will create a standing wave on this string. The longest possible wavelength for a standing wave is created with the fewest number of nodes: two. For this standing wave, the length of the string is equal to half a wavelength. Standing waves cause the string to resonate or vibrate at its natural frequency or resonant frequency. Since velocity is constant for a given medium, the equation $v = f\lambda$ can be used to find the resonant frequency for any given wavelength that creates a standing wave.

All mechanical structures have natural frequencies at which they resonate. If an outside driving force is applied to a structure at the resonant frequency, the structure will experience maximum vibration and maximum displacement amplitudes. The condition where the natural frequency and the driving frequency are equal is also called resonance. The resonating string discussed above reveals the driving force to be the reflected wave. This demonstrates that both definitions of resonance are the same. In a non-ideal situation, energy is lost to damping (described below) at the resonant frequency, and must be replaced by some outside driving force at the same frequency.

On the MCAT®, resonance will most likely appear as resonance in pipes and strings in the context of sound waves. In the case of a string, one or both ends may be fixed to a point. For a pipe, one or both ends may be open. If a string is fixed at both ends, as on a guitar, the ends of the string will be nodes. Those points are held in place and cannot vibrate. For a string secured at only one end, an antinode will be located at the unfixed end because, unlike a fixed point, this point will be in motion. If a standing wave has been established, no point on the string will have a larger displacement than the unfixed end, so its displacement will be equal to the amplitude of the wave.

The phenomenon of sympathetic resonance can be demonstrated by blowing across a bottle top and listening to an identical bottle held near. The sound will be repeated at a lower pitch.

---

Think back to the last time you got a cleaning at the dentist. There is a tool that "whirs" at a very high pitch and sounds like a very (scary) high-power drill. Those are called power scalers, and they vibrate at precisely the resonant frequency of tartar and other calculus around teeth. The calculus experiences maximum displacement at this frequency and is crushed easily by the power scaler.

---

Sound topics could appear on the MCAT® in the context of the voice. Lungs provide the power for the voice and the two vocal cords adjacent to the windpipe vibrate to produce sound. These vibrations resonate through the throat, mouth, and nose. Small changes to these openings can affect the sound produced. No two voices sound the same because the vocal cords vibrate with many different frequencies, and relative intensities of these frequencies determine the timbre of the voice.

---

**FIGURE 5.8** | Resonance in a Pipe or String: Both Ends Fixed

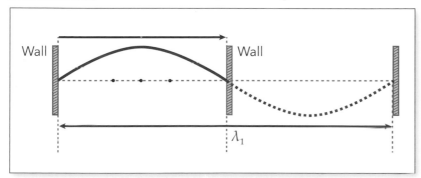

Wall    Wall

$\lambda_1$

## FIGURE 5.9 | Resonance on a String

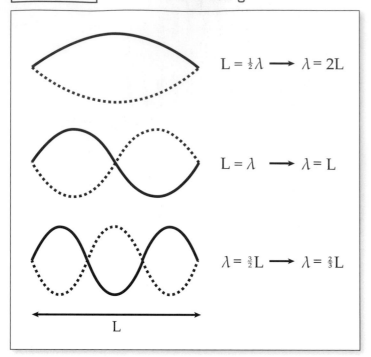

$L = \frac{1}{2}\lambda \longrightarrow \lambda = 2L$

$L = \lambda \longrightarrow \lambda = L$

$\lambda = \frac{3}{2}L \longrightarrow \lambda = \frac{2}{3}L$

L

## FIGURE 5.10 | Resonance in a Pipe

**Pipe open at both ends**

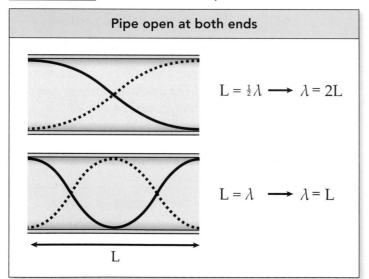

$L = \frac{1}{2}\lambda \longrightarrow \lambda = 2L$

$L = \lambda \longrightarrow \lambda = L$

L

**Pipe closed at one end**

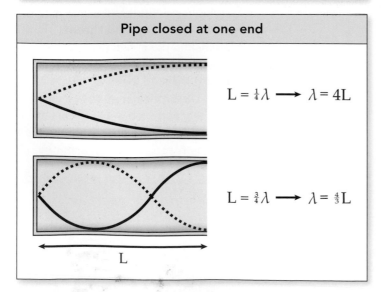

$L = \frac{1}{4}\lambda \longrightarrow \lambda = 4L$

$L = \frac{3}{4}\lambda \longrightarrow \lambda = \frac{4}{3}L$

L

Pipes create longitudinal waves, whereas strings generate transverse waves. Transverse waves are used in pipe diagrams to more easily illustrate the motion of particles. At regions with nodes, the particles in the standing wave have zero displacement. The regions with antinodes contain particles with maximum displacement. A pipe emitting sound can be open at one or both ends. At least one end must be open because disturbances in the fluid outside the pipe propagate the waves within. For that same reason, the air particles at the open end or ends must be moving with maximum displacement. A longitudinal wave travels by the vibrations of constituent particles. To imagine the propagation of a longitudinal wave, think about the particles like people in a crowded subway car. Some people are jostled more than others when the car shakes. The vibrations will not displace the people leaning against a wall at the end of a car because they are caught between a rigid surface and a crowd.

When a pipe is closed at one end, the molecules adjacent to that end cannot oscillate. If an incoming wave displaces nearby molecules, those will collide with the molecules against the end of the pipe. The molecules against the end will rebound against the end and once again collide with the nearby molecules, reversing the direction of the wave. For that reason the closed end of a pipe is the node for particle displacement. There are equations that can be used to describe resonance in pipes and strings mathematically, but they are beyond the scope of the MCAT®.

Figure 5.10 shows a transverse wave representing the particle displacement of a longitudinal wave. Transverse waves can also be used to represent the pressure differentials of a longitudinal wave. The pressure of the open end of a pipe must remain the same as atmospheric pressure, so the open end of the pipe is the pressure node. The pressure is greatest at the closed end of a pipe where the wave bounces against the wall, providing an equal reaction force in the opposite direction. Since the pressure differential is greatest at the closed end of the pipe, it is the pressure antinode. Either representation of a longitudinal wave could appear on the MCAT®. Remember, an open end is a particle displacement antinode and a pressure node. A closed end is a particle displacement node and a pressure antinode.

If you're having trouble imagining air in a pipe behaving like a wave, think of a spring in the pipe instead. Springs also propagate longitudinal waves. If you pushed the spring from both ends simultaneously, the ends would compress while the middle would not move at all. If the spring were put in a closed pipe, pressing the spring with your finger would result in displacement of the spring at the opening and no displacement for the parts of the spring at the closed end.

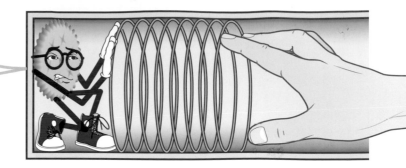

The particles in the spring can compress, but I can't move because my back is against the wall.

**FIGURE 5.11** Resonance in a Pipe or String: One End Unfixed

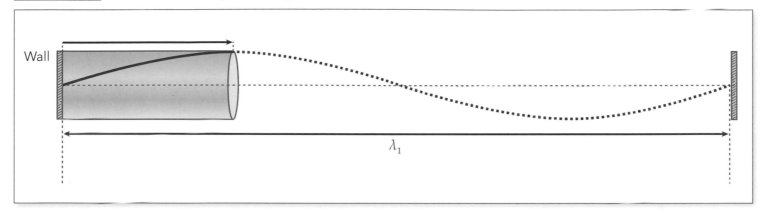

Wall

$\lambda_1$

As mentioned above, resonance is impacted by the fact that real waves undergo attenuation (damping): the decrease in the intensity of a wave propagating through a medium. One cause of attenuation is reflection. Attenuation of sound waves due to reflection makes it difficult to create ultrasonic images of a bone's interior. Because bone is so much denser than the surrounding tissue, almost all of the ultrasound waves are reflected at its boundary. As a result, very few sound waves continue into and reflect off of the interior of the bone. Another possible cause of attenuation is spreading; recall that as a sound wave spreads over a larger and larger area, its intensity is reduced. Yet another cause of attenuation is absorption, which is described later in this lecture.

When a wave attenuates, its intensity decreases. Recall that intensity depends on the square of both frequency and amplitude, as well as density of the medium and wave velocity. Frequency is a constant determined by the wave source, so it is the amplitude and velocity that decrease as intensity decreases. The loss of energy of the wave is most evident in its loss of amplitude. Are there ever any circumstances under which frequency changes? The frequency of an emitted wave does not change, but its perceived frequency can change when its source moves relative to an observer, as discussed in the following section.

> **MCAT® THINK**
>
> A flute is an example of an open pipe while a clarinet is a closed pipe. Which of these two instruments will have the greatest pressure differential between its two ends while it is being played?
>
> Answer on pg. 171.

## 5.8 | The Doppler Effect

The **Doppler effect** refers to the change in perceived frequency that occurs when a wave source and its observer move towards or away from each other. When the source or observer is moving toward the other, the observed frequency is higher than the source frequency. Conversely, when the source or observer is moving away from the other, the observed frequency is lower than the source frequency. Note that the source frequency—the frequency at which the waves are emitted—does not change. Only the observed frequency changes. With respect to sound waves, where pitch changes with frequency, the observer does not perceive the same pitch that the source emitted. With respect to light, the observer does not observe the same color that was emitted.

**FIGURE 5.12** Doppler Effect

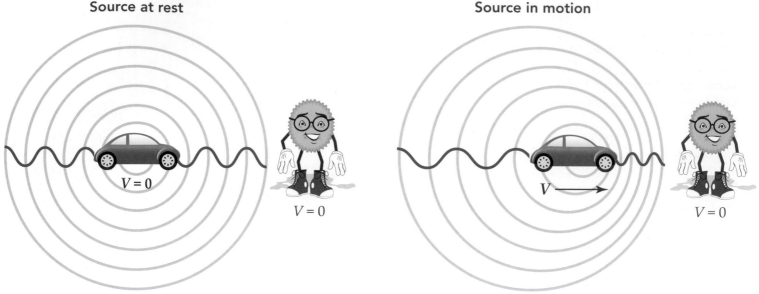

**Source at rest**          **Source in motion**

The Doppler effect occurs because a change in the relative motion of a source and observer changes the distance traveled by each wave front. When the source or observer is moving toward the other, the distance traveled is less than it would be if both were stationary. Each subsequent wave front is emitted closer to the observer, and the observer perceives a higher frequency. Conversely, when the source or observer is moving away from the other, the distance traveled is greater than it would be if both were stationary. Each wave front is emitted farther from the observer, and the observer perceives a lower frequency.

Recall that the speed of a wave is determined by the medium in which it travels. Once emitted, a sound wave with a given speed will continue traveling at that speed, regardless of the speed of the source. Because wave speed is constant, a change in distance traveled will change the time interval between wave fronts. Recall that $\text{speed} = \frac{\text{distance}}{\text{time}}$. As distance decreases, so, too, does the time interval between wave fronts. This decrease in time interval, or period, is perceived as an increase in frequency. Conversely, as distance increases, the interval between wave fronts also increases. This increase in period is perceived as a decrease in frequency.

If needed, the formula for the Doppler Effect will be given to you on the MCAT® as:

$$f_o = f_s\left(\frac{c \pm v_o}{c \pm v_s}\right)$$

where $f_o$ is the observed frequency, $f_s$ is the source frequency, $c$ is the velocity of the wave in the given medium, $v_o$ is the velocity of the observer and $v_s$ is the velocity of the source. Note that $c$ is not necessarily the speed of light. The difficult aspect of this formula is understanding when to use the plus sign and when to use the minus sign. The easy way to solve this problem is to follow these 3 steps:

1. assume that the observer is not moving;

2. if the source is moving toward the object, label that direction negative and use the minus sign for $v_s$;

3. check the direction that the observer is moving. If the direction is the same, use the same sign for $v_o$; if not, use the opposite sign for $v_o$.

This system is possible because velocity is a vector. Once you label a direction positive for one vector, it must be so for all vectors.

---

If you're still struggling to remember when to use which sign, here's one more way to think about it. When a source or observer is moving towards the other, $f_o > f_s$. Therefore, the factor by which $f_s$ is multiplied must be greater than one. So, in this instance, we add $v_o$ to $c$ in the numerator and/or subtract $v_s$ from $c$ in the denominator. When the numerator is larger than $c$ and/or the denominator is smaller than $c$, the ratio $\left(\frac{c \pm v_o}{c \pm v_s}\right)$ is greater than one. Conversely, when a source or observer is moving away from the other, $f_o < f_s$, and the factor by which $f_s$ is multiplied must be less than one. In this instance, we subtract $v_o$ from $c$ in the numerator and/or add $v_s$ to $c$ in the denominator.

---

You can simulate the Doppler Effect by allowing a tennis ball serving machine to pelt you with tennis balls. If you stand still, tennis balls come at you with a certain frequency, say one ball per second. If you run away from the machine, they still leave the machine at one ball per second, but as you run, they hit you with a lower frequency. If you run toward the machine, the balls hit you with a higher frequency.

Because tennis balls are particles and not waves, there is an important difference. Waves travel at the same speed through a medium regardless of whether or not the source moves. The tennis balls, on the other hand, if shot from a moving server, will travel at their original speed plus the speed of the server. This means that the frequency of tennis balls varies depending upon who is moving, the source or the observer. In a true Doppler Effect, the frequency change depends upon relative motion only, and who is actually moving cannot be distinguished.

For all waves, the Doppler Effect can be approximated by:

$$\frac{\Delta f}{f_s} = \frac{v}{c} \text{ and } \frac{\Delta \lambda}{\lambda_s} = \frac{v}{c}$$

where $v$ is the relative velocity of the source and observer and $c$ is the speed of the wave in the given medium. Use these formulae for any Doppler MCAT® problem, rather than the more complicated formula previously given. These formulae approximate the Doppler Effect when the relative velocity, $v$, of the source and the observer are much smaller than the wave velocity, $c$. $\Delta f$ and $\Delta \lambda$ are the change to the source frequency, $f$, and the source wavelength, $\lambda$.

Once this formula has been used to find the change in frequency or wavelength, that change must be added to the original value to find the observed value:

$$f_o = f_s \pm \Delta f \text{ and } \lambda_o = \lambda_s \pm \Delta \lambda$$

This method requires a qualitative judgment as to the direction of the change in frequency and wavelength. Remember this: when the relative velocity brings the source and observer closer, observed frequency goes up and observed wavelength goes down; in the opposite case, the opposite is true. If the object and source are getting farther apart, subtract $\Delta f$ from $f_s$ or add $\Delta \lambda$ to $\lambda_s$; if they are approaching each other, add $\Delta f$ to $f_s$ or subtract $\Delta \lambda$ from $\lambda_s$.

The relative velocity $v$ is sometimes difficult to grasp. It is simply the net speed at which the source and object are approaching each other. For objects moving in the same direction, subtract their individual speeds; for objects moving in opposite directions, add their individual speeds.

The Doppler effect is usually discussed in the context of a moving source or observer, but it can also occur due to the reflection of sound from a moving object. Although the source and observer are stationary, the moving object acts like a moving observer as the sound wave approaches and like a moving source

Another helpful way to remember the appropriate sign conventions in the Doppler Effect equation is to memorize the formula as $f_o = f_s\left(\frac{c \pm v_o}{c \mp v_s}\right)$. The only change in this equation is that the signs in the denominator are flipped. Now, for the source and the object, use the top sign if they are moving "towards" and the bottom sign if they are moving "away." Take, for instance, a bat that is gaining on a fleeing bug and emitting ultrasonic cries. If you wanted to calculate the frequency of the cries the insect experiences, consider the bat the source and the bug the object. The bat is moving toward the bug, so use the negative sign on the top in the denominator. The bug, the object, is moving away from the bat, so use the negative sign on the bottom in the numerator.

Calculation of beat frequency is an important skill for Test Day. It is the difference between the observed frequency and frequency omitted by the source. It can also represent the difference in the frequencies of two sounds, like tuning forks that are close in pitch.

These equations are only approximations of the Doppler effect, but they are close enough to find the correct answer on the MCAT®.

Apply Key 1: This is a method for solving Doppler effect problems that you may not have learned in physics class. Even though the equations may be unfamiliar, the concept can become intuitive. When an observer and source move toward each other, the frequency the observer perceives increases because it encounters more waves in a given amount of time. Add Δf to $f_s$. When the observer and source increase the distance between them, the observer encounters fewer waves for each moment in time. Subtract Δf from $f_s$.

Table 5.3 clarifies how to determine the relative velocities of two moving objects.

as the sound wave reflects, as described below. Police officers exploit this variation of the Doppler effect with the equipment they use to measure the speed of vehicles. Interference between the emitted sound wave, with the frequency set by the source, and the returning sound wave, with an altered frequency, causes *beats*. Beats occur when two waves with slightly different frequencies are superimposed. At some points they will be nearly in phase and experience constructive interference. At other points they will be out of phase and experience destructive interference. These points will alternate at the beat frequency, or the frequency equal to the difference between the frequencies of the original two waves. The beat frequency is represented by the formula:

$$f_{beat} = |f_o - f_s|$$

Notice that the beat frequency provides a measure of the change in frequency. The speed of the vehicle can then by calculated by the equation:

$$\frac{\Delta f}{f_s} = \frac{2v}{c} \ or \ v = \frac{c\Delta f}{2f_s}$$

This equation is nearly the same as the one given previously, except that the change in frequency is divided by two. This is necessary because unlike the situation where sound travels directly from a source to an observer, the Doppler effect occurs twice in this scenario. Imagine that a stationary police car emits a sound wave in the direction of a speeding vehicle. If we take the vehicle as a moving observer, the Doppler effect occurs and the original equation applies. Once the sound reflects off the vehicle and starts to return to the police car, the moving vehicle has become the source of the sound, and the Doppler effect occurs again. When the final sound wave is detected by the police car, the Doppler effect has occurred twice. When the detected frequency change is divided by two, it gives the change in frequency from just the first Doppler shift, which can then be used to calculate the velocity of the vehicle.

TABLE 5.3 > Relative Velocities and the Doppler Effect

| | Source | Observer | Relative velocity $v$ |
|---|---|---|---|
| Same direction | ← 5 m/s | ← 6 m/s | 1 m/s |
| Same direction | → 5 m/s | → 6 m/s | 1 m/s |
| Opposite directions | → 5 m/s | ← 6 m/s | 11 m/s |
| Opposite directions | ← 5 m/s | → 6 m/s | 11 m/s |

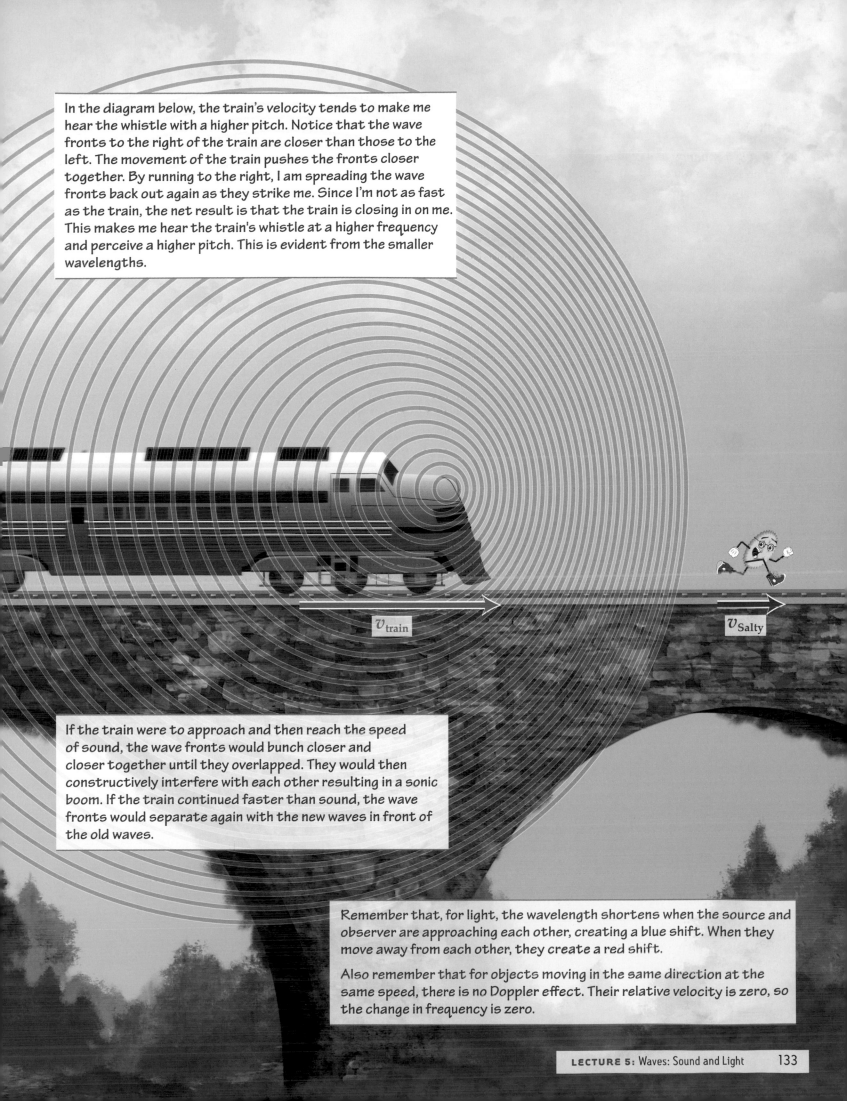

In the diagram below, the train's velocity tends to make me hear the whistle with a higher pitch. Notice that the wave fronts to the right of the train are closer than those to the left. The movement of the train pushes the fronts closer together. By running to the right, I am spreading the wave fronts back out again as they strike me. Since I'm not as fast as the train, the net result is that the train is closing in on me. This makes me hear the train's whistle at a higher frequency and perceive a higher pitch. This is evident from the smaller wavelengths.

$v_{train}$

$v_{Salty}$

If the train were to approach and then reach the speed of sound, the wave fronts would bunch closer and closer together until they overlapped. They would then constructively interfere with each other resulting in a sonic boom. If the train continued faster than sound, the wave fronts would separate again with the new waves in front of the old waves.

Remember that, for light, the wavelength shortens when the source and observer are approaching each other, creating a blue shift. When they move away from each other, they create a red shift.

Also remember that for objects moving in the same direction at the same speed, there is no Doppler effect. Their relative velocity is zero, so the change in frequency is zero.

This photograph demonstrates the shock waves produced by the explosion of a firing gun.

## Shock Waves

A shock wave is a conical wave front, produced when the velocity of the sound source exceeds the velocity of the sound wave. The ratio of the velocity of the source to the velocity of the wave, $\frac{v_s}{v}$, is known as the *Mach number*. Mach number increases as the velocity of the sound source increases. Like any sound wave, a shock wave consists of oscillations between high and low pressures. When the source moves faster than the speed of sound, many wave fronts overlap, generating a region of very low air pressure. Air moves in response to the pressure gradient, and the rapid movement creates a loud sonic boom.

**FIGURE 5.13** Shock Wave

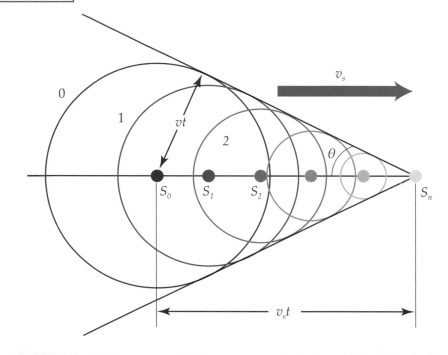

The jet is seen breaking the sound barrier. As air from the surroundings enters the region of low pressure, it condenses, creating the halo seen in this image.

## Question 97

One end of a string is shaken each second, sending a wave with an amplitude of 10 cm toward the other end. The string is 5 meters long, and the wavelength of each wave is 50 cm. How many waves reach the other end of the string in each 10 second interval?

○ **A.** 2
○ **B.** 5
○ **C.** 10
○ **D.** 50

## Question 98

The sound level of the chirping made by a bird at a distance of 5 meters is measured at 30 dB. When the same bird is 50 meters away the sound level is measured at 10 dB. How many times greater is the amplitude of the sound wave at 5 meters away compared to 50 meters away?

○ **A.** 3 times greater
○ **B.** 10 times greater
○ **C.** 20 times greater
○ **D.** 100 times greater

## Question 99

When the frequency of a sound wave is increased, which of the following will decrease?

   I.   Wavelength
   II.  Period
  III. Amplitude

○ **A.** I only
○ **B.** III only
○ **C.** I and II only
○ **D.** I and III only

## Question 100

If the intensity of a sound is doubled, the decibel level will increase by:

○ **A.** less than 10 dB.
○ **B.** exactly 10 dB.
○ **C.** more than 10 dB.
○ **D.** exactly 20 dB.

## Question 101

All of the following statements are true about a resonating string EXCEPT:

○ **A.** a resonating string forms a standing wave.
○ **B.** the wavelength created by a resonating string must coincide with one of its harmonics.
○ **C.** some spots on a resonating string will not move at all.
○ **D.** if left alone, the amplitude of a wave on a resonating string will grow infinitely large.

## Question 102

The human trachea behaves like an organ pipe in facilitating the production of sound. Researchers modeled the trachea with a pipe as shown below:

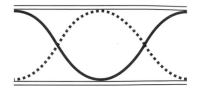

Which of the following statements is NOT true of this pipe?

○ **A.** The pipe can resonate at higher frequencies.
○ **B.** The pipe can resonate at lower frequencies.
○ **C.** The pipe resonates with transverse waves.
○ **D.** The pipe is capable of emitting multiple frequencies simultaneously.

## Question 103

Which of the following factors by itself will increase the frequency at which an observer hears a sound emanating from a source?

○ **A.** A wind blows from the source to the observer.
○ **B.** The source and the observer move away from each other at the same speed.
○ **C.** The source and the observer move in the same direction at the same speed.
○ **D.** The source moves away from the observer more slowly than the observer moves toward the source.

## Question 104

A piano creates a musical note when a metal wire stretched between two fixed ends is struck by a hammer, creating a standing wave. As the force with which the hammer strikes the string is increased, the amplitude of the string's motion is increased. Which of the following properties of the wave on the string will remain the same as the force of the hammer is increased?

   I.   Frequency
   II.  Wavelength
  III. Velocity

○ **A.** I only
○ **B.** I and II only
○ **C.** II and III only
○ **D.** I, II, and III

**STOP**

## 5.9 | Light Waves

Light is the transfer of energy through alternating electric and magnetic fields. As a charge vibrates, it accelerates and produces a changing electrical field. This movement of charge creates a changing magnetic field that, in turn, can induce a changing electrical field. As electrical and magnetic fields regenerate one another, an electromagnetic wave, a traveling oscillation of an electric and magnetic field, emanates from the vibrating charge. The electric and magnetic fields are perpendicular to one another, and the direction of propagation is perpendicular to both fields. Light becomes visible when electromagnetic radiation within a particular range of wavelengths is bent by the lens of the eye and focused on the retina, triggering transmission of electrical impulses to the brain.

**FIGURE 5.14** Electromagnetic Wave

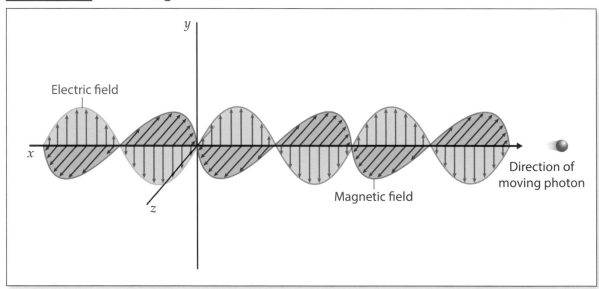

Recall that light acts like both a wave and a particle. The propagation properties of light can be described with wave theory, while the energy transformation properties of light are best described by particle theory. Neither wave nor particle theory alone can explain the phenomenon of light. In some cases (such as the discussion of optics), we can approximate light as a ray moving in a straight line, and represent it as an arrow.

## Emission of Light

The accelerating charges that produce light are electrons within atoms that gain speed as they transition from higher to lower energy states. Electrons are continuously undergoing rotational acceleration, but they only emit light during transitions from higher to lower energy states. The light emitted by electrons is in the form of photons, pulses of electromagnetic radiation that can be thought of as localized particles of energy. An emitted photon has a frequency, $f$, that is proportional to the energy change of the electron, $E$.

$$E = hf$$

where $h$ is a proportionality constant known as Plank's constant. When the frequency of the photon falls within the range associated with the visible spectrum, the resulting photon will be perceived as a color.

There are three common ways in which an electron can receive the energy needed to move from its ground state to an excited state. First, the atom in which the electron orbits could be bombarded by high speed particles, such as electrons. When it is bombarded by electrons subject to an alternating current voltage, mercury vapor emits light, much of which is in the ultraviolet region.

Second, the atom could absorb a photon of light. When an atom absorbs a photon of high-frequency light, such as ultraviolet light, its electrons can jump over intermediate energy states to reach higher energy states. When the electron loses energy, it falls into one of those intermediate states, emitting *fluorescent light* with wavelengths in the visible light range. A common type of fluorescent lamp first excites mercury vapor, which, when bombarded by high energy electrons, emits ultraviolet radiation. The energy from this ultraviolet light then excites a powdery material called phosphors, which emits lower frequency, visible light.

Finally, the atom could be subject to thermal agitation. When closely packed atoms, such as those in a solid, are subjected to high temperatures, their electrons transition not only between energy levels within a single atom, but also between atoms. Because their electrons can make an infinite number of transitions, they produce *incandescent light*, exhibiting a continuous range of wavelengths. The dominant frequency of emitted light is directly proportional to the temperature, so the temperature of an incandescent body can be measured by its color.

## Wavelength, Frequency, and Speed of Light

Electromagnetic radiation exists at all wavelengths. For the MCAT®, memorize that visible light includes all wavelengths from $390 \times 10^{-9}$ m to $700 \times 10^{-9}$ m. Also know that the shorter wavelengths correspond to violet light and the longer wavelengths to red light. Just beyond the visible spectrum on the smaller wavelength side is ultraviolet (beyond violet) light, and on the longer wavelength side is infrared (beyond red) light.

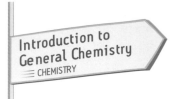

Introduction to General Chemistry
CHEMISTRY

Recall from chemistry that electrons exist in quantized orbits. Since light is emitted when electrons transition from higher to lower energy states, and only certain transitions exist within an atom, each atom can only produce light at specific wavelengths – not wavelengths across the electromagnetic spectrum.

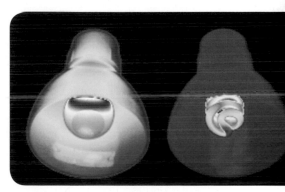

Shown here is a thermogram of two lamps, with an incandescent light bulb on the left and a fluorescent bulb on the right. The bulbs produce about the same amount of visible light, but compared to the incandescent bulb, the fluorescent bulb is several times more efficient and produces less wasted heat.

"Visibility" is not an intrinsic quality of the visible spectrum. This range is defined by the capabilities of the photoreceptors in the human eye, but there are other species that are able to see outside the visible spectrum.

## FIGURE 5.15 Various Wavelengths and Frequencies of Electromagnetic Waves

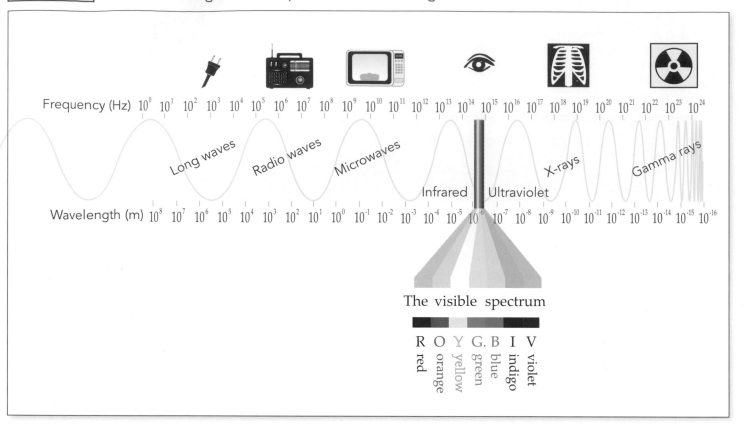

The visible spectrum

R O Y G.B I V
red orange yellow green blue indigo violet

Remember the order of the 3 primary colors of light, from low frequency to high frequency: red, then green, then blue. Once you know those, you know that orange follows red and yellow comes before green. If you need to think of all the colors in order quickly, just remember that Roy G. Biv invented the rainbow. O.K., not really, but Roy G. Biv is an acronym for the order of the colors in the visible spectrum (Red, Orange, Yellow, Green, Blue, Indigo, Violet). For the MCAT®, familiarize yourself with the individual parts of the electromagnetic spectrum and be able to compare them in terms of frequency and wavelength. One way to remember the order of the electromagnetic spectrum is to start with ultraviolet. It is easy to remember that ultraviolet (UV) is high energy because it can actually damage your DNA. Energy correlates with frequency, so UV rays are high frequency (and therefore short wavelength, making them the right size to damage tiny DNA base pairs). You know that violet is a purple-blue color, so remembering that UV is high frequency allows you to remember that blue must also have high frequency (and therefore short wavelength). Red is on the opposite side of the visible spectrum from blue and violet, so it must have the opposite characteristics: low frequency and long wavelength. Remember, the visible spectrum extends from $390 \times 10^{-9}$ m to $700 \times 10^{-9}$ m in wavelength. Since red has a lower frequency and longer wavelength than violet, it must be at the end with $700 \times 10^{-9}$ m.

To remember the general position of other parts of the electromagnetic spectrum—radio waves, microwaves, x-rays, and gamma rays—rely on your intuition about the relative safety of these wave types. You are exposed to microwaves and radio waves all the time; they are not harmful and must have low energy, meaning that they are on the side of the electromagnetic spectrum with the longest wavelengths and lowest frequencies. Gamma rays and x-rays have more potential to do harm because they are higher energy, so they lie on the end with the highest frequencies and shortest wavelengths.

Notice that each wavelength has a corresponding frequency. This is because the **speed of light** (or any other electromagnetic wave) **in** vacuo ($c$) is constant and equal to the ratio of the magnitudes of the electric field, $E$, and the magnetic field, $B$:

$$c = \frac{E}{B} = 3 \times 10^8 \tfrac{m}{s}$$

Although the electric field is much larger when compared in SI units, the energies of the two fields are exactly equal. The equation $c = \dfrac{E}{B}$ is useless for the MCAT®. It is given here to remind you of the nature of electromagnetic radiation. However, the fact that speed of light in a vacuum is equal to the constant $3 \times 10^8 \tfrac{m}{s}$ is necessary to know for the MCAT®. As described later in this lecture, light travels more slowly in a medium than it does in a vacuum.

Because c is a constant, we can derive frequency $f$ from wavelength $\lambda$. From our wave equation, $v = f\lambda$, we have:

$$f = \frac{c}{\lambda}$$

## Absorption of Light

As waves propagate through media, they undergo **absorption**. The likelihood that a wave will be absorbed depends both on the medium and on the frequency of the wave. The waves most likely to be absorbed are those whose frequencies match the resonant frequencies of the medium.

To illustrate, consider light waves of three different frequencies—one in the ultraviolet region, one in the visible light region, and a third in the infrared region—all of which encounter a glass window pane. The resonant frequencies of the electrons in the glass are in the ultraviolet range, so when ultraviolet light strikes glass, much of it is absorbed. The electrons in the glass begin to vibrate strongly and the vibrations dissipate through the glass as heat, preventing much of the ultraviolet light from passing through. At the frequencies of visible light, the electrons of the glass do not resonate, and the wave passes through. The visible light wave proceeds through the glass unchanged, but the transfer of energy creates a slight delay that accounts for the slower speed of light through glass. The low frequency of infrared light causes entire glass atoms to vibrate, warming the glass and preventing most infrared light from passing through.

> Grass isn't green! The color you see when you look at an object is determined by the colors that are reflected and NOT absorbed by the object. Grass absorbs red and blue light, and reflects green light, which is why it appears green. When an object absorbs all visible wavelengths of light, the "color" you observe is black. When it cannot absorb any visible light, the "color" you observe is white. Black and white are not technically colors: black is the absorption of all visible light, while white is the reflection of all visible light.

**FIGURE 5.16** Glass Blocks Ultraviolet and Infrared Light, but Is Transparent to Visible Light

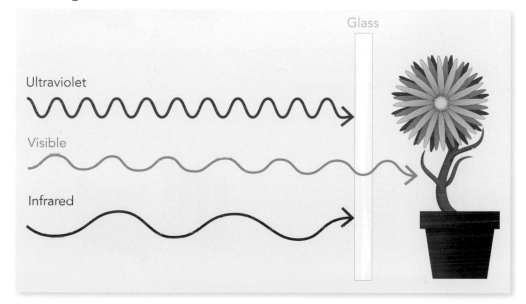

The differential absorption of electromagnetic radiation is exploited in many laboratory techniques, including nuclear magnetic resonance (NMR) spectroscopy, infrared (IR) spectroscopy, and ultraviolet-visible (UV-Vis) light spectroscopy. See the Laboratory Techniques lecture found in the *Biochemistry* manual for more information.

## Polarization of Light

When something is polarized, it exhibits a particular alignment, separation, or orientation. When a molecule is polarized, for instance, it exhibits a separation of positive and negative charge. When light is **polarized**, its electric and magnetic fields are oriented in a particular, rather than a random, way. Light is commonly described as horizontally, vertically, circularly, or randomly polarized. If the electric field oscillates parallel to the y-axis, then the light is said to be vertically polarized. If it oscillates parallel to the x-axis, then it is said to be horizontally polarized. In all cases, magnetic fields oscillate in planes perpendicular to the planes in which electric fields oscillate.

Polarized lenses are handy for fishing because the sun creates a glare when it strikes water. Photons are reflected in many directions, creating a sheen that disguises the fish from the fisher. With microscopic slits in the lenses, only photons vibrating in the direction of the slits will reach the eyes. Plane polarizers act like light sieves.

Polarizing topics are topics that separate, or create divisions between, people who align themselves with different positions.

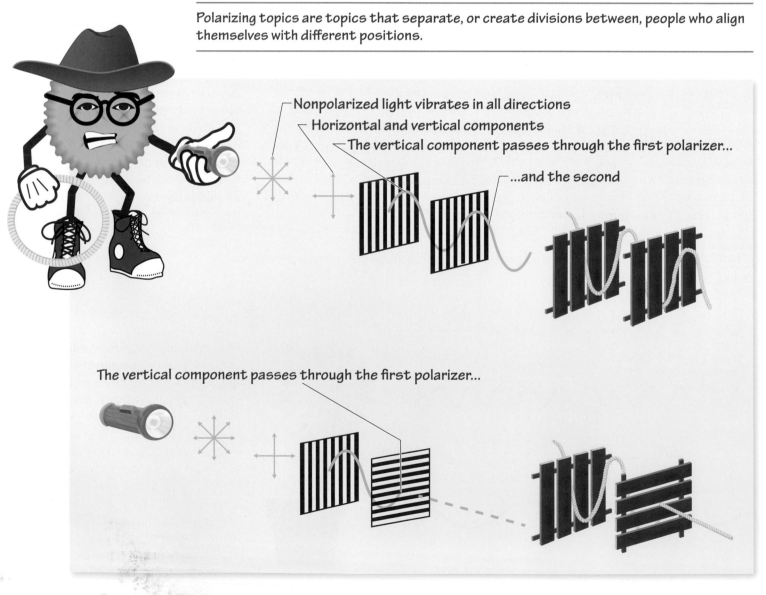

Nonpolarized light vibrates in all directions
Horizontal and vertical components
The vertical component passes through the first polarizer...
...and the second

The vertical component passes through the first polarizer...

Recall that the source of light is a vibrating charge. If the charge accelerates vertically, then the light it emits will be vertically polarized. Vertically polarized light is conventionally represented by a double-headed, vertical arrow. If it accelerates horizontally, then the light it emits will be horizontally polarized. Horizontally polarized light is conventionally represented by a double-headed, horizontal arrow.

Light is said to be **circularly polarized** when it consists of electric fields of constant magnitude that change direction in a rotary manner. The fields can rotate in either a clockwise or counterclockwise direction.

**FIGURE 5.17** Vertically and Horizontally Polarized Light

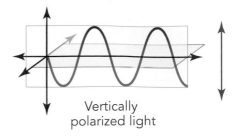

Vertically polarized light

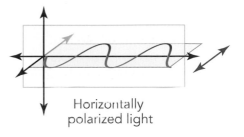

Horizontally polarized light

**FIGURE 5.18** Circularly Polarized Light

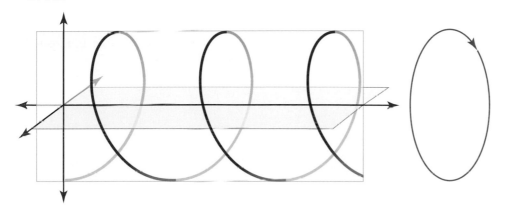

Most common light sources emit light that is randomly polarized; the electrons emitting the light have no preferred vibrational direction. Randomly polarized, or unpolarized, light can be represented a couple of ways. First, it can be drawn as a mess of double-headed arrows, each representing a distinct electric field orientation, and all with a common intersection point. Alternatively, it can be represented as two intersecting, double-headed arrows, one vertical and one horizontal. The vertical arrow represents the vertical component of each of the electric field vectors and the horizontal arrow represents the horizontal component of each of the field vectors.

**FIGURE 5.19** Randomly Polarized Light

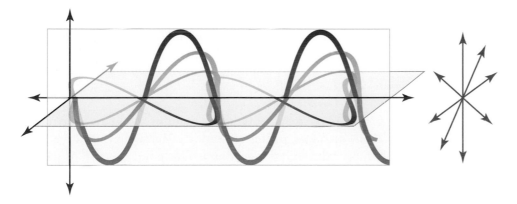

Light that is unpolarized when it is emitted can subsequently be polarized by reflection, scattering, or polarizing filters.

The sections that follow will present the four things that light is most likely to do on the MCAT®: reflect, refract, diffract, or disperse. Reflection is light *bouncing* off the boundary between media. Refraction is light *bending* as it passes into a new medium. Dispersion, a type of refraction, is the *splitting* of light according to frequency. Diffraction is the *spreading* of light when it encounters an edge.

## Reflection and Refraction

When a wave reaches an interface between two media, it can be altered through either **reflection** or **refraction**. A wave is reflected when, at the boundary between media, it bounces back to return into the medium from which it came. By contrast, a wave is refracted when bends as it continues on from one medium to the next. Because light reflects when it encounters a mirror and refracts when it encounters a lens, an understanding of reflection and refraction is crucial for the discussion of optics later in this lecture.

Unlike the hypothetical wave on a string, which strikes the boundary between media at a ninety degree angle and reflects back along the path it came, a light or sound wave can strike a boundary at any angle. The angle at which a wave strikes an interface is called the **angle of incidence** and the angle at which it reflects is called the **angle of reflection**. The angle of incidence is equal to the angle of reflection when light reflects off a **plane** (flat) **surface**. Both angles are measured from a line normal to the interface.

$$\theta_{\text{incidence}} = \theta_{\text{reflection}}$$

**FIGURE 5.20** Upright and Inverted Reflections

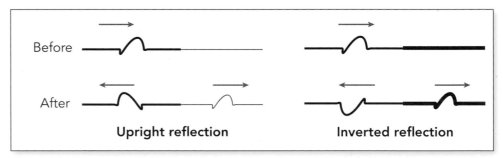

| Upright reflection | Inverted reflection |

A wave that bends as it passes from one medium to another is said to be refracted. All waves refract. Sound waves bend as they move from air of one temperature to air of another temperature. However, the MCAT® only tests refraction of light waves.

The degree to which light bends when it passes from one medium to the next depends on the change of speed that it experiences. Recall that in a vacuum, the speed of light is a constant, $c$, equal to $3 \times 10^8$ m/s. Light is slower when it propagates through a medium. The ratio of the speed of light in a vacuum, $c$, to the speed of light in a particular medium, $v$, is known as the medium's **index of refraction** ($n$).

$$n = \frac{c}{v}$$

Since no waves can exceed the speed of light in a vacuum, all media have refractive indices greater than one. The greater the index of refraction for a medium, the more slowly light moves through that medium. This point can also be seen by rearranging the equation above to write it as $v = 1/n \times c$. This form of the equation shows more clearly that the velocity of light in a medium is a fraction of the speed of light in a vacuum. Since n is in the denominator, the fraction gets smaller as the refractive index gets larger. In other words, the velocity decreases to become an even smaller fraction of the speed of light in a vacuum.

*n is the ratio of the speed of light in a vacuum to its velocity in the particular medium.*

*For the MCAT®, be familiar with the indices of refraction for water (1.3) and glass (1.5), and air (1.0).*

The extent to which a change in speed will bend a light ray is predicted by Snell's law:

$$n_1 \sin\theta_1 = n_2 \sin\theta_2$$

where $n_1$ and $n_2$ are the indices of refraction for the media on either side of the interface, $\theta_1$ is the angle of incidence and $\theta_2$ is the **angle of refraction**. Like angles of incidence and reflection, angles of refraction are measured from a line normal to the interface between media.

The lens of the eye is not the only medium in the eye that refracts light. The cornea, aqueous humor, and vitreous humor also have higher indexes of refraction than air, and refraction occurs at all of those boundaries before light reaches the retina.

**FIGURE 5.21** Refraction and Reflections

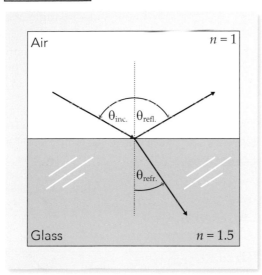

All angles in Snell's law are measured from the normal, an imaginary line that is perpendicular to the surfaces that interface. This use of "normal" should sound familiar: the normal force is a force that is perpendicular to a surface.

At first glance, Snell's law seems to violate the conservation of energy. Since the frequency of the light wave does not change from one medium to the next, both the reflected light and the refracted light must have the same energy. This appears to be twice the energy with which the light started. The trick is that the light still has the same energy per photon, but some of the photons have reflected and some have refracted. The sum of the intensities of the refracted and reflected beam is equal to the intensity of the incident beam, and energy is conserved.

In order to understand why light bends as it moves from one medium to another with a different index of refraction, consider how the transition between media affects the wave fronts that comprise light. Imagine a light source so distant that its circular wave fronts appear as straight lines. The ray approximating the traveling light wave emitted by the source is drawn perpendicularly to the wave fronts. The greater the distance between wave fronts, the greater the wavelength and speed of the light. Remember, $v = f\lambda$, where frequency is a constant determined by the light source. For a given wave, a larger $\lambda$ is associated with greater speed.

As light transitions from a medium with a lower index of refraction to one with a higher index of refraction, its speed decreases and its wave fronts cluster closer together. If the light approaches the interface at any angle other than ninety degrees, one part of the wave slows down before the rest. The light ray, which remains perpendicular to the wave fronts, bends towards the normal. By contrast, when light transitions from a medium with a higher index of refraction to a lower index of refraction, its speed increases and its wave fronts spread out. As a result, the light ray bends away from the normal.

One reason we blink frequently is to maintain the tear layer. When light enters the eye, it is first refracted by the tear layer. The tear layer may also act as a thin film, filtering incoming light.

To visualize refraction, try laying down a rope, linking arms with several friends, and walking toward the rope at an angle. The rule is that once any person's foot goes over the line, that person must slow down just like light does when it enters medium with a higher index of refraction. You'll notice that your line will bend when you cross the boundary because the people on the end were moving so quickly while the people who stepped over the rope slowed down.

**FIGURE 5.24** A Method for Visualizing Refraction

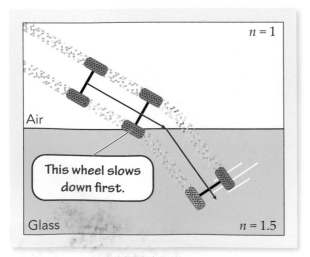

**FIGURE 5.22** Changes in Wave Fronts and Light Rays as Light Transitions between Media at 90⁰

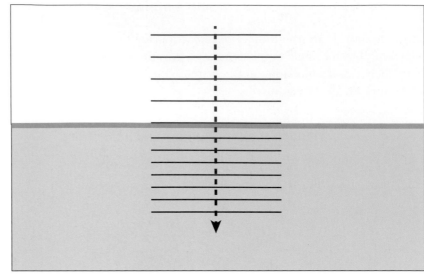

When light approaches a medium with a higher index of refraction at 90°, its wave fronts change speed uniformly and the light ray does not bend.

**FIGURE 5.23** Changes in Wave Fronts and Light Rays as Light Transitions between Media at an Angle

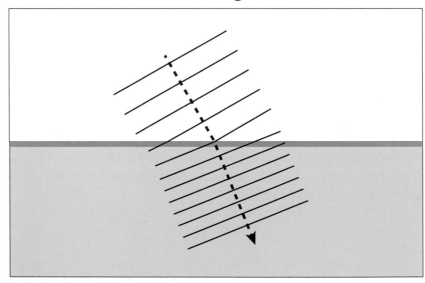

When light approaches a medium with a higher index of refraction at an angle other than 90°, one part of the wave front changes speed before the other and the light ray, which remains perpendicular to the wave fronts, bends at the interface.

Another simple way to choose the direction that light will bend is to imagine a pair of wheels on an axle. The wheels rotate the most rapidly where light travels the fastest, and they always straddle the light ray. When the wheels hit the interface, the first wheel to make contact will speed up if light would speed up (n decreases), or slow down if light would slow down (n increases). Since the wheels hit the interface at different times, the axle will turn to accommodate the different speeds of the wheels. The direction in which the axle turns is the direction in which light will bend.

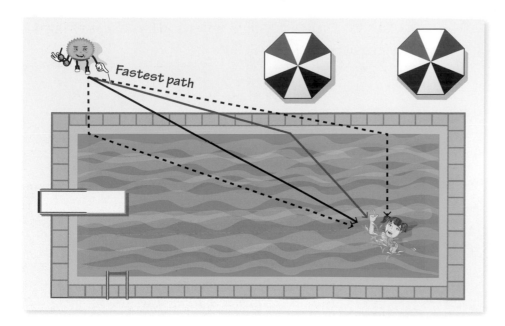
Fastest path

Light traveling between any two points takes the path requiring the least amount of time. This should help you decide which way light will bend at any interface. Imagine that I must rescue a child floundering in a swimming pool. We are both several feet from the edge of the pool. I must approximate at what point I should enter the water in order to reach her the most rapidly. I could either find a pen and paper and calculate Snell's law based upon my velocity on land and in the water, or I could just guess that since I am faster on land, I should travel farther on land. I am looking for the path requiring the least amount of time, and I will bend my path at the edge of the pool, just like light.

Know that when light crosses into a new medium, the frequency remains the same while the wavelength and velocity change. If the medium's index of refraction is higher, the wavelengths become shorter; if the index is lower, then the wavelengths become longer. The phase of the wave does not change due to refraction at an interface.

Refraction does NOT change the phase of the wave at the interface between two media.

## Total Internal Reflection

When light is coming from a medium with a higher index of refraction, the angle of incidence can be so great as to cause total internal reflection. In other words, if the angle of incidence is large enough, all photons will be reflected at the angle of reflection, and none will refract. This angle is called the critical angle. The critical angle is derived from Snell's law by recognizing that the angle of refraction is $90°$ and that $\sin 90° = 1$:

$$\theta_{critical} = \sin^{-1}\left(\frac{n_2}{n_1}\right)$$

The concept of the critical angle is used in fiber optics, where a beam of light is trapped inside a glass tube and signals are sent using the energy of the beam.

If you find it difficult to remember the relationships among $n$, $v$ and $\lambda$, spend some time with the following two equations: $n = c/v$ and $v = f\lambda$. An increase in $n$ is associated with a decrease in $v$, which is associated with a decrease in $\lambda$. What is a decrease in $n$ associated with?

**FIGURE 5.25** Total Internal Reflection

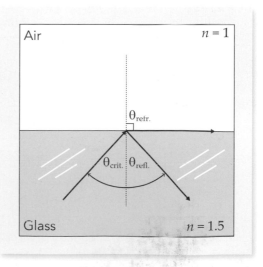

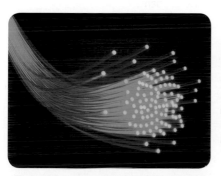

These fibers use the principle of total internal reflection to transmit light down their entire length.

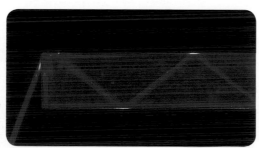

Because light in this glass is incident on the glass-air interface at an angle that equals or exceeds the critical angle, all of the photons are reflected within the glass.

**R** ed
**O** range
**Y** ellow
**G** reen
**B** lue
**I** ndigo
**V** iolet

*Chromatic dispersion is the result of refraction. In dispersive media, distinct wavelengths move at slightly varying speeds, resulting in slightly different angles of refraction.*

## Dispersion

**Dispersion** is the separation of light into different frequencies due to their different indices of refraction in a medium. Recall that light refracts at boundaries because it travels at varying speeds in different media. The speed of light in a given medium depends on the extent to which it is absorbed and re-emitted by that medium. Light that is more frequently absorbed and re-emitted will travel more slowly. Because most objects are more likely to absorb higher-frequency light than lower-frequency light, blue light travels more slowly than red light. As a result, blue light is refracted, or bent, more than red light. In other words, the index of refraction varies slightly with frequency (and therefore with wavelength). As a result, white light, which is made up of all light frequencies in the visible spectrum, is split by a prism in the phenomenon known as **chromatic dispersion**.

Dispersion can occur simply due to refraction, as described above, but light can also be separated into different frequencies according to a more complex process combining reflection, refraction, and interference. This phenomenon is described in the following section.

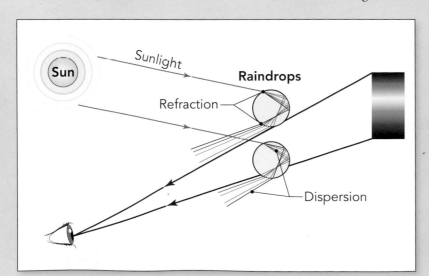

When we observe rainbows in the sky or from prisms, we are viewing multiple photons from different angles. These angles produce the spectra characteristic of these media.

**FIGURE 5.26** Reflection of Parallel Light Rays

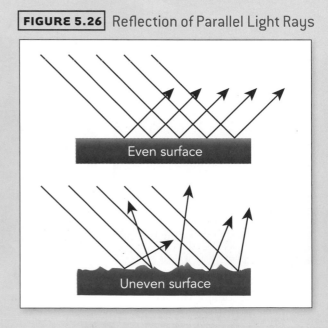

Thin film interference is a particular type of interference that can be used in technology for the purpose of enhancing or diminishing certain wavelengths of light. Because of differences in wavelength and path length, light of one color may experience constructive interference while another experiences destructive interference, resulting in dispersion of white light.

Thin film interference occurs when a thin layer of a substance is placed between two layers of another substance that has a different index of refraction. At each interface, light can either reflect or refract. If it refracts, it changes wavelength but not phase. If it reflects off a medium that is denser, it changes phase but not wavelength. If it reflects off a medium that is less dense, it changes neither wavelength nor phase. Depending on the changes to wavelength, phase, and path length, either constructive or destructive interference can occur.

To better understand the mechanism of thin film interference, examine the figure to the right, which depicts the reflection and refraction of light rays incident on a soap film. When light ray $i_1$ strikes the surface of soapy water, it both reflects ($r_\alpha$) and refracts ($r_\gamma$). Recall that waves reflecting off a denser medium (in this case a medium with a greater index of refraction) change phase by one half of a wavelength, while refracted waves never change phase. As the refracted ray, $r_\gamma$, travels through the soap film, it has a shortened wavelength due to the larger index of refraction of the film. The refracted ray strikes the back surface of the thin layer and both reflects ($r_\delta$) (without phase change since it is reflecting off a medium with a lower index of refraction) and refracts ($r_\zeta$). Ignoring the refracted ray, we follow the reflected ray ($r_\delta$) back to the front surface where it reflects ($r_\epsilon$) and refracts ($r_\beta$) again. The refracted ray, $r_\beta$, follows the same path as the reflection of the incident ray, $i_2$, so the two rays interfere either constructively or destructively.

Because the values of the film thickness and wavelength determine whether the interference is constructive or destructive, manufacturers can create thin films that are the correct thickness for the desired effect. Destructive interference results when the thickness of the film is equal to a multiple of half the wavelength of light within the medium of the thin film. This is because the light travels twice the thickness of the film (to the back surface and then returning to the front) before emerging. When the thickness of the film is equal to half the wavelength, the wave will travel one full wavelength. The light ray with which interference will occur underwent a phase shift of half a wavelength when it reflected off the film surface. As a result, the two waves are out of phase by half a wavelength and will undergo destructive interference. Constructive interference occurs when the thickness of the thin film is equal to a multiple of one quarter of the wavelength of light within the thin film. Rather than traveling a full wavelength, the light only travels a half wavelength before re-emerging. Since the reflecting light underwent a half wavelength phase shift, the two light rays are in phase and interfere constructively.

**FIGURE 5.27** Thin Film Interference

Parallel light rays $i_1$ and $i_2$ strike a soap film. Some photons from this incident light ray refract into the soap film ($r_\gamma$), reflect off the right soap-air interface, and refract back out along path $r_\beta$. Some of the photons from incident light ray $i_2$ reflect off the soap bubble and also follow path $r_\beta$. Path $r_\beta$ is then traveled by photons that have originated from multiple incident rays. The photons will interfere either destructively or constructively depending upon the phase difference, as determined by the thickness of the film.

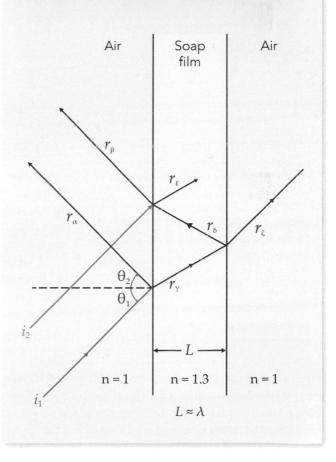

To take advantage of thin film interference, eyewear and camera stores sell solutions that, when applied to lenses, leave a film with the right index of refraction and thickness to produce destructive interference in reflecting photons. This serves to eliminate glare.

The equations for thin film interference maxima (bright portions created by constructive interference) and minima (dark portions created by destructive interference) are:

$$2L = (m + \tfrac{1}{2})\frac{\lambda}{n_2} \qquad for\ m = 0, 1, 2...$$

$$2L = (m)\frac{\lambda}{n_2} \qquad for\ m = 0, 1, 2...$$

where air with an index of refraction of 1 is assumed to surround the thin layer, $n_2$ is the index of refraction of the thin layer, L is the thickness of the thin layer, $\lambda$ is the wavelength in air, and m is an integer. Each value of m that is plugged into each equation returns a wavelength and thickness combination that creates a bright or dark portion, according to the equation.

These equations can be used to quantitatively demonstrate the relationship between wavelength, film thickness, and the type of interference, as described above. Recall that the velocity of light in a medium is represented by the equation $v = c/n$. This can also be written as $v_n = v/n$, where $v_n$ is the velocity of light in a medium with refractive index $n$ and $v$ is the velocity of light in a vacuum. A similar equation can be written for wavelength: $\lambda_n = \lambda/n$. In the equations above, $\lambda/n_2$ can be rewritten as $\lambda_n$. When the equation for destructive interference is then rearranged as $L = \tfrac{1}{2}m\lambda_n$, it shows that destructive interference results when the thickness of the thin film is equal to a multiple of half the wavelength of light within the thin film. A similar rearrangement for the equation for constructive interference shows that constructive interference occurs when the thickness of the thin film is equal to a multiple of a quarter of the wavelength of light within the thin film.

Thin film interference also occurs when the back layer of air is replaced by a substance with a higher index of refraction. In such a case, $r_\beta$ undergoes a phase shift upon reflection. This additional phase shift affects the interference between the reflection of the refracted ray and the light reflected from the front surface. The equations given above remain the same, but the top equation applies to minima while the bottom equation applies to maxima. Under these conditions, constructive interference occurs with a thin film whose thickness is equal to a multiple of half of the wavelength of light within the film, while destructive interference occurs when the thickness is instead a multiple of a quarter of the wavelength.

If, in the figure, width L of the soap film is much smaller than the wavelength of the incident light (i.e., $L < 0.1\ \lambda$), the phase difference is due only to the reflective phase shift. In such a case, the phase difference is approximately one half of a wavelength and the two waves are completely out of phase; destructive interference occurs and the film is dark.

---

To remember the extra ½ term in the maxima equation, remember that maxima have more while minima have less.

---

Thin film interference is the result of:

1. phase changes associated with reflections off media that are more dense,

2. path length differences, and

3. wavelength changes associated with changes in media.

---

Hold your horses! You do not need to memorize these equations or the rearrangement, which was given to help you understand how to use the equations if they are given to you. Instead, focus on understanding how and why thin film interference occurs.

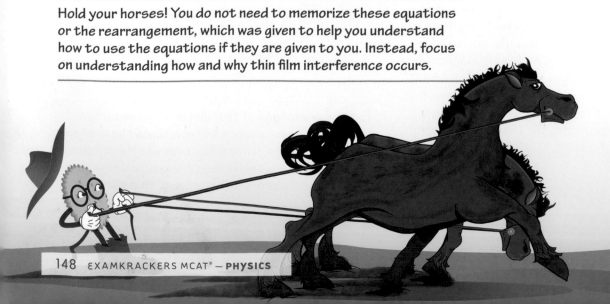

## Diffraction

Diffraction is the spreading of light that occurs when a wave bends around the edges of an object or opening. All types of waves diffract, and waves diffract around all objects. The extent to which a wave diffracts depends on the size of the object or opening relative to the wavelength of the wave. Significant diffraction occurs when the size of the object or opening is on the order of the wavelength or smaller.

Diffraction is a limiting factor for geometric optics. If we attempt to create a sharply defined ray of light by shining light through a small circle, diffraction will occur and the light will spread out, frustrating our efforts. The smaller we make the circle, the larger the spread of the light. Because light diffracts, it cannot be used to produce an image of an object whose size is orders of magnitude smaller than the wavelength of the light. To reduce diffraction and produce images of objects smaller than the wavelength of light, electron microscopes use electron beams that have smaller wavelengths than visible light.

*Remember, diffraction is significant when the size of an object or opening is small relative to the wavelength of a wave. The smaller the object or opening and the larger the wavelength, the greater the bending of the wave.*

---

Light bends in only three ways: 1. refraction, 2. reflection, and 3. diffraction. Notice that longer wavelengths diffract more but refract less than shorter wavelengths.

---

**FIGURE 5.28** Diffraction

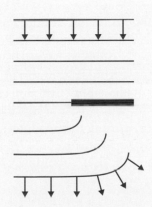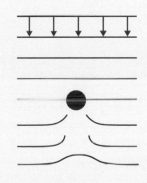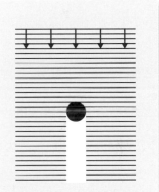

Each of these three images shows a series of wave fronts that passes the edges of an object. The relative wavelength of each wave is indicated by the distance between wave fronts. In the first image, a wave diffracts around the edges of a rectangular object. In the second image, the same wave passes the edge of a more compact, circular object. In this instance, the object is about the same size as the wavelength, and significant diffraction occurs. Finally, in the third image, a wave with smaller wavelength passes the same compact, circular object. In this instance, the object is larger than the wavelength, and minimal diffraction occurs.

It is important to realize that the diffraction of light through a single opening involves diffraction off of multiple surfaces. If light is shone through a slit, it diffracts off of each edge of the slit. Light spreading from one edge interferes with the light spreading from the other edge, forming concentric light and dark rings around a central circle of light. The tendency of light to both interfere and diffract can be observed in Young's double-slit experiment.

**FIGURE 5.29** Rings Created By Light Diffracting Through a Small Circle

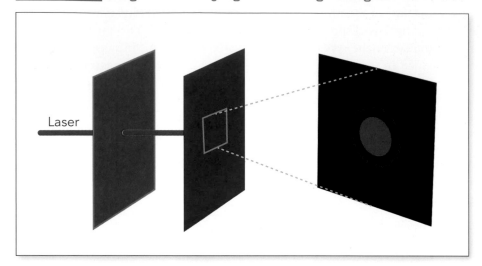

In **Young's double-slit experiment**, light is projected onto a screen with two small slits. The light is monochromatic and *coherent* (able to be forced into a parallel beam that spreads and weakens very little over great distances). The light waves diffracting through the two slits interfere with one another and produce a predictable pattern of alternating light and dark bands (maxima and minima) on the detector screen. The waves from each slit start out in phase but travel different path lengths to meet on the detector. The difference in path length brings them alternately in and out of phase up and down the detector, causing them to interfere either constructively to form maxima or destructively to form minima. Waves interfere constructively when the difference in path length, $\delta$, is a multiple of $\lambda$, and destructively when $\delta$ is a multiple of $\lambda/2$.

**FIGURE 5.30** Bright and Dark Areas in Double Slit Diffraction

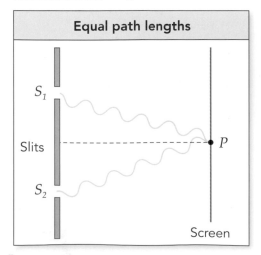
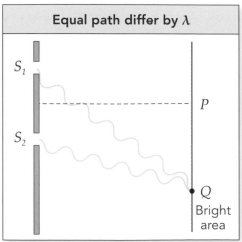
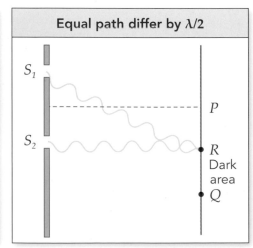

**FIGURE 5.31** Young's Double Slit Experiment

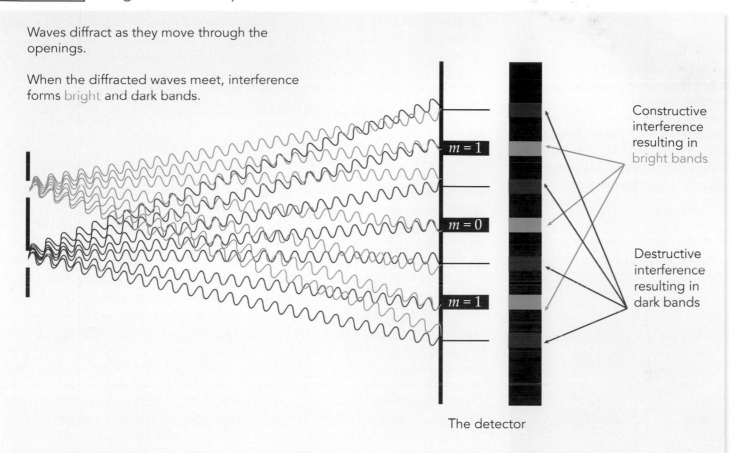

Waves diffract as they move through the openings.

When the diffracted waves meet, interference forms bright and dark bands.

$m = 1$

$m = 0$

$m = 1$

Constructive interference resulting in bright bands

Destructive interference resulting in dark bands

The detector

Notice that the light is coherent. Coherence is typically created by placing a single slit screen in front of the double slit screen and using a monochromatic light source. The single slit acts as a point source. Point sources create spatially coherent light.

**FIGURE 5.32** Path Difference in Double Slit Diffraction

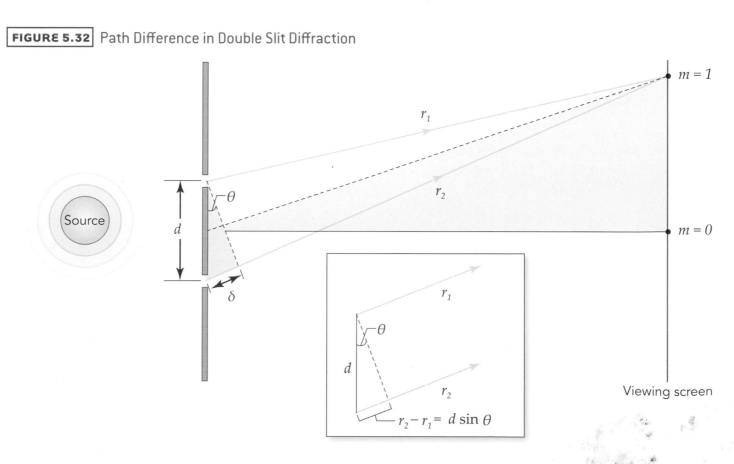

$m = 1$

$r_1$

$r_2$

Source

$\theta$

$d$

$\delta$

$m = 0$

$\theta$

$d$

$r_1$

$r_2$

$r_2 - r_1 = d \sin \theta$

Viewing screen

Because the distance between the slits and the screen is so much greater than the distance between the slits, the paths of the waves can be considered approximately parallel and the difference in path length, δ, can be considered to be equal to $d \sin\theta$.

As a result, maxima occur when path difference, δ, equals:

$$d \sin\theta = m\lambda, \text{ for } m = 1, 2, 3\ldots$$

and minima occur when path difference, δ, equals:

$$d \sin\theta = (m + \tfrac{1}{2})\lambda, \text{ for } m = 1, 2, 3\ldots$$

where $d$ is the distance between the slits, $m$ is the order of the maxima, $\theta_m$ is the angle between the zeroth order maximum and the $m^{th}$ order maximum, and $\lambda$ is the wavelength of the incident wave.

Interference patterns can also be observed when light is passed through more than two slits. A **diffraction grating** is a series of many small slits that diffracts a light source into its component colors. The slits are called *rulings*. A grating may contain as many as several thousand rulings per millimeter. Rulings may be perforations that allow light to pass through, or they may be grooves that reflect light. Like double-slit diffraction, a diffraction grating creates maxima and minima. For each maximum, other than the zeroth order maximum, the component parts of the light source are spread out in spectra from shorter wavelengths (violet) to longer wavelengths (red). Higher order maxima exhibit a wider spread. The spread may be made up of discrete vertical lines or a smear of blended color depending upon whether the source light is made up of a few discrete wavelengths or a continuous spectrum. The more rulings a grating has, the narrower and more defined each maximum and the wider the dark regions between the maxima. The formula for the maxima produced by a diffraction grating is the same as that for the double slit experiment shown earlier:

$$d \sin\theta = m\lambda, \text{ for } m = 1, 2, 3\ldots$$

X-rays are electromagnetic radiation with wavelengths on the order of 1 Å. This is about 5000 times smaller than the wavelength for visible light and approximately equal to the diameter of an atom. Since diffraction works best when the opening is the size of the wavelength or smaller, it is impossible to mechanically construct a diffraction grating for x-rays. The atoms of crystals are roughly the correct distance apart to act as a natural diffraction grating for x-rays. In **x-ray diffraction**, x-rays that are projected at a crystal scatter and create regular interference patterns unique to the structure of the crystal. X-ray diffraction is visualized as rays reflecting off distinct surfaces (or reflecting planes) created within the crystal. Bragg's law describes x-ray diffraction as follows:

$$2 \sin\theta = m\lambda, \text{ for } m = 1, 2, 3\ldots$$

where $d$ is the distance between reflecting planes, $\theta$ is the angle from the reflective plane to the ray (NOT the normal to the ray), $m$ is the order number of the maximum, and $\lambda$ is the wavelength of the x-ray.

---

Notice that the parentheses in these equations for maxima and minima are opposite those used for thin film interference!

---

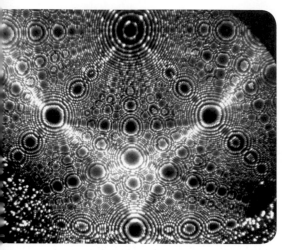

X-ray diffraction is used in crystallography to find the shape or structure of a molecule. This is a color enhanced x-ray diffraction of platinum crystal.

Laboratory Techniques
BIOLOGY 1

---

**Please don't spend your time memorizing Bragg's law. It is very unlikely to appear on the MCAT®. If for some reason you do get a question on x-ray diffraction, and you need Bragg's law, it will be given. Even the fact that the angle is measured from the surface will be given to you. We discussed it here so that you have been exposed to it and won't be surprised or confused if you see it again. What do you need to know to answer an MCAT® question on x-ray diffraction? Understand normal diffraction and the principles behind diffraction gratings; understand what an x-ray is; and understand that x-ray diffraction is used to analyze crystalline structure.**

---

## Questions 105–112 are NOT related to a passage.

### Question 105

A ray of light strikes a flat window as shown. Which ray most closely approximates the path of light as it exits the window?

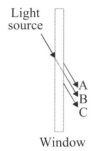

- ○ **A.** A
- ○ **B.** B
- ○ **C.** C
- ○ **D.** Some light will follow all three paths.

### Question 106

Compared to humans, bees perceive a slightly higher frequency of electromagnetic waves. Based on only this information, to which of the following flower colors is a bee more likely to be attracted?

- ○ **A.** Green
- ○ **B.** Red
- ○ **C.** Yellow
- ○ **D.** Blue

### Question 107

Which of the following properties of waves is primarily responsible for attenuation?

- ○ **A.** Refraction
- ○ **B.** Diffraction
- ○ **C.** Reflection
- ○ **D.** None of the above

### Question 108

All of the following are indicative of the wave nature and not the particle nature of light EXCEPT:

- ○ **A.** diffraction.
- ○ **B.** interference.
- ○ **C.** dispersion.
- ○ **D.** reflection.

### Question 109

A piece of glass shaped as shown, with a refractive index of 1.5 allows light to pass through it striking point B. In order to make the light strike point A, the piece of glass should be:

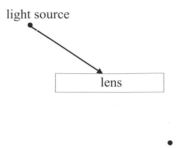

Note: diagram not drawn to scale

- ○ **A.** raised.
- ○ **B.** lowered.
- ○ **C.** made thicker from top to bottom.
- ○ **D.** made thinner from top to bottom.

### Question 110

If a light on a dimmer switch is gradually turned down, it will generally show a red glow at the moment before it is turned off. This is because red light:

- ○ **A.** moves more slowly through air than light of any other color.
- ○ **B.** moves more quickly through air than light of any other color.
- ○ **C.** has more energy than light of any other color.
- ○ **D.** has less energy than light of any other color.

### Question 111

The index of refraction of glass is 1.5. How long does it take for light to pass through a plate of glass that is 1 cm thick?

- ○ **A.** $5 \times 10^{-8}$ s
- ○ **B.** $5 \times 10^{-11}$ s
- ○ **C.** $2 \times 10^{-8}$ s
- ○ **D.** $2 \times 10^{-11}$ s

### Question 112

All of the following are examples of wave diffraction EXCEPT:

- ○ **A.** a light wave bends when passing from air to water.
- ○ **B.** music is audible around a corner from the source.
- ○ **C.** the shadow cast by statue is blurred at the edges.
- ○ **D.** ripples in water become semicircular after passing through a small space.

## 5.10 Optics: Convergers and Divergers

The remaining sections of this lecture will discuss the creation of images. Light waves reflect off of the objects around us. The cornea and lens of the human eye refract these light waves, focusing them on the retina. The retina then generates a cascade of nerve impulses that transmit information to the brain, which in turn processes the information provided by the reflected and refracted light waves and generates images of the objects. Vision is essentially the creation of images from reflected and refracted light. The workings of mirrors and lenses demonstrate how images are created.

The MCAT® requires an understanding of the fundamental similarities and differences between mirrors and lenses. The properties of lenses and mirrors are described by a shared vocabulary, which will be discussed in the following sections. The shape of both mirrors and lenses is key to understanding how they affect light rays. Mirrors and lenses both function to change the direction of light rays reflected off an object, and, as a result, produce an image of that object. The size and direction of the image is affected by the focal length of the lens or mirror, which is a set distance defined by the shape, or curvature, of the lens or mirror.

Without an observer, an image has no meaning. The observer of an image can be an organism, such as a person, or an inanimate object, such as the photographic film in an old-fashioned camera. In this lecture, "the eye" will sometimes be used as a shorthand for the observer. Keep in mind that there are many types of observers and that the eye works with the brain to perceive and make sense of images.

Lenses and mirrors are categorized as convergers or divergers. Light rays converge at a particular point after reflecting from a converging mirror or passing through a converging lens. Light rays diverge after reflecting from a diverging mirror or passing through a diverging lens, so the image is created by a virtual extension of these rays--the real rays never converge. Like the focal point, the converging or diverging nature of a mirror or lens is determined by its shape.

Lenses and mirrors can also each be categorized as concave or convex, according to the shape of the glass. There are two distinct ways to talk about mirrors and lenses: referring to what they do to light (converge or diverge) or referring to their physical shape (concave or convex).

These mirrors are examples of convex mirrors.

**FIGURE 5.33** Mirrors and Lenses

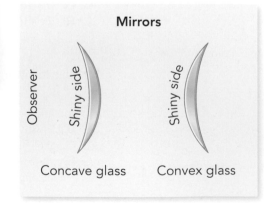

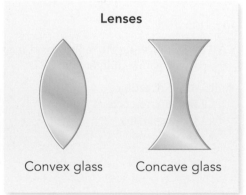

While mirrors and lenses can be described and understood according to a shared vocabulary, they have a fundamental difference: light reflects when it encounters a mirror and refracts when it encounters a lens. Unlike lenses, mirrors have a shiny side (the reflective side) and an opaque side through which light cannot pass. When light from an object encounters a mirror, it is reflected at an angle equal to the angle of incidence. **Spherical mirrors** are mirrors in the shape of a portion of a sphere. If the mirror is part of the inside curve of a sphere, it is a concave or converging mirror. If it is part of the outside, it is a convex or diverging mirror. A spherical mirror forms images of objects by reflecting the light from those objects. Thin lenses form images of objects by refracting the light from those objects.

A lens is any transparent object consisting of two curved surfaces that refract light according to Snell's law: $n_1 \sin\theta_1 = n_2 \sin\theta_2$. A thin lens is a lens whose maximal thickness is small relative to the radius of curvature, object distance and image distance (characteristics that are described in detail later in this lecture). Recall that when light encounters an interface between two media, it is either reflected, absorbed or transmitted. A lens forms images by transmitting and, in the process, bending light.

---

On the MCAT®, assume that all lenses are thin lenses and all mirrors are spherical mirrors.

---

This key difference between mirrors and lenses—that light passes through lenses but does not pass through mirrors—determines the position of the observer. The object and observer must be on the same side of a mirror, the shiny side; otherwise the reflected light rays could not be seen by the observer. With a lens, the observer has to be on the opposite side from an object so that the light from the object can be bent by the lens before reaching the observer.

---

Thinking about everyday examples will help you remember where the observer has to be for lenses and mirrors. When you look in the bathroom mirror in the morning, the object (you) and the observer (also you!) are on the same side of the mirror. As for a lens, think about a pair of glasses. Having the object and observer on the same side of the lens would be like holding your glasses on the other side of a book and thinking they will help you see it!

---

The purpose of mirrors and lenses is to produce an image of an object by bending light rays that reflect off of that object. Depending on the type of mirror or lens, the image that is produced can be real, meaning that light rays actually meet at a physical point, or virtual, meaning that the brain of the observer fills in an image at the point where the light rays would converge if they were traced back to an imaginary origin. These types of images will be described in more detail later in this lecture.

---

If you understand the fundamental principles described above, you're in good shape to understand the more detailed discussion of optics that follows. If necessary, read the introduction above again before you continue to make sure you have a full understanding.

---

Mirrors are used in optical instruments and biomedical technology, which are fair game for the MCAT®.

## Focal Point

Every mirror or lens has a characteristic **focal point** at which parallel light rays converge or appear to converge after reflecting off of the mirror or passing through the lens. (Light rays approaching at any angle will have a real or apparent point of convergence, but only parallel, horizontal light rays converge, or focus, at the focal point.) A *real focal point* is a point at which light rays actually converge, whereas a *virtual focal point* is a point at which light only appears to converge. Because a mirror has a single curve, it has only one focal point, defined by the shape of the mirror. Imagine a spherical mirror to be part of a complete sphere. At the center of the imaginary sphere would be a point called the **center of curvature**. Each point along the mirror's surface is equidistant from the center of curvature. This distance between the surface of the mirror and its center of curvature is known as the **radius of curvature**. A smaller radius of curvature indicates a sharper curve. The larger a mirror's radius of curvature, the flatter its surface. The focal point of a concave mirror lies in front of the mirror, while the focal point of a convex mirror is located behind the mirror, where the rays appear to converge.

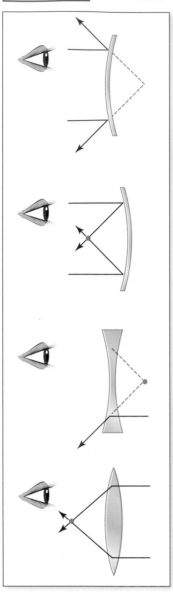

**FIGURE 5.34** Focal Point

---

You are likely to see only spherical mirrors on the MCAT®, rather than planar mirrors. Notice that it would be impossible to determine the radius of curvature for a planar mirror; it would lie at infinity. Remembering this will help you remember that a flatter spherical mirror has a larger radius of curvature.

---

The distance between a mirror and its focal point is known as the focal length. The focal length of a mirror is equal to half the radius of curvature.

$$f = \frac{R}{2}$$

where $f$ is the focal length and $R$ is the radius of curvature. This equation shows that the focal length is half the radius of curvature, which means the focal point of a mirror lies halfway between the mirror's surface and its center of curvature.

Unlike a mirror, a lens has two focal points because it has two curved surfaces. Recall that a mirror will reflect only the light rays that strike its reflective surface. By contrast, a lens will refract light that strikes either one of its curved surfaces. Depending on which surface they strike, parallel light rays can converge or appear to converge at one of two focal points. The focal length for a lens is affected by the refractive index of the lens and the substance surrounding the lens. The lens strength of a lens, also called power, is determined by its focal length. This power is not the same as the power in mechanics. The power of a lens is measured in diopters, which have the equivalent units of $m^{-1}$. The power of a lens is the inverse of the focal length:

$$P = \frac{1}{f}$$

---

Express the focal length in meters when calculating power. If you use the thin lens equation, described later in this lecture, to calculate focal length, you have to convert to meters before using the equation for power. You can bet that the MCAT® will provide an incorrect answer choice equal to the number that you would get if you left the focal point in centimeters.

---

If a lens has two focal points, how can I determine which sign to use for the focal length? The rule for both lenses and mirrors is to use a positive sign if light actually travels to that focal point, and negative if light does not actually travel there. For this reason, convergers have positive focal points and divergers have negative focal points. If a diverging lens problem refers to a focal point that lies between the observer and the lens, that focal length should be negative because the photons travel through the lens, refract, and never travel through the focal point.

---

## Converging and Diverging Lenses and Mirrors

As described above, both mirrors and lenses can be categorized by the way in which they interact with light rays. Converging mirrors and lenses converge light. A **converging mirror** reflects light rays such that they converge at a point in front of the mirror. If the light rays approaching the mirror are parallel, the point at which the reflected rays converge is the focal point. A **converging lens** refracts light rays such that they converge at a point on the side of the lens opposite the light source. Since the observer is on the same side as the light source for a mirror and the opposite side of the light source for a lens, this means that light converges on the same side as the observer.

Recall that lenses and mirrors can be described in terms of both their shape and how they affect light. Converging mirrors and lenses interact with light in the same way, but they do not have the same shape. A converging mirror is concave, while a converging lens is convex. From the perspective of the observer, a **concave mirror** looks like the entrance to a cave. Its surface is "caved in." A **convex lens** has a center that is thick relative to its periphery.

In reality, only a parabolically curved mirror will reflect all parallel light rays such that they converge at a single point. In other words, only a parabolically curved mirror has a single focal point. Mirrors that are spherical rather than parabolic can produce distorted images, a phenomenon called spherical aberration. Unless specifically stated otherwise, assume that all spherical mirrors appearing on the MCAT® behave like parabolic mirrors. When the radius of curvature is relatively large and the angles of incidence are relatively small, a spherical mirror reflects light approximately as a parabolic mirror would.

**FIGURE 5.35** Converging Mirror and Lens

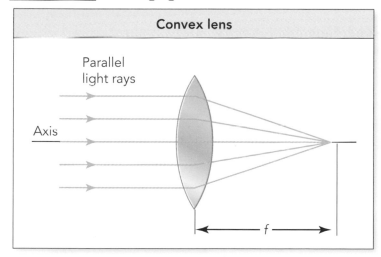
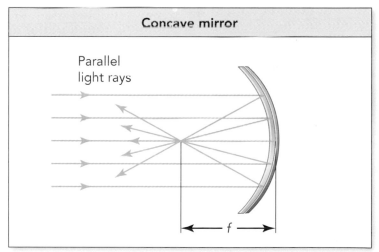

The behavior of divergers is opposite to that of convergers: when parallel light rays encounter a diverging mirror or lens, they spread out such that they will never intersect. The reason that divergers produce an image of the object, despite the fact that the light rays do not converge at a point, is that the observer cannot see the bending of light. As a result, the brain traces back the path of the reflected or refracted light rays and perceives an image at the point at which they would have originated if they had been travelling in a straight line, as described in the following section.

A **diverging mirror** reflects light rays such that the observer perceives them as converging at a point on the opposite side of the mirror from the observer. Similarly, a **diverging lens** refracts light rays such that they appear to converge at a point on the same side of the lens as the light source, opposite from the side of the observer. Diverging lenses and mirrors are differentiated by shape, just like converging lenses and mirrors. A diverging lens is a **concave lens**, meaning that its center is thin relative to its periphery. A diverging mirror is a **convex mirror**, which, in contrast to the caved-in surface of a concave mirror, has a surface that "bulges out" towards the observer.

---

For the MCAT®, practice the skill of quickly identifying a mirror or lens as converging or diverging. If you ever run into trouble, start by thinking about mirrors. Imagine light rays reflecting perpendicularly from the surface of a concave or convex mirror. The light rays reflecting from the concave mirror must head inwards and converge; those reflecting from a convex mirror must go off in all directions and will never converge. This is a simple way to remember that a concave mirror is converging and a convex mirror is diverging. Since lenses follow the opposite pattern, you now also know that a concave lens is diverging and a convex lens is converging.

The shape of the side from which light emerges is the same for convergers and divergers. In other words, the back of a convex lens (converging) has the same shape as the front of a concave mirror (also converging), while the back of a concave lens (diverging) has the same shape as the front of a convex mirror (also diverging).

---

---

Generally the light from the object originates from some other source and reflects off the object. To avoid confusion, when working with mirrors or lenses, assume that light originates from the object.

Here's a little trick to help identify a converging lens. Just remember the three C's: A thick center converges light.

Thicker
center
converges

---

**FIGURE 5.36** Convex and Concave Lenses

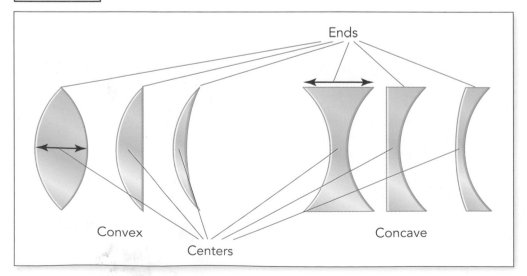

Ends

Convex          Concave

Centers

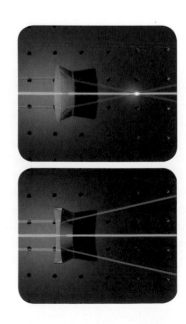

If the center of a lens is thicker than its ends, it will converge light, regardless of its shape or which direction light moves through the lens. If the center is thinner, it will diverge light.

**FIGURE 5.37** Diverging Mirror and Lens

| Concave lens | Convex mirror |
|---|---|
| 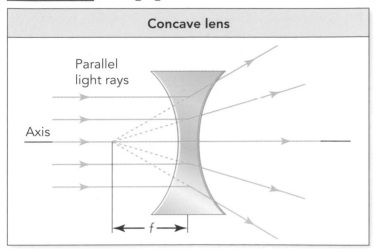 | 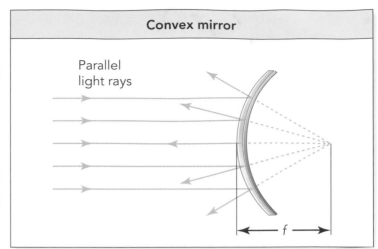 |

## Types of Images

The previous sections described the fundamental characteristics of mirrors and lenses that allow them to bend light for the purpose of creating images. An image is a representation of an object derived from the light reflected from the object. Depending on how an object reflects light, inferences can be made about its shape, orientation, texture, and color. The visual system continuously forms images of the environment by processing the information provided by light.

There are two kinds of images. The first type is real, inverted, on the same side of the mirror or lens as the observer, and positive. The other type is virtual, upright, on the opposite side of the mirror or lens from the observer, and negative. All four characteristics are always found together, so if any one characteristic is given, the other three are also known. The description of an image as positive or negative is redundant with the description of the side of the observer: an image on the same side as the observer is, by convention, defined as positive, while an image on the opposite side from the observer is defined as negative. Assigning a positive or negative sign to the distance between an image or object and the lens or mirror is necessary for the thin lens equation, described in the following section.

One way to think of the difference between real and virtual images is that a real image can be captured on a screen, while a virtual image cannot. (This means the observer of a virtual image must be a living observer. An inanimate observer, such as the example of photographic film, can only receive real images.) A **virtual image** is produced by the apparent convergence of light rays; there are no light rays actually present at the location of the perceived virtual image. Virtual images are always **upright**, rather than inverted. In other words, the top of the object is also the top of the image. Virtual images are located on the opposite side of the lens or mirror from the observer, so they are called negative. Diverging lenses and mirrors always form virtual, upright images located on the opposite side from the observer.

A **real image** is derived from the actual convergence of light rays. Real images are always **inverted**, meaning that the top of the object appears at the bottom of the image. They are also on the side as the observer, so a positive value is assigned to image distance. Convergers usually form images that are inverted, real, and located on the side of the observer, but unlike divergers, which always form the same kind of image regardless of the position of the object, convergers are capable of forming both real and virtual images. When the object is located beyond the focal point, convergers will always produce a real, inverted image, located on the side of the observer. If the object is instead placed within the focal length, the image formed will be virtual and upright. (For a converger, when an object

> Thinking about a magnifying glass can be a useful way to remember the focal point exception for convergers. You know that a magnifying glass must be converging because it is convex, and that usually a converging lens produces a real, inverted image. But when you place it right above a page, the image that you see is upright and must be virtual. That's because the magnifying glass is close enough that the page lies within its focal length.

is placed at the focal point, parallel light emerges, and no image is formed.) The mirrors and lenses on the MCAT® are usually small, meaning that they have tiny focal distances. For that reason, most objects will be located beyond the focal point. This means that convergers almost always create images that are real, inverted, on the same side as the observer, and positive. The creation of an image that is virtual, upright, on the opposite side from the observer, and negative is an important exception to this general rule, and takes place only when the object is placed between the focal point and the concave mirror or converging lens.

> An image formed by a mirror is real if it is on the same side of the mirror as the object. An image formed by a lens is real if it is on the opposite side of the lens as the object. The real image is always on the same side as the observer.

**FIGURE 5.38** Your Eyes Cannot Detect the Bending of Light

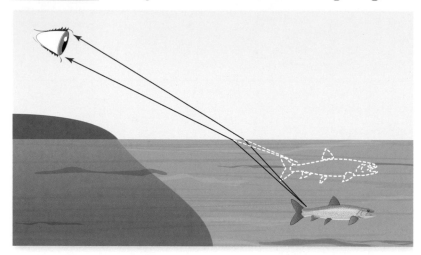

The eye by itself cannot detect whether or not light rays have been bent. Without other visual cues, the mind assumes that light travels in a straight line. As a result, the mind traces straight back along the path of the light rays entering the eye and perceives an image. To the person in the figure above, the fish appears to be where the image is formed because the person's eyes cannot detect the bending of the light.

## The Thin Lens Equation

The previous section described the qualitative features of images formed by converging and diverging mirrors and lenses. Object and image distances can be calculated precisely using the thin lens equation, which relates the image distance ($d_i$) from the mirror or lens and the object distance ($d_o$) to the focal length, also known as the focal distance, $f$, of a mirror or lens.

$$\frac{1}{f} = \frac{1}{d_o} + \frac{1}{d_i}$$

> On the MCAT®, object distance will probably be represented by $p$ and image distance will usually be represented by $q$. You could also see object distance as $d_o$ and image distance as $d_i$. This lecture will use both ways, and you need to be familiar with both.

The values used in this equation will often be expressed in centimeters because the optical instruments being considered are built to be compatible with the eye, which is very small. However, recall that the equation for lens power $\left( P = \frac{1}{f} \right)$ uses m⁻¹. If the thin lens equation is used to find focal length, the value must be converted to meters to find the correct value of power.

> Despite the name, the thin lens equation applies to both lenses and mirrors.

The thin lens equation is additive, so it is necessary to understand the sign conventions for focal, object, and image distances. Each of these characteristics is arbitrarily assigned a positive or negative value according to its location. The thin lens equation will only find the correct answer if each variable is given the correct sign.

Recall that the focal point is a fixed characteristic determined by the shape of the lens or mirror and cannot be changed. For the thin lens equation, the focal distance of a converging lens or mirror is given a positive sign and the focal distance of a diverging mirror or lens is given a negative sign.

Object distances are given a positive sign in the equation when objects are "where they belong." Recall that objects belong on the same side as an observer for mirrors (on the shiny side), and on the opposite side from an observer for lenses. In a single lens system, object distance is always positive.

Finally, the signs for image distance must be correct when using this formula. As described in the previous section, real images are always positive. A positive image sign means it is on the same side as the observer. By contrast, virtual images are always negative. Negative image sign means it is on the opposite side from the observer.

Using the wrong sign for focal length, object distance, or image distance is a common mistake. Memorize the conventions and take a few extra seconds to check the signs when using the thin lens equation.

Real images are images that form where photons actually travel. Virtual images, on the other hand, are "tricks of the eye" – they appear where light does not actually travel. They are just perceived to be at that location by the observer.

TABLE 5.4 > Putting it All Together

| p | Convergers: $f$ is + | Divergers: $f$ is - |
|---|---|---|
| | Image | Image |
| $> f$ | Side of the eye, positive $q$, real, inverted | Opposite side from the eye, negative $q$, virtual, upright |
| $< f$ | Opposite side from the eye, negative $q$, virtual, upright | |
| $= f$ | No image formed | |

Know the four characteristics of images that always go together. A real (1), inverted (2) image is always on the side of the eye (3) and therefore has a positive q (4). On the other hand, a virtual (1), upright (2) image is always on the opposite side from the eye (3) and so has a negative q (4). There are no exceptions. This means that if you are provided with any one characteristic, you automatically know the other three. For example, if a question provides only the information that q is negative, you know that the image is virtual, upright, and on the opposite side from the eye.

In the next section, we present a system for predicting the behavior of light in lenses and mirrors. It's a good idea to practice drawing ray diagrams for lenses and mirrors in case you get tripped up on the test.

## Magnification

When a mirror or lens produces an image, it may magnify it. In everyday language, to magnify something is to make it larger. In optics, magnification, $m$, is a measure of the image's size and orientation relative to the size and orientation of the object it represents.

$$m = -\frac{d_i}{d_o} = \frac{h_i}{h_o}$$

where $d_i$ is the distance from the mirror or lens to the image, $h_i$ is the height of the image, $d_o$ is the distance from the mirror or lens to the object and $h_o$ is the height of the object. The sign conventions previously established for the thin lens equation apply to the magnification equation as well. In addition, the image height is positive when the image is upright and negative when the image is inverted.

An image that is smaller than the object has a magnification smaller in magnitude than one, an image that is the same size as the object has a magnification equal in magnitude to one, and an image that is larger than the object has a magnification greater in magnitude than one. An image that has the same orientation as the object will have a positive magnification and an image that has an orientation opposite to the orientation of the object will have a negative magnification.

Note that an image's magnification provides two pieces of information about it. First, the magnification tells the size of the image relative to the size of the object. Second, it tells the orientation of the image relative to that of the object.

Don't worry too much about the negative sign in the magnification equation. You can tell whether or not the image is inverted just by knowing the characteristics of the lens or mirror. The main point of this equation is that if you know the distances of the object and image, you can find out whether the image is larger or smaller than the object. If the height of the image is greater than the height of the object, the image is larger than the object.

You can remember the magnification equation by thinking of it as saying "Di do, hi ho!"

Diverging mirrors and lenses always form images that are smaller than the objects they represent. Converging mirrors and lenses form images whose sizes vary based on object distance. If you memorize the magnification equation, it is not necessary to memorize the table below.

Don't spend too much time with this table. Instead, memorize the magnification equation and move on. Just know that diverging mirrors and lenses always form smaller images whereas converging mirrors and lenses form larger images unless the object is at or outside the radius of curvature.

TABLE 5.5 > Magnification

| | Image Size | |
|---|---|---|
| $d_o$ | Convergers | Divergers |
| $d_o > R$ | Smaller | |
| $d_o = R$ | Same size | Smaller |
| $d_o < R$ | Larger | |
| $d_o = f$ | No image | |

## MCAT® THINK

1. Have you ever wondered why $m = -\dfrac{d_i}{d_o} = \dfrac{h_i}{h_o}$ ? If so, take a look at the figure below.

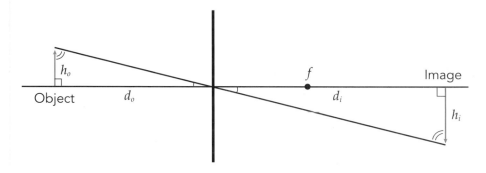

A converging lens forms a real, inverted, larger image of an object placed inside its radius of curvature and outside its focal distance. Notice that, when a line is drawn from the top of the object to the bottom of the image, two similar triangles are formed. Because they are similar, their corresponding sides are all in the same proportion. The magnitude of the ratio $\dfrac{d_i}{d_o}$ is equal to the magnitude of the ratio $\dfrac{h_i}{h_o}$ .

Don't worry if you see a plane mirror question on the MCAT®—the reason that plane mirrors usually aren't tested is that they are too easy! You know from experience that the image in a plane mirror is the same size as the object. In other words, $\dfrac{h_i}{h_o}$, and $m = 1$. Since $m = -\dfrac{d_i}{d_o} = \dfrac{h_i}{h_o}$, this also means that $d_i = d_o$; the image formed by a plane mirror is the same distance from the mirror as the object. You also already know from looking in flat mirrors that they create upright images, so the images are also virtual, on the opposite side of the mirror from the eye, and negative.

A System for Mirrors and Lenses

Understand Key 3: Mirrors and lenses may seem tricky, but, luckily, I have a system. My system, with only three rules and one exception, makes it easy to find the positives and negatives. After that, it's just plug and chug with only three equations to memorize.

The diagram on the facing page provides a visual representation of my system and the three rules. There is one column for convergers and one for divergers. Each column is divided into a row for mirrors and a row for lenses. Each eye represents an observer. Remember, in order to view the image formed by a mirror, an observer must stand on the same side of the mirror as the object. In order to view the image formed by a lens, an observer must stand on the opposite side of the lens as the object.

With these diagrams in hand, you are now ready to learn and apply my three rules!

Rule #1: Converging Mirrors and Lenses...

Converging lenses have positive focal points. Diverging lenses have negative focal points.

Rule #2: The Object Rule

An object belongs on the same side of a mirror and the opposite side of a lens as the eye. When this is true, object distances are positive.

Rule #3: The Image Rule

Converging mirrors make positive, real, and inverted images, except when an object is placed within the focal distance, in which case they make negative, virtual and upright images.

Diverging mirrors and lenses make negative, virtual, and upright images.

The image rule can be summed up by the sentence "I (Eye) am positive that the real is inverted." Images on the side of the eye will always be positive, real, and inverted. This sentence describes images produced by convergers (unless the object is within the focal point), but you can also use it to remember what divergers do. Just remember that a diverging lens or mirror produces an image with the opposite characteristics: not eye, not positive (i.e. negative), not real (i.e. virtual), and not inverted (i.e. upright.)

In the case of a double lens or mirror system, simply find the image for the first lens or mirror, and use that image as the object of the second lens or mirror. Be careful when applying the image rule in a double lens or mirror system, since the image of the first lens or mirror, which is the object of the second lens or mirror, may not be where it belongs.

My last piece of advice is to memorize the three formulas I've written at the bottom of my diagram, which are crucial for success on the MCAT®.

| Convergence (+F) | Divergence (-F) |
|---|---|
| **Mirrors** 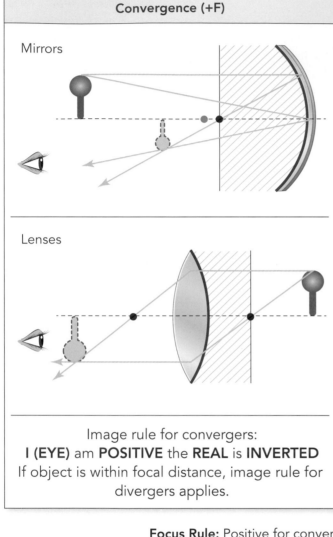 | **Mirrors** 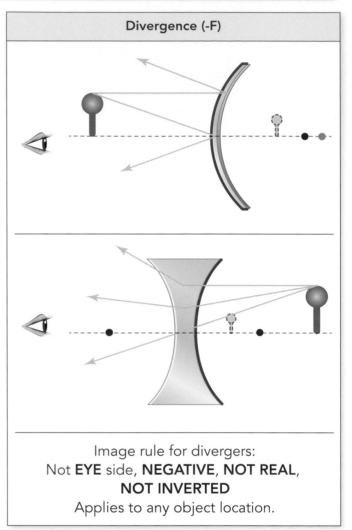 |
| **Lenses** | **Lenses** |
| Image rule for convergers:<br>**I (EYE) am POSITIVE the REAL is INVERTED**<br>If object is within focal distance, image rule for divergers applies. | Image rule for divergers:<br>Not **EYE** side, **NEGATIVE, NOT REAL,**<br>**NOT INVERTED**<br>Applies to any object location. |

**Focus Rule:** Positive for converging, negative for diverging
**Object Rule:** If object is where it should be, $d_o$ is +. If not, $d_o$ is -.
**Image Rule:** Eye side is positive, opposite of eye is negative
Usually only negative for multiple lens/mirror systems

$$P = \frac{1}{f} = \frac{1}{d_o} + \frac{1}{d_i} \qquad \text{Sign matters!}$$

+ and - important for inputting information in lens maker's formula

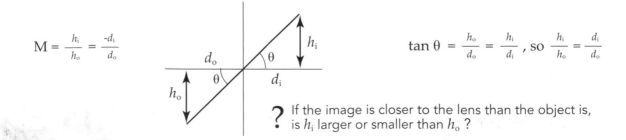

$$M = \frac{h_i}{h_o} = \frac{-d_i}{d_o}$$

$$\tan \theta = \frac{h_o}{d_o} = \frac{h_i}{d_i} \text{, so } \frac{h_i}{h_o} = \frac{d_i}{d_o}$$

**?** If the image is closer to the lens than the object is, is $h_i$ larger or smaller than $h_o$?

# 5.12 | Lens Aberrations

In theory, thin lenses produce focused images. In reality, images are often blurred and exhibit departures from theoretical images called **lens aberrations**. Two common departures are chromatic and spherical aberrations.

*Chromatic aberrations* arise when light of higher frequencies focuses closer to a lens than does light of lower frequencies. Recall that index of refraction varies slightly with frequency and that higher frequency light is bent more than lower frequency light. This means that violet light will focus closer to a lens than red light. Chromatic aberration can be reduced by combining a converging lens of one index of refraction with a diverging lens of another index of refraction.

> The big idea here is that light with a greater frequency tends to bend more sharply when passing through a lens. This sharper bend creates a smaller focal length for light at higher frequencies.

**FIGURE 5.39** Chromatic Aberration

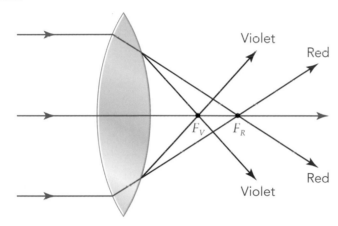

Chromatic aberrations occur only when different frequencies of light pass through a lens simultaneously. If only monochromatic light passed through the lens, chromatic aberrations would not be visible. By contrast, spherical aberrations can be seen even when monochromatic light is used.

*Spherical aberrations* arise when rays farther from the center of a lens focus at different points than do rays closer to the center of the lens. Images produced by lenses with spherical aberrations are clear only when viewed through the center of the lens. Spherical aberration can be reduced by allowing light rays to pass only through the central portion of the lens.

**FIGURE 5.40** Spherical Aberration

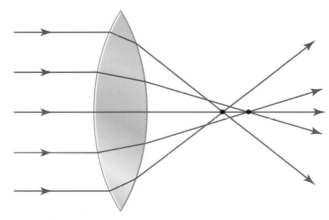

| Multiple Lens Systems

In a single lens system, objects are always "where they belong" and object distances are positive. This is not the case in a system with a **combination of lenses**. The best way to deal with a two lens system is to consider one lens at a time. Use the image of the first mirror or lens as the object of the second mirror or lens. Sometimes the image from the first mirror or lens is formed behind the second mirror or lens. The object distance for the second mirror or lens is negative in this case.

The lateral magnification of a two lens system is the product of the lateral magnification of each lens:

$$M = m_1 m_2$$

Two lenses in contact with each other have an effective power equal to the sum of their individual powers:

$$P_{eff} = P_1 + P_2$$

On the MCAT®, multiple lens systems will likely appear in the context of optical instruments, which manipulate the properties of light to produce viewable images. (A magnifying glass is an example of a simple, single lens optical instrument.) *Compound microscopes* and *refracting telescopes* are two examples of multiple lens optical instruments that allow humans to view objects that cannot be seen with the naked eye. They are used for several types of objects (very small but close objects in the case of microscopes, and very large but far in the case of telescopes), but they are both used for the purpose of creating an enlarged image, and they use similar mechanisms. The two converging lenses used in a microscope or telescope are called the *objective* and the *eyepiece*. Light from an object placed outside the focal point first encounters the objective, which forms a real, inverted image that acts as the object for the eyepiece. The eyepiece then forms an enlarged image that can be seen by the observer. Because the image formed by the objective falls inside the focal length of the eyepiece, the eyepiece forms a virtual, upright image. Since the first image was inverted, this means that the image viewed by the observer appears inverted. For both microscopes and telescopes, even though the object of the second lens is the image of the first one, the object is still "where it belongs" (that is, on the other side of the lens from the observer) and is therefore designated positive.

---

You don't need to memorize the workings of microscopes and telescopes, but these or other optical instruments could be presented in a passage. Being comfortable with these examples of optical instruments will help you deal with any that appear on the MCAT®. Optical instruments could be used to test your understanding of magnification. For example, you could see a question asking where the image formed by the objective falls relative to the radius of curvature of the eyepiece. Since the purpose of the microscope is to enlarge the object, and a converging lens forms an enlarged image when the object is within the radius of curvature, the image formed by the objective should be within the radius of curvature of the eyepiece.

---

## The Human Eye

As discussed in the Nervous System Lecture in *Biology 2: Systems*, the human eye acts as an optical instrument by refracting incoming light so that it focuses on an area at the back of the eye known as the retina. Two structures in the eye, the *cornea* and the *lens*, bend incoming light rays as needed to converge on the retina. After encountering the transparent *cornea*, which is responsible for the most extreme bending, incoming light is further bent by the *crystalline lens*. Despite the name, the lens does not bend light as much as the cornea; instead the lens is responsible for the fine control necessary to precisely focus light on the retina.

Slight variations in the shape of the lens allow the eye to focus light reflected off of both near and far objects. To focus light from near objects, the muscle surrounding the lens contracts, causing the lens to bulge, thus reducing the focal length of the lens. To focus light from far objects, the muscle relaxes, causing thin filaments that run from the muscle to the edge of the lens to tighten and flatten the lens. In this way, the eye increases the focal length of the lens.

Nervous System
BIOLOGY 2

The cornea bends incoming light rays in the general direction of the retina. Light rays that have already been bent by the cornea are then bent again by the lens to produce a clear image.

---

**FIGURE 5.41** The Eye

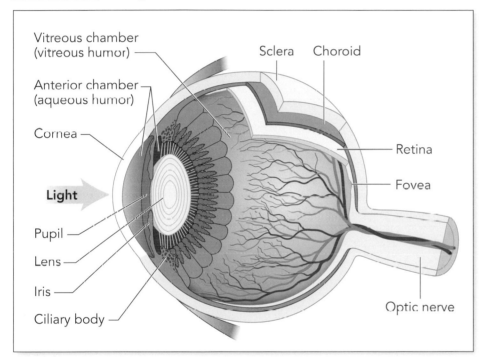

Do not spend time memorizing the names of the components of the eye. Instead, focus on understanding how the eye works. Try to integrate what you already know about thin lenses with what is presented here.

---

The commonly used terms of *near-sighted* (myopia) and *far-sighted* (hyperopia) describe opposite deficits in vision, each caused by the inability of the eye to correctly focus light on the retina. A near-sighted person can see near objects clearly but has difficulty seeing far objects. Think of the lens of a near-sighted person as being particularly good at bending light, since light that reflects off of a nearby object will approach the eye at a sharp angle and must be bent significantly to focus on the retina. When light rays reflecting off of a far object approach the eye, the lens of a near-sighted person bends the light too sharply, and the rays converge in front of the retina. As a result, the object is not seen clearly. The distance vision of a person who is near-sighted can be corrected with a diverging lens, which causes the light rays to spread out before encountering the eye's lens, allowing them to be focused at the retina.

A far-sighted person has the opposite problem. The lens of someone who is far-sighted is not very good at bending light. This does not present a problem for light rays reflecting off of a far object (remember that the farther the source of the light, the closer the light rays are to being parallel). When light approaches from a nearby object, the lens is not able to bend the light rays sufficiently, and they do not converge until they have passed the retina. A converging lens corrects the

NEAR-sighted people can see NEAR objects clearly. The lens of a NEAR-sighted person causes light to focus too NEAR the front of the eye. FAR-sighted people can see FAR objects clearly. The lens of a FAR-sighted person causes light to focus too FAR from the front of the eye.

---

A far-sighted person can see far but not near objects. This means their near point must be farther than average. A near-sighted person can see near but not far objects. This means their far point must be nearer than average.

vision of a far-sighted person by bending light rays enough that the lens can focus them on the retina.

A more technical understanding of nearsightedness and farsightedness involves differences in the position of the near point and far point. The near point is the closest distance at which the eye can see an object clearly. By contrast, the far point is the farthest distance at which the eye can see an object clearly. A person with normal vision can see distant objects and is considered to have a far point at infinity.

A far-sighted person has a near point that is farther than average. The near point tends to increase with age as the lens stiffens and resists the bulging necessary to reduce the focal length. A converging lens corrects for farsightedness by converging the light rays from a nearby object, making them closer to parallel and so making the light rays appear as though they are coming from farther away.

**FIGURE 5.42** Farsightedness

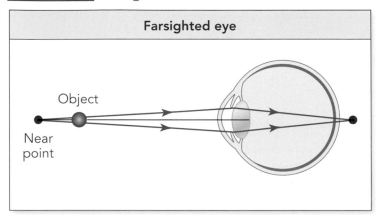

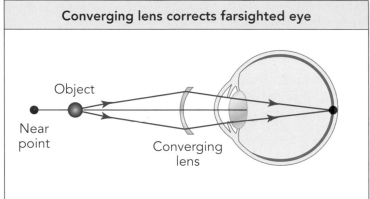

A near-sighted person has a far point that is closer than average. Diverging lenses correct nearsightedness by spreading the light rays out more, making them appear as they would if they were coming from a nearer object.

**FIGURE 5.43** Nearsightedness

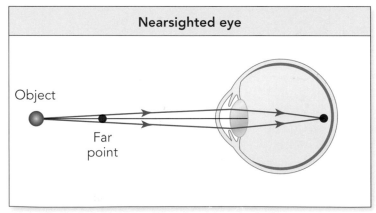

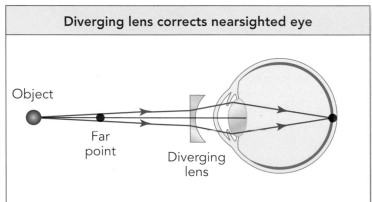

How are the focal lengths of eyeglasses and contact lenses different? Eyeglasses sit on the bridge of the nose about 2 cm from the cornea. A contact lens sits on the outer surface of the eye, closer to the retina, so it has a smaller focal length.

## Question 113

A glass magnifying lens is submerged in water to view an underwater object. Compared to viewing the object with the magnifying lens out of water, this will:

- ○ **A.** increase the magnification.
- ○ **B.** decrease the magnification.
- ○ **C.** not change the magnification.
- ○ **D.** The magnifying glass will not work at all under water.

## Question 114

Which of the following statements is (are) true?

- I. Virtual images can be projected onto a screen.
- II. Real images can never be seen.
- III. Real images can only be created by converging lenses and concave mirrors in a single lens or single mirror system.

- ○ **A.** III only
- ○ **B.** I and II only
- ○ **C.** I and III only
- ○ **D.** I, II, and III

## Question 115

An increase in which of the following lens properties will increase the power of a lens?

- I. Index of refraction
- II. Focal length
- III. Radius of curvature on one side of the lens

- ○ **A.** I only
- ○ **B.** I and II only
- ○ **C.** II and III only
- ○ **D.** I, II, and III

## Question 116

An object stands 4 cm in front of a converging lens. If the lens has a focal distance of 1 cm, where is the image formed?

- ○ **A.** 0.75 cm in front of the lens
- ○ **B.** 0.75 cm behind the lens
- ○ **C.** 1 cm behind the lens
- ○ **D.** 1.33 cm behind the lens

## Question 117

An inverted image is created by an object 5 m in front of a mirror. Which of the following could be true about the mirror and the object?

- ○ **A.** The mirror is convex with less than a 5 m focal distance.
- ○ **B.** The mirror is concave with less than a 5 m focal distance.
- ○ **C.** The mirror is convex with more than a 5 m focal distance.
- ○ **D.** The mirror is concave with more than a 5 m focal distance.

## Question 118

A 1 cm candle stands 4 cm in front of a concave mirror with a 2 cm focal distance. The image is:

- ○ **A.** inverted and 1 cm tall.
- ○ **B.** inverted and 2 cm tall.
- ○ **C.** upright and 1 cm tall.
- ○ **D.** upright and 2 cm tall.

## Question 119

A lens is manufactured in such a way as to allow the object and the image to be at the same distance from the lens. If the lens is not flat, the only way this could be true is if the lens were:

- ○ **A.** a diverging lens with the object at the focal distance.
- ○ **B.** a diverging lens with the object at twice the focal distance.
- ○ **C.** a converging lens with the object at the focal distance.
- ○ **D.** a converging lens with the object at twice the focal distance.

## Question 120

The diagram below shows an object placed in front of an unknown optical device and the image produced.

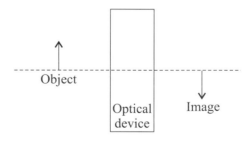

The optical device is a:

- ○ **A.** convex mirror.
- ○ **B.** concave mirror.
- ○ **C.** converging lens.
- ○ **D.** diverging lens.

### Waves

$$v = f\lambda \qquad T = \frac{1}{f}$$

### The Doppler Effect

$$\frac{\Delta f}{f_s} = \frac{v}{c} \qquad\qquad \frac{\Delta \lambda}{\lambda_s} = \frac{v}{c}$$

### Sound

$$\beta = 10 \log \frac{I}{I_0}$$

$$f_{\text{Beat}} = |f_1 - f_2|$$

$$L = \frac{n\lambda_n}{2} \quad (n = 1, 2, 3, ...)$$

$$L = \frac{n\lambda_n}{4} \quad (n = 1, 3, 5, ...)$$

### Electromagnetic radiation

$$c = f\lambda$$

$$E = hf$$

$$n = \frac{c}{v}$$

$$n_1 \sin \theta_1 = n_2 \sin \theta_2$$

### Mirrors and lenses

$$f_{\text{mirror}} = \frac{1}{2} r$$

$$P = \frac{1}{f}$$

$$m = -\frac{d_i}{d_o} = \frac{h_i}{h_o}$$

$$\frac{1}{f} = \frac{1}{d_o} + \frac{1}{d_i}$$

# MCAT® THINK ANSWERS

pg. 129:   The clarinet. The flute is open to the atmosphere at both ends, so no net differential exists at the ends. Regions of pressure differential will develop as the air within oscillates, but neither end of the instrument is sensitive to pressure differentials. The clarinet, on the other hand, has one end that is closed to the atmosphere. At that end, no displacement of air molecules occurs, and the difference in pressure from atmospheric pressure at the open end is greatest. (Again, think of a compressed spring in the pipe. Pressure will be at a maximum at the closed end of the pipe.)

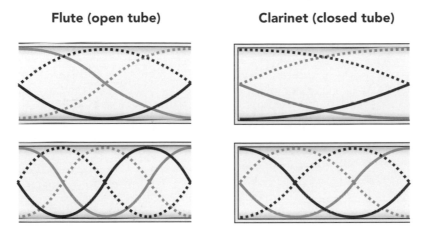

pg. 168:   (top of page) It will decrease. As the near point gets farther and farther, the lens will have to bend light more, requiring a decreased focal length. Another way to think about it is that an aging person will need increasingly powerful lenses, and lens power is inversely related to focal length.

pg. 168:   (bottom of page) Remember that nearsightedness is corrected with a diverging lens. Divergers always have negative focal points, so they must have negative power. Farsightedness is corrected with a converging lens. Since convergers always have positive focal points, they must have positive power.

Absorption
Amplitude
Angle of incidence
Angle of reflection
Angle of refraction
Attenuation (damping)
Center of curvature
Chromatic dispersion
Circularly polarized
Combination of lenses
Concave lens
Concave mirror
Constructive interference
Converging lens
Converging mirror
Convex lens
Convex mirror
Critical angle
Decibels (dB)
Destructive interference
Diffraction
Diffraction grating
Diopters
Dispersion
Diverging lens
Diverging mirror

Doppler effect
Electromagnetic waves
Focal length
Focal point
Frequency (f)
Image
In vacuo
Index of refraction (n)
Infrared
Intensity level
Inverted
Lens aberrations
Lens strength
Light
Logarithmic scale
Longitudinal waves
Mechanical waves
Natural frequency
Optical instruments
Oscillations
Phase
Photons
Pitch
Plane surface
Polarized
Power

Production of sound
Radius of curvature
Real image
Reflection
Reflection of sound
Refraction
Require a medium
Resonance
Resonance in pipes and strings
Resonant frequency
Resonate
Shock wave
Sound
Speed of light in vacuo (c)
Spherical mirrors
Thin lens
Transverse waves
Total internal reflection
Ultraviolet
Upright
Velocity
Virtual image
Wave
Wavelength (λ)
X-ray diffraction
Young's double-slit experiment

### THE 3 KEYS

1. To solve for the Doppler Effect: when a wave source and observer move towards one another, *frequency* increases—add $\Delta f$ to $f_s$ to get $f_o$. When a wave source and observer move away from each other, frequency decreases—subtract $\Delta f$ from $f_s$ to get $f_o$.

2. Determine whether a wave is undisturbed, reflected, refracted, diffracted, or dispersed.

3. Lenses and mirrors follow the three optics rules: the focal point rule, the object rule, and the image rule.

# STOP!

## DO NOT LOOK AT THESE EXAMS UNTIL CLASS.

**30-MINUTE IN-CLASS EXAM FOR LECTURE 1**

## Passage I (Questions 1-5)

Muscular contractions generate force and can be classified as isometric, concentric, or eccentric. During an isometric contraction, the muscle length remains constant; during a concentric contraction, the muscle shortens; during an eccentric contraction, the muscle lengthens. Performing a biceps curl by flexing the elbow is an example of concentric contraction of the biceps, and slowly lowering the weight is an example of eccentric contraction. Researchers examined the relationship between muscular activation and force output in all three contraction types.

### Experiment 1

In the laboratory, muscles isolated from frogs were attached to an apparatus in which they can be electrically stimulated to contract with weights suspended from them. The device allows measurement of muscle force and motor unit recruitment during contractions. First, the muscles were sufficiently stimulated to suspend 5 kg and 10 kg discs. Next, the stimulation was increased and the discs were lifted 0.08 m. Then, the stimulation was decreased and the discs were slowly lowered to the starting position. Finally, a large stimulus was given to lift the 10 kg disc. The measured average motor unit recruitment and average muscle force is presented in Table 1.

| Contraction type | Disc Mass (kg) | Force (N) | Motor unit recruitment (%) |
|---|---|---|---|
| Isometric | 5 | 50 | 26 |
| Isometric | 10 | 100 | 55 |
| Concentric | 5 | 55 | 29 |
| Concentric | 10 | 105 | 59 |
| Concentric – large stimulus | 10 | 145 | 94 |
| Eccentric | 5 | 45 | 22 |
| Eccentric | 10 | 80 | 44 |

**Table 1** Average Muscle Force versus Motor Unit Recruitment Percentage

This passage was adapted from "Motor Unit Firing Behavior of Soleus Muscle in Isometric and Dynamic Contractions." Kallio J, Søgaard K, Avela J, Komi PV, Selänne H, et al. *PLoS ONE*. 2013. 8(2): e53425 doi:10.1371/journal.pone.0053425 for use under the terms of the Creative Commons Attribution 4.0 License (http://creativecommons.org/licenses/by/4.0/legalcode).

### Question 1

How much greater was the acceleration of the 10 kg disc with the larger stimulus compared to the acceleration of this disc with the original stimulus?

- ○ **A.** 4.5 m/s$^2$
- ○ **B.** 4 m/s$^2$
- ○ **C.** 5 m /s$^2$
- ○ **D.** 10 m/s$^2$

### Question 2

What is the final expected velocity for the 10 kg disc when it is lifted with a force of 145 N?

- ○ **A.** 0.60 m/s
- ○ **B.** 0.85 m/s
- ○ **C.** 1.20 m/s
- ○ **D.** 1.52 m/s

### Question 3

Which of the following is most likely the maximum disc mass that could be suspended from an average frog muscle during an isometric contraction with maximal stimulation?

- ○ **A.** 10 kg
- ○ **B.** 12 kg
- ○ **C.** 16 kg
- ○ **D.** 22 kg

### Question 4

Which of the following is true of a disc at the moment when concentric contraction of the muscle ceases and eccentric contraction begins?

- ○ **A.** Both its kinetic and gravitational potential energies are at a maximum.
- ○ **B.** Both its kinetic and gravitational potential energies are at a minimum.
- ○ **C.** Its kinetic energy is at a maximum and its gravitational potential energy is at a minimum.
- ○ **D.** Its kinetic energy is at a minimum and its gravitational potential energy is at a maximum.

### Question 5

Suppose the experiment is repeated at a very high altitude, where the force of gravity is slightly lower. After adjusting the stimulation to the level needed to achieve isometric contraction, concentric contraction is achieved by increasing the stimulation the same amount that it was increased during the original experiment. How will the results obtained during concentric contraction be different from those of the original experiment?

- ○ **A.** Both the muscle force and the disc acceleration will be reduced.
- ○ **B.** Both the muscle force and the disc acceleration will be greater.
- ○ **C.** The muscle force will be the same, and the disc acceleration will be greater.
- ○ **D.** The muscle force will be reduced, and the disc acceleration will be the same.

## Passage II (Questions 6-10)

Pulmonary arterial hypertension (PAH), caused by vascular remodeling of the small pulmonary arteries, is characterized by mean pulmonary arterial pressure $\geq 25$ mmHg and pulmonary capillary wedge pressure $\geq 15$ mmHg at rest, as assessed by right heart catheterization. As pulmonary vascular resistance increases, the overloaded right ventricle (RV) changes morphologically and functionally.

Echocardiography is the most common and convenient method used to evaluate RV function. Researchers assessed the value of two echocardiographic parameters in predicting right ventricular ejection fraction (RVEF), which is the percentage of end diastolic volume ejected with each contraction.

First, both RVEF and average tricuspid annular systolic excursion velocity (S') were measured. During ventricular diastole, the leaflets of the tricuspid valve project into the right ventricle, allowing passage of blood from the right atrium to the right ventricle. The base of each leaflet on the valve is secured to the annulus, a fibrous ring that surrounds the atrioventricular orifice. Tricuspid annular systolic excursion velocity is an indicator of right heart systolic function.

| Tricuspid Annular Systolic Excursion Velocity (S') | Right Ventricular Ejection Fraction (RVEF) |
|---|---|
| 6 cm/s | 20% |
| 8 cm/s | 24% |
| 10 cm/s | 30% |
| 12 cm/s | 36% |

**Table 1** Tricuspid annular systolic excursion velocity (S') and right ventricular ejection fraction (RVEF)

Next, RV isovolumetric acceleration (IVA) was calculated as the peak isometric myocardial velocity divided by time to peak velocity. RVEF was plotted as function of IVA.

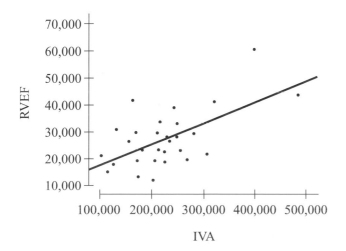

**Figure 1** Right ventricular ejection fraction (RVEF) as a function of right ventricle isovolumetric acceleration (IVA)

After adjusting for mean right atrial pressure, mean pulmonary arterial pressure, and pulmonary vascular resistance, only IVA was an independent predictor of RVEF.

This passage was adapted from "Echocardiographic Parameters in Patients with Pulmonary Arterial Hypertension: Correlations with Right Ventricular Ejection Fraction Derived from Cardiac Magnetic Resonance and Hemodynamics." Yang T, Liang Y, Zhang Y, Gu Q, Chen G, et al. *PLoS ONE*. 2011. 8(8): e71276. doi:10.1371/journal.pone.0071276 for use under the terms of the Creative Commons CC BY 3.0 license (http://creativecommons.org/licenses/by/3.0/legalcode).

### Question 6

If average IVA was calculated to be 3.2 m/s$^2$ and peak isometric myocardial velocity was measured at 8 cm/s, how long did it take to reach peak velocity? Assume initial myocardial velocity was 0 cm/s.

- A. 0.25 s
- B. 0.025 s
- C. 40 s
- D. 4 s

### Question 7

RVEF is positively correlated with right ventricle function. Compared to a healthy patient, would a patient with pulmonary arterial hypertension be expected to have higher or lower S' and IVA measurements?

- A. Higher S' but lower IVA
- B. Higher S' and higher IVA
- C. Lower S' but higher IVA
- D. Lower S' and lower IVA

### Question 8

As RVEF increases, would the force with which the right ventricle contracts decrease or increase?

- A. Decrease because IVA decreases
- B. Decrease because IVA increases
- C. Increase because IVA increases
- D. Increase because IVA decreases

## Question 9

Blood returning to the right atrium from the lower extremities must flow against the force of gravity, but the magnitude of blood flow velocity increases as blood moves from the capillaries to the heart. Given that venous blood flow velocity is in the positive direction, in which directions are net force and acceleration?

- A. Both net force and acceleration are in the negative direction.
- B. Net force is in the negative direction but acceleration is in the positive direction.
- C. Net force is in the positive direction but acceleration is in the negative direction.
- D. Both net force and acceleration are in the positive direction.

## Question 10

At the onset of ventricular diastole, the net forces acting on the leaflets of the tricuspid valve are directed:

- A. into the right ventricle.
- B. into the right atrium.
- C. into the pulmonary artery.
- D. into the venae cavae.

## Passage III (Questions 11-14)

The activation of T cells is a key process in the adaptive immune system. T cells regulate the activity of many other cells in the immune system, especially B cells, which produce antibodies that are vital to fighting off specific pathogens.

When the appropriate antigens are presented, T cell receptors (TCRs) bind to major histocompatibility complexes (MHCs) on antigen presenting cells (APCs), and are, thereby activated. Once activated, T cells exert pushing and pulling forces on APCs. Some of these mechanical forces are generated by actin polymerization and increases in intracellular calcium. Additionally, the membrane protein integrin has been shown to play a role in generation of T cell mechanical forces.

To quantify the pushing and pulling forces exerted by activated T cells, researchers created a model APC by coating a bead with antibodies against the TCR-CD3 subunit. When in close proximity to the bead, TCRs bound to the antibodies and were activated by them. In this way, researchers were able to simulate the activation of TCRs by MHCs on antigen presenting cells. The bead coated with antibodies was connected to a red blood cell with a known stiffness of 50 pN/μm. Researchers recorded deformation of the red blood cell following activation of the TCRs.

This passage was adapted from "Force Generation upon T Cell Receptor Engagement." Husson J, Chemin K, Bohineust A, Hivroz C, Henry N. *PLoS ONE*. 2011. 6(5) doi: 10.1371/journal. pone.0019680 for use under the terms of the Creative Commons CC BY 3.0 license (http://creativecommons.org/licenses/by/3.0/legalcode).

## Question 11

Which of the following would be true if red blood cell stiffness was overestimated?

- A. The researchers would overestimate the mechanical force generated.
- B. The researchers would underestimate the mechanical force generated.
- C. The T cell would not be activated by the model APC.
- D. The results would not be affected.

## Question 12

How much force would a T cell need to exert on a red blood cell in order to compress it 0.5 μm?

- A. 200 pN
- B. 100 pN
- C. 25 pN
- D. 12.5 pN

Next ▶

## Question 13

What change to the experimental conditions would be most likely to decrease the measured force?

○ **A.** Using a cell with a stiffness of 25 pN/μm instead of a red blood cell

○ **B.** Administering Latrunculin A, a compound that prevents actin polymerization

○ **C.** Increasing the pH of the cellular medium that the experiment takes place in

○ **D.** Using a cell with a stiffness of 75 pN/μm instead of a red blood cell

## Question 14

Which of the following could accurately describe changes in the velocity of an antigen-presenting cell accelerated, first, by the pushing and, then, by the pulling forces exerted by a T cell receptor?

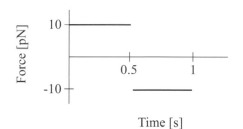

○ **A.**

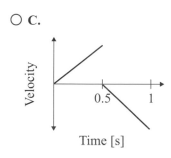

○ **B.**

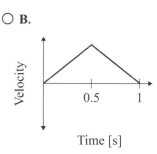

○ **C.**

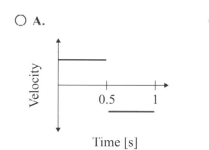

○ **D.**

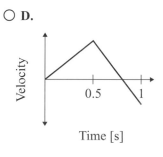

## Passage IV (Questions 15-18)

Bone morphogenetic protein 2 (BMP2) plays critical roles in the skeleton. As a result, BMP2 has been used clinically in orthopedic and dental settings to stimulate growth. Extensive research has focused on BMP2's ability to enable differentiation of precursor cells into osteoblasts and enhance osteoblast function. BMP2 is highly expressed in osteoblasts, but little is known about how a deficiency of BMP2 affects differentiated osteogenic cells.

Surprisingly, BMP2 knockout mice are similar to wild-type mice at birth. However, as early as one week postnatally they begin to exhibit defects in both cartilage and bone formation, and as they mature the phenotype worsens. Knockout mice have thinner, less dense bones that spontaneously fracture. It is unclear if one cell type (progenitor, chondrocyte, osteoblast, osteocyte) is the major contributor of BMP2 causing the phenotype or if the phenotype is a result of knockout from all chondro- and osteo- cells. Also, it is unknown if the spontaneous fractures are due solely to the smaller size of the knockout bones or if there is a defect in the bone material of knockout mice.

Researchers sought to better identify the role of tissue specific BMP2 during post-natal skeletal growth and determine if BMP2 knockout affects the ability of terminally differentiated cells to create normal quality bone material. They targeted BMP2 knockout to two differentiated cell types known to express BMP2 during growth and healing, osteoblasts and vascular endothelial cells (VEC), and then assessed various bone characteristics in each transgenic line.

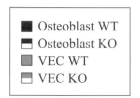

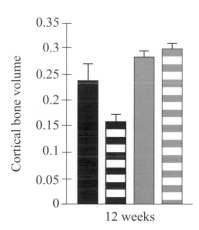

**Figure 1** Cortical bone volume in conditional BMP2 knockout mice

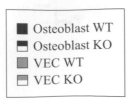

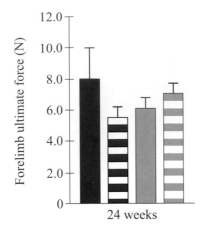

**Figure 2** Forelimb ultimate force (a measure of bone strength) in conditional BMP2 knockout mice

This passage was adapted from "Long Bone Structure and Strength Depend on BMP2 from Osteoblasts and Osteocytes, but Not Vascular Endothelial Cells." McBride SH, McKenzie JA, Bedrick BS, Kuhlmann P, Pasteris JD, et al. *PLoS ONE*. 2014. 9(5) doi:10.1371/journal. pone.0096862 for use under the terms of the Creative Commons CC BY 4.0 license (http://creativecommons.org/licenses/by/4.0/legalcode).

## Question 15

One major source of discomfort and pain is the friction of direct contact between bones. Which of the following affects the degree of friction between two bones that are in contact?

   I. Surface area of the bones that are in contact

   II. The amount of force that each bone exerts on the other

   III. Texture of each bone

  ○ **A.** I only

  ○ **B.** I and II

  ○ **C.** II and III

  ○ **D.** I, II, and III

## Question 16

Which of the following bones has the greatest inertia?

  ○ **A.** 142 g, 64 cm³

  ○ **B.** 130 g, 64 cm³

  ○ **C.** 71 g, 25 cm³

  ○ **D.** 65 g, 25 cm³

## Question 17

During a bone test, a 0.03 kg bone is accelerated from rest by a constant 0.004 N force for 5 seconds. What final speed does this bone reach?

  ○ **A.** 0.133 m/s

  ○ **B.** 0.335 m/s

  ○ **C.** 0.67 m/s

  ○ **D.** 37.5 m/s

## Question 18

A bone from each of the four genotypes of mice has a constantly increasing force exerted on it. Which genotype's bone will be the first to crack?

  ○ **A.** VEC WT

  ○ **B.** VEC KO

  ○ **C.** Osteoblast WT

  ○ **D.** Osteoblast KO

**Questions 19 through 23 are NOT based on a descriptive passage.**

## Question 19

Some proteins bound to microtubules during anaphase form "gas springs" that behave like ideal springs. Which of the following graphs accurately represents the relationship between force and tension in an ideal spring?

—— Potential energy (s) vs. distance
- - - Force (N) vs. distance

○ A)

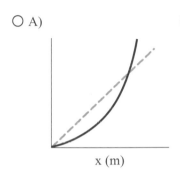

x (m)

○ B)

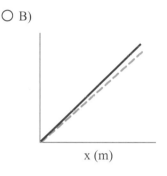

x (m)

○ C)

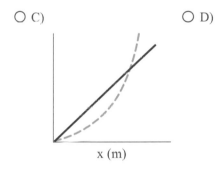

x (m)

○ D)

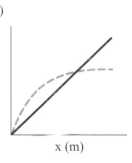

x (m)

## Question 20

A red blood cell (RBC) is traveling through a vein in the $+x$ direction. It is subject to the forces shown below:

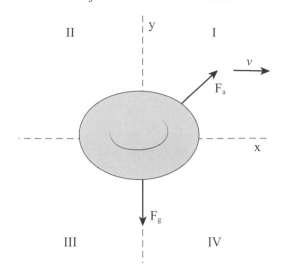

A third force is applied such that a component of acceleration is in the $-x$ direction. The net force MUST lie:

○ **A.** in quadrant III.

○ **B.** in quadrant IV.

○ **C.** along the $-x$ axis.

○ **D.** in quadrant II, III, or the $-x$ axis.

## Question 21

A ball is rolled down a 1 m ramp placed at an angle of 30° to the horizontal. The same ball is then rolled down a 1 m ramp placed at an angle of 60° to the horizontal. Which of the following statements is true?

○ **A.** The ball required the same amount of time for both trips.

○ **B.** The ball had the same displacement at the end of both trips.

○ **C.** The ball accelerated at the same rate for both trips.

○ **D.** None of the above

## Question 22

In a 'tug of war,' two groups of men pull in opposite directions on either end of a rope. Each group applies 2000 N of force. What is the magnitude of the tension in the rope? Assume that the rope is massless.

○ **A.** 0 N

○ **B.** 1000 N

○ **C.** 2000 N

○ **D.** 4000 N

## Question 23

A 5 kg mass hangs from a spring distending it 10 cm from its resting point. What is the spring constant $k$ of the spring?

○ **A.** 50 N/m
○ **B.** 100 N/m
○ **C.** 250 N/m
○ **D.** 500 N/m

---

**STOP.** IF YOU FINISH BEFORE TIME IS CALLED, CHECK YOUR WORK. YOU MAY GO BACK TO ANY QUESTION IN THIS TEST BOOKLET.

---

STOP

# 30-MINUTE IN-CLASS EXAM FOR LECTURE 2

## Passage I (Questions 24-27)

Recently, artificial electrical stimulation of neuromuscular systems has been used not only for experimental purposes, but also for exercise training, physical therapy, and medical rehabilitation. To improve these applications, researchers have investigated the relationship between the velocity of muscle shortening and the load applied to the muscle, where the velocity of shortening decreases with the progressive increase in load. This relationship allows for the estimation of the maximal shortening velocity of muscle ($V_{max}$) from the extrapolation of the experimental data. An alternative approach, referred to as the slack test, consists of multiple quick releases applied to an isometrically contracting muscle fiber. This test measures unloaded shortening velocity ($V_0$) of single muscle fibers. As with $V_{max}$, $V_0$ is among the most important variables of muscle contractile function. The difference between these two properties is that $V_0$ is a measure of the shortening velocity of the fastest fibers, whereas $V_{max}$ is a function of the force–velocity characteristics of all the fibers.

Previous studies have shown that $V_0$, expressed as an angular velocity of the ankle joint, increased with muscle activation level defined as a fraction of maximal voluntary contraction torque (MVC). Similar results have been shown in studies investigating $V_{max}$ of human wrist flexors and elbow extensors. To further study the contraction of muscle fibers, researchers applied the slack test to voluntary and electrically-elicited contractions of human dorsiflexors.

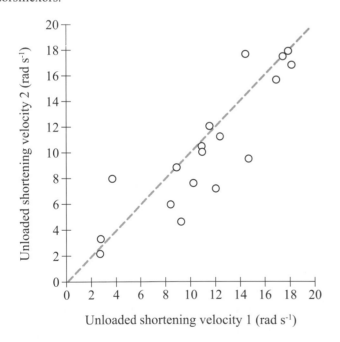

**Figure 1** Unloaded shortening velocity in consecutive trials of the slack test

This passage was adapted from "Unloaded Shortening Velocity of Voluntarily and Electrically Activated Human Dorsiflexor Muscles In Vivo." Sasaki K and Ishii N. *PLoS ONE*. 2010. 5(9) doi:10.1371/journal.pone.0013043 for use under the terms of the Creative Commons CC BY 3.0 license (http://creativecommons.org/licenses/by/3.0/legalcode).

## Question 24

What is the work done by the muscles in the hand and the arm as a person walks 10 m across a room as he holds up a 10 kg object flat on his hand?

- ○ **A.** 0 J
- ○ **B.** 1 J
- ○ **C.** 10 J
- ○ **D.** 100 J

## Question 25

If torque is directly proportional to MVC for a given muscle, the torque at 50% MVC would be equivalent to the torque when:

- ○ **A.** the magnitude of the force is quadrupled.
- ○ **B.** the magnitude of the force is doubled.
- ○ **C.** the distance from the muscle's insertion point to the joint is doubled.
- ○ **D.** the angle between the direction of the force and the plane of rotation is changed from perpendicular to 30°.

## Question 26

Velocity of shortening decreases with increase in load. A muscle initially has a velocity of shortening of 5 rad/s when the load on the muscle is 100N. What is the velocity of shortening of the fibers in the muscle if the load increase to 250 N?

- ○ **A.** 0 rad/s
- ○ **B.** 2.7 rad/s
- ○ **C.** 5 rad/s
- ○ **D.** 9 rad/s

## Question 27

As a person moves an object, the bones in the arm rotate about a joint at a constant rotational velocity, while the translational velocity is 0 m/s. This system is known to be:

    I. in dynamic equilibrium.

    II. in static equilibrium.

    III. gaining potential energy.

- ○ **A.** I only
- ○ **B.** I and III
- ○ **C.** II only
- ○ **D.** II and III

Next ▶

## Passage II (Questions 28-32)

Fatigue can be defined as a reduction in the force generating capacity of the neuromuscular system, regardless of the level of force required. During exercises of maximal intensity, fatigue can result in a decline in force, contraction velocity, or power. Following a series of contractions performed at moderate velocity, it has been shown that evoked peak twitch responses are reduced by up to 75%, directly leading to a reduction in force generation.

A study was conducted to understand the mechanisms behind fatigue. The primary aim of this study was to evaluate the relative contribution of reductions in the rate of torque development (RTD) and diminutions of the peak torque on the decrease of the average torque. These variables were measured during repeated maximal contractions performed at a moderate velocity. The exercise protocol consisted of total of 160 isokinetic maximal knee extensions that were performed at a constant velocity of $240° \times s^{-1}$. The knee joint angle changed from 90° to 30°, where 0° corresponds to full knee extension. Each contraction lasted roughly 250 milliseconds. The exercise protocol was performed in such a way that the femur remained in a horizontal position throughout the exercise. The 160 contractions were performed such that participants completed 20 sets of eight repetitions each and were given 24 seconds of recovery between each set. Immediately after completion of the exercise protocol, participants performed a post-exercise neuromuscular testing. Figure 1, below, shows average torque over time on the knee joint during knee extensions in the first set and in the twentieth set.

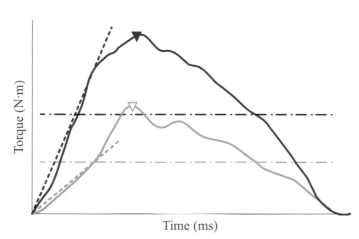

**Figure 1** Average torque trace recording on the knee joint and associated changes in the RTD and $T_{mean}$

### Question 28

The human leg can be modeled as a 30 cm massless lever from knee to ankle. If the knee is extended at the end of the exercise as described in the study, how much work is performed in one knee extension with a 500 N weight attached at the ankles?

- **A.** The patient performs 150 J of work.
- **B.** The patient performs 0 J of work.
- **C.** The patient performs 600 J of work.
- **D.** The patient performs 75 J of work.

### Question 29

Which joint angle would require the most force for the subject to maintain a constant velocity knee extension?

- **A.** The force must be highest at 30°.
- **B.** The force must be highest at 60°.
- **C.** The force must be highest at 90°.
- **D.** The force remains constant at all angles.

### Question 30

What conclusion about muscle fatigue is best supported by data in Figure 1?

- **A.** Fatigued muscles experience a reduction in energy as evidenced by lower peak torque values.
- **B.** Fatigued muscles experience a reduction in power as evidenced by lower RTD values.
- **C.** Fatigued muscles experience an increase in energy as evidenced by higher peak torque values.
- **D.** Fatigued muscles experience an increase in power as evidenced by higher RTD values.

### Question 31

If a subject uses a pulley to lift the weight to the same height as in the knee extensions, which of the following is true?

- **A.** The subject is using less power than in the knee extensions.
- **B.** The subject is using the same amount of force as in the knee extensions.
- **C.** The subject is performing the same amount of work as in the knee extensions.
- **D.** The subject uses more force than in the knee extensions.

## Question 32

A patient performs one set of weighted knee extensions, ending with the knee extended. Is the force applied by the patient on the weight a conservative force?

- ○ **A.** The force is a conservative force because the total mechanical energy in the weighted system is conserved.
- ○ **B.** The force is not a conservative force because the total mechanical energy in the weighted system is not conserved.
- ○ **C.** The force is not a conservative force because it acts against gravity, a conservative force.
- ○ **D.** The force is a conservative force because it converts chemical energy from the muscle to increase the potential energy of the weight.

## Passage III (Questions 33-37)

When asked to complete a motor task, people will commonly perform more mechanical work than is necessary to complete the task. For example, when asked to complete a vertical jump, people may increase the work performed by the muscles of the legs in order to decrease deformation of soft tissues.

Figure 1 shows the mechanical power generated by the muscles of the legs during each of the five phases of a representative vertical jump as a function of time.

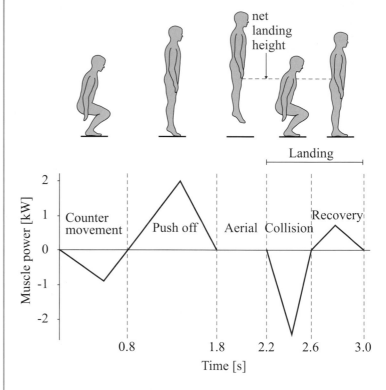

**Figure 1** Total mechanical power during jumping and landing as a function of time

Work that moves the center of mass towards the ground is considered to be negative, whereas work that moves the center of mass away from the ground is considered to be positive.

In a series of experiments, researchers calculated the work done by muscles during vertical jumps of varying heights and landings. Landings were divided into the following three categories: stiff, preferred, and soft.

A stiff landing was defined as one in which an individual lands with the hips and knees vertically aligned such that no joint rotations occur during landing. Associated work was assumed to equal the change in gravitational potential energy associated with vertical displacement.

In order to measure muscle work associated with preferred and soft landings, participants were asked to, first, stand at rest with their arms crossed and each foot on an in-ground force plate and, then, jump vertically, land back on the same force plates, and return to the original rest posture. Kinematic data were collected using an infrared motion capture system.

Next ▶

Work associated with preferred landings was assumed to equal work performed when no additional instruction was given. Work associated with soft landings was assumed to equal work performed when participants were subsequently instructed to land as softly as possible.

Figure 2 shows, by landing strategy, the work done by the muscles during collision and recovery as a function of displacement of center of mass.

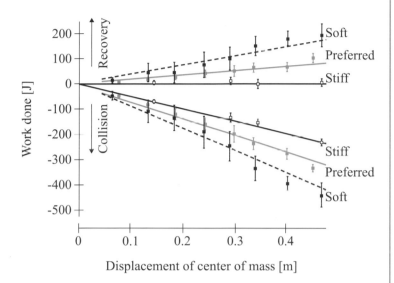

**Figure 2** Work done as a function of displacement of center of mass

This passage was adapted from "Mechanical Work as an Indirect Measure of Subjective Costs Influencing Human Movement." Zelick KE, Kuo AD. *PLoS ONE*. 2012. 7(2): e31143 doi: 10.1371/journal.pone.0031143 for use under the terms of the Creative Commons CC BY 3.0 license (http://creativecommons.org/licenses/by/3.0/legalcode).

## Question 33

During the aerial phase of a vertical jump, as displacement of the individual's center of mass increases, the kinetic energy generated during push-off is converted to gravitational potential energy. Which of the following forms of energy is converted into the kinetic energy required for push-off?

○ **A.** Gravitational potential energy

○ **B.** Rest energy

○ **C.** Chemical potential energy

○ **D.** Thermal energy

## Question 34

If an individual wanted to minimize the magnitude of negative work done by muscles during collision and recovery, which of the following landing strategies should she prefer?

○ **A.** Soft because the most positive work is done during collision

○ **B.** Preferred because the most positive work is done during recovery

○ **C.** Stiff because the least negative work is done during collision

○ **D.** Stiff because no work is done during recovery

## Question 35

Which of the following statements best describes the work done during the aerial phase of a vertical jump? Assume a constant vertical posture.

○ **A.** Work is done by the force of gravity.

○ **B.** Work is done by the forces generated by muscle contractions.

○ **C.** Work is done by both the force of gravity and the forces generated by muscle contractions.

○ **D.** No work is done.

## Question 36

According to Figure 1, how much work is done during the push-off phase of a representative jump?

○ **A.** $2.00 \times 10^3$ J

○ **B.** $1.00 \times 10^3$ J

○ **C.** $2.50 \times 10^2$ J

○ **D.** 1.00 J

## Question 37

If you assume that total mechanical power measurements remain accurate, and if the infrared motion capture system underestimated collision time by a factor of 4, the work done would be:

○ **A.** underestimated by a factor of 2.

○ **B.** underestimated by a factor of 4.

○ **C.** overestimated by a factor of 2.

○ **D.** overestimated by a factor of 4.

## Passage IV (Questions 38-41)

After spinal surgery, the physical performance of patients is often drastically reduced because of preoperative sparing and postoperative decline in fitness due to pain or reduced mobility. Physical exercise, such as walking or cycling, is an effective way to improve the fitness of such patients. However, patients often do not know which exercises can be performed without overloading an implant or bone and consequently endangering surgical success (e.g., implant subsidence). Few experimental studies have been conducted on the actual spinal loads during cycling and how they compare to those during walking.

One way to quantify spinal loads is to measure the induced change in spinal length, termed 'spinal shrinkage'. Measurements indicate that after 1 h of cycling at a constant speed of 12 km/h, the shrinkage is only half of that after 1 h of erect standing. However, this method of measurement provides only relative values and does not predict the real spinal forces acting on an implant during different activities.

A severe fracture of a vertebral body and tumors of the spine are often surgically treated by implantation of a vertebral body replacement (VBR). Scientists sought to document the effect of power level on the forces on a VBR during ergometer cycling.

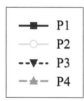

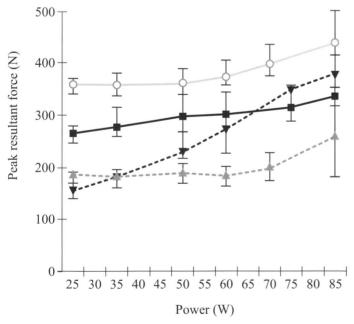

**Figure 1** Peak resultant force on VBR of four patients at various powers

This passage was adapted from "Spinal Loads during Cycling on an Ergometer." Rohlmann A, Zander T, Graichen F, Schmidt H, Bergmann G. *PLoS ONE*. 2014. 9(4) doi:10.1371/journal. pone.0095497 for use under the terms of the Creative Commons CC BY 4.0 license (http://creativecommons.org/licenses/by/4.0/legalcode).

## Question 38

P1 has a mass of 80 kg, while P2 has a mass of 60 kg. The maximum speed reached by P1 is 10 km/hr, while the maximum speed reached by P2 is 20 km/hr. What is the ratio of the kinetic energy of P1 to that of P2 at their respective maximum speeds?

- ○ **A.** 1:1
- ○ **B.** 1:4
- ○ **C.** 3:1
- ○ **D.** 1:3

## Question 39

As part of another VBR stress test, a person pushes a box horizontally across a floor. A constant force of 17 N is applied over a distance of 8 m, and this interaction occurs over 10 s. What is the average power?

- ○ **A.** 4.7 W
- ○ **B.** 13.6 W
- ○ **C.** 16.3 W
- ○ **D.** 21.25 W

## Question 40

A subject rides a stationary bike that is hooked up to a power generator. What is the path of energy conversion that occurs as the subject pedals?

- ○ **A.** Kinetic energy → chemical potential energy → electric potential energy
- ○ **B.** Chemical potential energy → kinetic energy → electric potential energy
- ○ **C.** Electric potential energy → kinetic energy → chemical potential energy
- ○ **D.** Electric potential energy → chemical potential energy → kinetic energy

## Question 41

Which subject generated the greatest work during the test shown in Figure 1?

- ○ **A.** P1
- ○ **B.** P2
- ○ **C.** P3
- ○ **D.** Cannot be determined

## Questions 42 through 46 are NOT based on a descriptive passage.

### Question 42

A machine uses 600 J of fuel and outputs work at 80% efficiency. If this work occurs over 15 s, what is the average power of the machine?

- ○ **A.** 32 W
- ○ **B.** 40 W
- ○ **C.** 7,200 W
- ○ **D.** 9,000 W

### Question 43

Which of the following objects is in equilibrium?

- ○ **A.** An object thrown up in the air, at the top of its arc
- ○ **B.** An object falling at terminal velocity
- ○ **C.** An object swinging from a rope like a pendulum
- ○ **D.** An object experiencing a single non-zero force

### Question 44

When the biceps muscle contracts, the forearm is lifted, raising the hand. The biceps tendon inserts into the forearm very close to the elbow joint. Which of the following increases net torque on the forearm when it is accelerating upward in a lifting motion?

- ○ **A.** Increasing weight of the forearm
- ○ **B.** Redistributing forearm mass so more of it is in the hand
- ○ **C.** Insertion of the biceps tendon further from the elbow
- ○ **D.** Decreasing mass of the biceps muscle

### Question 45

A 5 kg mass is hung from the right end of a massless meter stick. 20 cm from its left end, the meter stick is attached to the ceiling by a string. What downward force $F$ should be applied to the left end of the meter stick to balance it horizontally and in rotational equilibrium?

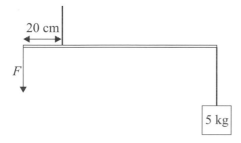

- ○ **A.** 20 N
- ○ **B.** 50 N
- ○ **C.** 100 N
- ○ **D.** 200 N

### Question 46

A pulley system is attached to a massless board as shown below. The board pivots only at the pivot point. A 10 kg mass $M$ sits exactly in the middle of the board.

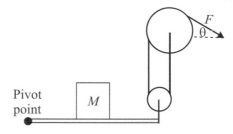

If the angle $\theta$ is 30°, what is the force necessary to lift the 10 kg mass? (Note: $\sin 30° = 0.5$).

- ○ **A.** 12.5 N
- ○ **B.** 25 N
- ○ **C.** 50 N
- ○ **D.** 100 N

---

**STOP.** IF YOU FINISH BEFORE TIME IS CALLED, CHECK YOUR WORK. YOU MAY GO BACK TO ANY QUESTION IN THIS TEST BOOKLET.

---

# 30-MINUTE IN-CLASS EXAM FOR LECTURE 3

## Passage I (Questions 47-51)

Changes in blood cell counts are a well-known feature of malarial infections. These changes involve major cell lines, including red blood cells (RBC), leukocytes and thrombocytes. The average masses of these cells are 0.5 ng, 2 ng, and 5 ng, respectively.

Hyperparasitemia has been listed as one of the criteria of severe malaria. Previous studies have shown that there is a correlation between parasite density and severity of malarial infections. Mortality is also correlated with the degree of parasitemia. Additionally, high parasitemia due to *Plasmodium falciparum* infection takes a serious turn in anemia. Moreover, excessive hemolysis of parasitized RBCs in malaria infection may lead to anemia.

Researchers found that *P. falciparum* and *P. vivax* infections, as well as different parasite densities on blood cell parameters in malaria patients, profoundly impacted hematological parameters (RBC, leukocyte, platelets, hemoglobin level (Hb), mean corpuscular volume (MCV), mean corpuscular hemoglobin (MCH), mean corpuscular hemoglobin concentration (MCHC). However, total blood volume (5L average for adult humans) was not altered.

This passage was adapted from "Effects of Malaria Parasite Density on Blood Cell Parameters." Kotepui M, Piwkham D, PhunPhuech B, Phiwklam N, Chupeerach C, et al. *PLoS ONE*. 2015. 10(3) doi:10.1371/journal.pone.0121057 for use under the terms of the Creative Commons CC BY 4.0 license (http://creativecommons.org/licenses/by/4.0/legalcode).

## Question 47

A person jumps into a pool foot-first. Where in the body is the hydrostatic pressure the greatest?

○ **A.** Head
○ **B.** Shoulder
○ **C.** Thigh
○ **D.** Foot

## Question 48

If the volume of an RBC is half that of a leukocyte, what is the ratio of their densities?

○ **A.** An RBC is half as dense as a leukocyte.
○ **B.** An RBC is one fourth as dense as a leukocyte.
○ **C.** An RBC is twice as dense as a leukocyte.
○ **D.** An RBC is four times as dense as a leukocyte.

## Question 49

A clump of malaria parasites blocks ¼ of the cross-sectional area of a horizontal, cylindrical artery. Which of the following statements is true regarding flow through the blocked area, assuming ideal flow?

○ **A.** Blood flows slower through the artery.
○ **B.** Blood in the blocked area has a higher pressure.
○ **C.** Blood in the blocked area has a lower pressure.
○ **D.** Blood in the blocked area has more potential energy.

## Question 50

While a regular sample of blood forms an upward meniscus in the tube, an infected sample forms a downward meniscus. Which of the following is most likely correct?

○ **A.** Parasite presence increases both cohesive and adhesive forces.
○ **B.** Parasite presence increases cohesive forces and decreases adhesive forces.
○ **C.** Parasite presence decreases both cohesive and adhesive forces.
○ **D.** Parasite presence decreases cohesive forces and increases adhesive forces.

## Question 51

The presence of parasites in the bloodstream increases the viscosity of blood. Which of the following statements is most likely to be true?

○ **A.** Blood flow is less ideal during severe infections.
○ **B.** Blood flow is more ideal during severe infections.
○ **C.** Severe infection reduces the number of blood vessels.
○ **D.** Severe infection increases the number of blood vessels.

## Passage II (Questions 52-55)

Transcapillary exchange of fluid between the intravascular and interstitial spaces is facilitated by differences in hydrostatic and oncotic pressures. Scientists and clinicians have long studied transcapillary exchange in an attempt to understand and better regulate drug delivery.

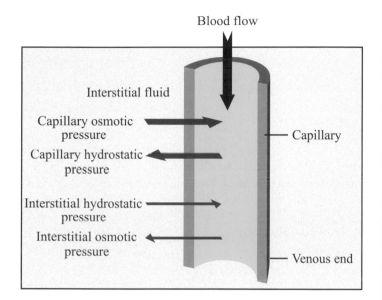

**Figure 1** Transcapillary exchange

More than 85% of human cancers involve solid tumors, and current chemotherapy depends on the adequate delivery of therapeutic agents to tumor sites. The blood supply to a solid tumor is highly heterogeneous, with vascularized well-perfused areas only on the outside walls of the tumor. Little or no drug reaches 90% of the tumor; however, for successful cancer treatment, all areas of the tumor must be exposed to chemotherapy agents. If just the tumor's outer cells are killed, the tumor will eventually regrow.

In a mathematical model assuming ideal fluid flow, the value of the radially outward fluid velocity at the tumor rim for a 42 g tumor with a 1 cm radius was calculated to be 0.1 mm/s. Researchers performed another study of 2 cm diameter mouse fibroadenomas, and found that changes in hydrostatic pressure depended on the relative size of the necrotic center.

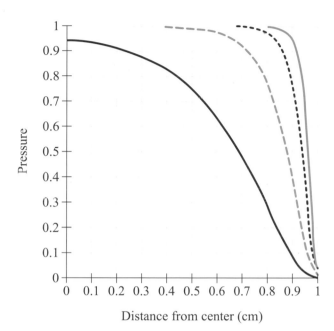

**Figure 2** Interstitial pressure as a function of distance from the center for 2 cm mouse fibroadenomas of different size necrotic centers

This passage was adapted from "Numerical Modeling of Fluid Flow in Solid Tumors." Soltani M, Chen P. *PLoS ONE*. 2011, 6(6) doi:10.1371/journal.pone.0020344; for use under the terms of the Creative Commons CC BY 3.0 license (http://creativecommons.org/licenses/by/3.0legalcode).

## Question 52

The average capillary size in the mathematical model was estimated to be 10 micrometers in diameter. Assuming the density of blood is the same as water, what is the average mass flow rate?

- ○ **A.** $7.85 \times 10^{-12}$ kg/s
- ○ **B.** $5.42 \times 10^{-10}$ kg/s
- ○ **C.** $3.48 \times 10^{-7}$ kg/s
- ○ **D.** $8.12 \times 10^{-14}$ kg/s

## Question 53

To predict the diffusion rate of cisplatin, a chemotherapeutic agent, capillary filtration was measured 0.9 cm from the necrotic center of two 2 cm tumors, one with a necrotic core of 0.5 cm and the other 0.1 cm. Assuming constant rate of flow through the capillaries, filtration rate to the tumor with the smaller necrotic core is:

- O **A.** smaller than in those which perfuse the tumor with the 0.5 cm necrotic core.
- O **B.** larger than in those which perfuse the tumor with the 0.5 cm necrotic core.
- O **C.** the same as in those which perfuse the tumor with the 0.5 cm necrotic core.
- O **D.** larger or smaller than in those which perfuse the tumor with the 0.5 cm necrotic core.

## Question 54

Drug delivery to the center of a tumor depends on delivery via vessels that travel to the center and on diffusion in the interstitial fluid. Which of the following would decrease drug delivery to the center?

- O **A.** Smaller drug concentrations in the tumor center because this would increase interstitial fluid static pressure.
- O **B.** Smaller interstitial hydrostatic pressures in the tumor center because this would weaken the osmotic gradient.
- O **C.** Larger drug plasma concentrations because this would increase blood viscosity.
- O **D.** A decrease in capillary diameter because this would decrease capillary hydrostatic pressure.

## Question 55

Assuming that drug delivery in a large vein, like the femoral vein, depends primarily on the capillary hydrostatic pressure, which is true?

- O **A.** Increasing the height of the location in the leg would increase drug delivery.
- O **B.** Increasing the drug mass in the leg vein would increase drug delivery.
- O **C.** Increasing the cross-sectional area of the vein would decrease drug delivery.
- O **D.** Increasing the density of the drug would decrease drug delivery.

## Passage III (Questions 56-60)

High intrathoracic pressure can depress venous return to the right atrium, thus affecting the output of blood from the right ventricle (RV). In chronic obstructive pulmonary disease (COPD), airway obstruction leads to an increase in intrathoracic pressure during expiration. In order to better understand cardiopulmonary interactions in patients with COPD, researchers investigated the effects of intrathoracic pressure changes and consequent expiratory airflow limitations on right ventricular function in spontaneously breathing patients at rest. Patients with moderate to very severe COPD participated in the study.

Esophageal pressure served as an indicator of intrathoracic pressure, and changes in pulmonary artery pulse pressure served as an indicator of changes in RV output. Systolic and diastolic pressure in the pulmonary artery were measured beat by beat over at least 10 consecutive respiratory cycles. A decline in pulmonary artery pressure during expiration was observed in all subjects. A schematic representation of the results is shown in Figure 1.

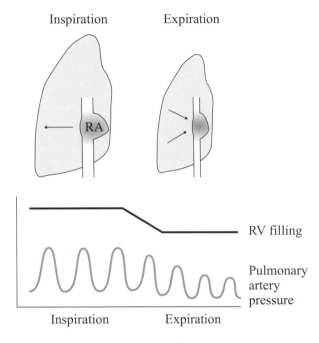

**Figure 1** Schematic illustration of the effect of changing intrathoracic pressure on RV filling and pulmonary artery pressure

Next ▶

## Question 56

In what way is the blood in the pulmonary artery most likely to differ from an ideal fluid?

- ○ **A.** Blood always has laminar flow, unlike an ideal fluid.
- ○ **B.** Blood has viscosity, unlike an ideal fluid.
- ○ **C.** The characteristics of blood flow cannot be predicted qualitatively or quantitatively, unlike those of an ideal fluid.
- ○ **D.** None of the above; blood acts as an ideal fluid.

## Question 57

Which of the following best describes the change in pressure as blood flows from the pulmonary artery through the lungs and back to the pulmonary vein?

- ○ **A.** The pressure decreases and then increases back to the starting pressure.
- ○ **B.** The pressure increases and then decreases back to the starting pressure.
- ○ **C.** The pressure stays constant throughout the circulatory system.
- ○ **D.** The pressure decreases and does not return to the starting pressure.

## Question 58

What is the most likely explanation for the finding demonstrated in Figure 1?

- ○ **A.** Decreased intrathoracic pressure during inspiration decreases the driving pressure of blood flow, leading to decreased venous return.
- ○ **B.** Increased intrathoracic pressure during expiration decreases the driving pressure of blood flow, leading to decreased venous return.
- ○ **C.** Decreased intrathoracic pressure during expiration increases the driving pressure of blood flow, leading to increased venous return.
- ○ **D.** Increased intrathoracic pressure during inspiration increases the driving pressure of blood flow, leading to increased venous return.

## Question 59

Assuming that other factors are constant, if the researchers compared the pulmonary artery pressure to the pressure in another blood vessel in which blood was moving more slowly, they would most likely find that:

- ○ **A.** the pressure is the same in both vessels because velocity does not affect pressure.
- ○ **B.** the pressure is higher in the other blood vessel because the slower velocity must indicate a larger surface area.
- ○ **C.** the pressure is higher in the other blood vessel because the fluid has higher random translational motion.
- ○ **D.** the pressure is lower in the other blood vessel because the fluid has lower random translational motion.

## Question 60

Researchers conducted a follow-up study during which they measured the radius of the obstructed area of the airway in patients with COPD. They found that the average radius in patients with COPD was reduced by ½ when compared to individuals without COPD. The rate of airflow through the airway in patients with COPD is most likely:

- ○ **A.** decreased by a factor of 2.
- ○ **B.** decreased by a factor of 4.
- ○ **C.** increased by a factor of 16.
- ○ **D.** decreased by a factor of 16.

## Passage IV (Questions 61-64)

At high intensities of exercise in normal oxygen levels, above the respiratory compensation threshold (RC), hyperventilation-induced hypocapnia (reduced $CO_2$) constricts the cerebral vessels, thereby reducing cerebral blood flow (CBF) and lowering cerebral oxygen delivery. In conditions of hypoxia, in spite of vasodilation (widening of blood vessels), the hypocapnia-induced limitation of CBF at high exercise intensities is further aggravated due to a greater ventilatory drive. Exaggerated hyperventilation-induced hypocapnia and subsequent reduction in CBF during heavy exercise might account, in part, for the impaired physical performance in hypoxia.

For climbing 8,000 m peaks, a strong ventilatory response at altitude is believed to be a factor for success, but increases the risk of brain damage because of excessive hyperventilation-induced cerebral hypoxemia. Acclimatized elite climbers with a smaller ventilatory response to hypoxia at 5,200 m were more successful climbing to extreme altitudes such as the summits of Everest and K2, perhaps due to a greater ventilatory reserve (difference between maximal voluntary ventilation and effective minute ventilation) at these altitudes. The effect of augmenting $CO_2$ on ventilation during exercise is of interest, particularly in the presence of enhanced ventilatory drive associated with hypoxia. Researchers measured middle cerebral artery blood velocity (MCAν) in subjects in conditions of normoxia and hypoxia in controls as well as subjects given supplemental $CO_2$.

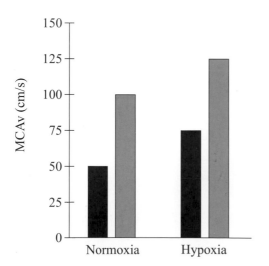

**Figure 1** MCAν in conditions of hypoxia and normoxia

This passage was adapted from "The Effect of Adding $CO_2$ to Hypoxic Inspired Gas on Cerebral Blood Flow Velocity and Breathing during Incremental Exercise." Fan J, Kayser B. *PLoS ONE*. 2013. 8(11) doi:10.1371/journal.pone.0081130 for use under the terms of the Creative Commons CC BY 3.0 license (http://creativecommons.org/licenses/by/3.0/legalcode).

## Question 61

Air has a density of roughly 1.225 kg/m³. What is the specific gravity of air relative to water?

- A. 0.0001225
- B. 0.001225
- C. 0.01225
- D. 1.225

## Question 62

Which object experiences the greatest buoyant force?

- A. A 1 L object fully submerged in water
- B. A 1 L object fully submerged in a fluid with a specific gravity of 1.5
- C. A 1 L object fully submerged in a fluid with a specific gravity of 3.0
- D. A 1 L object fully submerged in a fluid with a specific gravity of 6.0

## Question 63

A person inspires 1.2 L of air in a 1 second period. If the trachea is a circle with a diameter of 4 cm, what is the average velocity of air through the trachea during this single inspiration? ? (1 L = 1000 cm³)

- A. 0.0955 cm/s
- B. 0.1 cm/s
- C. 95.5 cm/s
- D. 100 cm/s

## Question 64

A person climbs an 8,000 m mountain starting from the base. Considering the information in Figure 1, which of the following statements is most likely true?

   I. The difference in pressure between blood in the head and the foot has increased.

   II. The velocity of blood in the MCA has increased.

   III. The volumetric flow rate through the MCA has decreased.

- A. I only
- B. I and II
- C. II only
- D. I, II, and III

**Questions 65 through 69 are NOT based on a descriptive passage.**

## Question 65

What is the net force acting on a 5 kg, 1 L object that is sitting at the bottom of a pool of water?

○ **A.** 9.8 N

○ **B.** 39.2 N

○ **C.** 49 N

○ **D.** 0 N

## Question 66

What is the pressure difference between the water at the top of an open container to the water coming out of a large opening 1.5 m below the top?

○ **A.** 0 Pa

○ **B.** 1,500 Pa

○ **C.** 15,000 Pa

○ **D.** 101,325 Pa

## Question 67

A 5 L container weighing 2 kg is thrown into a lake. What percentage of the container will float above the water? Assume that the density of lake water is 1 kg/L.

○ **A.** 10%

○ **B.** 40%

○ **C.** 60%

○ **D.** 90%

## Question 68

A brick sits on a massless piece of Styrofoam floating in a large bucket of water. If the Styrofoam is removed and the brick is allowed to sink to the bottom:

○ **A.** the water level will remain the same.

○ **B.** the water level will fall.

○ **C.** the water level will rise.

○ **D.** more information is needed to predict whether the water level will rise or fall.

## Question 69

A water tower is filled with water to a depth of 15 m. If a leak forms 10 m above the base of the tower, what will be the velocity of the water as it escapes through the leak?

○ **A.** 10 m/s

○ **B.** 14 m/s

○ **C.** 17 m/s

○ **D.** 20 m/s

---

**STOP.** IF YOU FINISH BEFORE TIME IS CALLED, CHECK YOUR WORK. YOU MAY GO BACK TO ANY QUESTION IN THIS TEST BOOKLET.

---

# 30-MINUTE IN-CLASS EXAM FOR LECTURE 4

## Passage I (Questions 70-74)

The human body's ability to conduct electricity is used in bioelectrical impedance analysis (BIA), a means of assessing body composition. This technology has been of particular value in estimating body fat percentage as an indicator of obesity. In BIA, a small current is passed between electrodes placed on the skin, and voltage is measured between electrodes. BIA makes use of the fact that electrical conductivity of lean tissue is greater than that of fat, given the higher electrolyte content of lean tissue.

Since the human body is a relatively good conductor of electricity it remains at the same potential as the ground and the electric field in the air adjusts around the body accordingly as shown in Figure 1. Under normal conditions, an electric field exists in the air near the surface of the Earth with an average strength of approximately 100 V/m.

The atmosphere is about 50,000 m deep and the total potential difference between the ground and the top of the atmosphere is approximately 400,000 V. Air is a poor conductor, so the average current is only about $10^{-12}$ A/m$^2$.

A lightning strike occurs when the bottom of a cloud has a negative electric charge that is greater than the negative charge below it on the ground. This temporarily reverses the electric field between the ground and the cloud, allowing electrons to flow from the cloud to the ground. The current in a lightning strike is about 10,000 A and a typical strike will deliver a charge of 20 C.

This passage was adapted from "Percentage of Body Fat Assessment Using Bioelectrical Impedance Analysis and Dual Energy X-Ray Absorptiometry in a Weight Loss Program for Obese or Overweight Chinese Adults." Li Y-C, Li C-A, Lin W-Y, Liu C-S, Hsu H-S, Lee C-C, Chen F-N, Li T-C, and Lin C-C. *PLoS ONE*. 2013. 8(4) doi:10.1371/journal.pone.0058272 for use under the terms of the Creative Commons CC BY 3.0 license (http://creativecommons.org/licenses/by/3.0/legalcode).

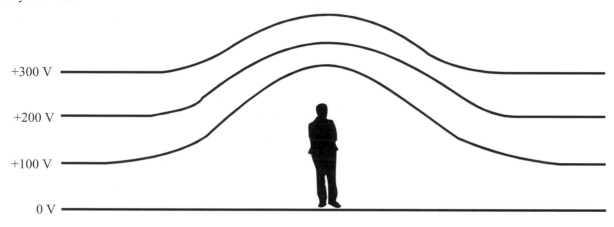

**Figure 1** Potential gradient near the surface of the earth

## Question 70

If the current produced by the biological impedance analysis is constant, how would resistance and voltage between electrodes change as the fraction of fat tissue increased? Assume that fat tissue functions approximately as an Ohmic device.

- **A.** Both resistance and voltage would increase
- **B.** Resistance would increase but voltage would decrease.
- **C.** Resistance would decrease but voltage would increase.
- **D.** Both resistance and voltage would decrease.

## Question 71

What is the approximate duration of the lightning strike described in the passage?

- **A.** 2 s
- **B.** 0.5 s
- **C.** $2 \times 10^{-3}$ s
- **D.** $5 \times 10^{-6}$ s

## Question 72

What is the average resistance of the atmosphere?

- **A.** $0\ \Omega(m^2)$
- **B.** $4\ \Omega(m^2)$
- **C.** $4 \times 10^7\ \Omega(m^2)$
- **D.** $4 \times 10^{17}\ \Omega(m^2)$

## Question 73

If the total electric current reaching the Earth's surface is nearly constant at 1800 A, approximately how much electrical energy is dissipated each second by the atmosphere?

- **A.** $4 \times 10^{-7}$ J
- **B.** $4 \times 10^5$ J
- **C.** $7.2 \times 10^8$ J
- **D.** $1.3 \times 10^{24}$ J

## Question 74

Which of the following describes the direction of current flow during a lightning strike?

- A. From a cloud at high potential to the ground at lower potential
- B. From a cloud at low potential to the ground at higher potential
- C. From the ground at high potential to a cloud at lower potential
- D. From the ground at low potential to a cloud at higher potential

## Passage II (Questions 75-79)

Neuromodulation is the application of therapeutic levels of electrical current for the treatment of medical diseases. Clinically, this is achieved by surgically inserting an implanted pulse generator (IPG) to deliver electrical stimuli to tissue. The electrical stimuli generates an action potential which modulates the release of neurotransmitters. Some examples of neuromodulators used in medical practice include deep brain stimulation (DBS), and spinal cord stimulation (SCS), which inhibits the release of neurotransmitters that signal for pain. SCS may be used for patients with chronic back pain who fail medical therapy.

The devices are powered by a sealed medical grade battery within the IPG. The device's lifetime depends on the energy capacity of the battery and the rate of energy depletion, which is dictated by the circuit elements. The power consumed during electrical stimulation depends on the three major components: the current, the resistance of the tissue ($R_t$), and the internal resistance of the battery ($R_i$). In order to prolong the life of the battery, engineers design IPGs that deliver the majority of power to the tissue, while minimizing power lost through internal resistance.

Additionally, adjacent tissue can also be added in parallel to the circuit to achieve neuromodulation at multiple sites.

If the electrodes of the IPG are attached to an axon, the axon may exhibit resistive properties analogous to a wire, as given in Equation 1, where $R$ – resistance, $L$ = length, $A$ = cross-sectional surface area, and $\rho$ = electrical resistivity.

$$R = \rho \frac{L}{A}$$

**Equation 1**

In general, the axonal resistance is negligible relative to the resistance of the neuromodulation circuit. However, in the event that the axonal resistance becomes contributory, it must be factored in when computing an IPG's lifetime due to additional power consumption.

This passage was adapted from "Energy Efficient Neural Stimulation: Coupling Circuit Design and Membrane Biophysics." Foutz TJ, Ackermann DM Jr, Kilgore KL, McIntyre CC. *PLoS ONE* 7(12): e51901. doi:10.1371/journal.pone.0051901 for use under the terms of the Creative Commons CC BY 3.0 license (http://creativecommons.org/licenses/by/3.0/legalcode).

## Question 75

Which of the following conditions will maximize the power delivered to the tissue?

- A. Increasing the internal resistance
- B. Increasing the tissue resistance
- C. Decreasing the tissue resistance
- D. Decreasing the battery voltage

## Question 76

The current delivered to the tissue is given by:

- A. $V/(R_t)$.
- B. $V/(R_i)$.
- C. $V/(R_t+R_i)$.
- D. $V(1/R_t+1/R_i)$.

## Question 77

Another tissue is added in parallel to the circuit. Assuming both tissues have the same resistance, and all other resistances are negligible, by what factor will the current change?

○ **A.** 4
○ **B.** 2
○ **C.** No change
○ **D.** ½

## Question 78

How much work is done to move a point charge ($q$) a distance of x, at an angle of 30° to the lines of force of an electric field ($E$)?

○ **A.** $qEx$
○ **B.** $qEx \sin(30°)$
○ **C.** $qEx \cos(30°)$
○ **D.** Zero

## Question 79

Increasing which of the following would decrease the resistance of an axon?

○ **A.** Diameter
○ **B.** Voltage
○ **C.** Current
○ **D.** Length

## Passage III (Questions 80-83)

Chromaffin cells are neuroendocrine cells in the adrenal glands of mammals. These cells exocytose vesicles containing signaling molecules, primarily epinephrine and norepinephrine. Vesicles are first primed, or made ready to exocytose, by an excitatory stimulus. Then, they are secreted by the cell in response to changes in intracellular calcium concentration.

Researchers measured the degree of exocytosis by counting the number of vesicles secreted in response to electrical stimulation. Vesicle exocytosis is very hard to observe, as these events can only be visualized for about 200 ms.

Total internal reflection microscopy (TIRF-Microscopy) was used to count the number of vesicles leaving the chromaffin cell's membrane. This technique could only accurately observe the area of the cell attached to the glass slide, called the footprint. The number of vesicles secreted from the footprint was then extrapolated to the entire membrane based on the fraction of the membrane that the footprint represented. For example, if the footprint represented half of the membrane, then twice as many vesicles were expected to be secreted by the whole membrane as were secreted by the footprint.

In addition to the number of vesicles, the change in capacitance of the cell membrane following exocytosis was also measured. In this context, the cell membrane is comparable to a parallel plate capacitor, separating opposite charges on the cytoplasmic and extracellular face of the membrane. A correlation was found between the change in capacitance and the number of vesicles secreted.

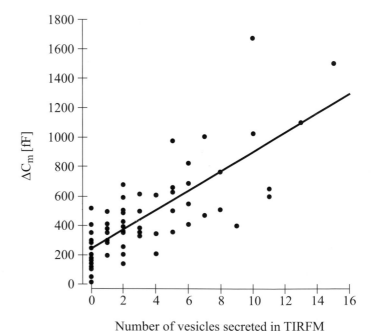

**Figure 1** Relationship between change in membrane capacitance ($\Delta C_m$) and number of vesicles observed by TIRF-Microscopy.

This passage was adapted from "Quantifying Exocytosis by Combination of Membrane Capacitance Measurements and Total Internal Reflection Fluorescence Microscopy in Chromaffin Cells." Becherer U, Pasche M, Nofal S, Hof D, Matti U, Rettig J. *PLoS ONE*. 2010. 2(6) doi: 10.1371/journal.pone.0000505 for use under the terms of the Creative Commons CC BY 3.0 license (http://creativecommons.org/licenses/by/3.0/legalcode).

Next ▶

## Question 80

If 5 vesicles are observed by TIRF-Microscopy on a certain cell, and 25 vesicles are secreted in total, what percentage of the total cell membrane does the footprint make up?

○ A. 100%

○ B. 50%

○ C. 20%

○ D. 10%

## Question 81

Which of the following would most drastically compromise the researchers' results?

○ A. Accidental use of a different type of cell growth medium designed for another subgroup of adrenal cells

○ B. Overestimation of the ratio of the footprint to the entire membrane on all trials

○ C. The finding that vesicle exocytosis from the footprint is not representative of exocytosis from the whole membrane

○ D. Underestimation of the ratio of the footprint to the entire membrane on all trials

## Question 82

Which of the following changes would decrease the capacitance of a chromaffin cell's membrane?

○ A. Increasing expression of a membrane protein that increases the dielectric constant of the membrane

○ B. Secretion of 10 vesicles

○ C. Decreasing the width of the membrane

○ D. Decreasing the surface area of the chromaffin cell

## Question 83

What is the electric field of the membrane of a chromaffin cell if the membrane is 8 nm thick and the membrane potential is 70 mV?

○ A. $8.75 \times 10^6$ N/C

○ B. $8.75 \times 10^{-6}$ N/C

○ C. $1.14 \times 10^7$ N/C

○ D. $1.14 \times 10^{-7}$ N/C

## Passage IV (Questions 84-87)

Whenever electricity is generated, transmitted or consumed, electromagnetic fields (EMF) are created. The abundant use of high voltage transmission (HVT) lines has resulted in much concern being raised about the impact of EMF exposure from HVT lines on human health, especially in children. In fact, extremely low frequency electromagnetic fields (ELF-EMF) have been classified as a possible carcinogen.

Potential associations between exposure to ELF-EMF and adverse health outcomes have mostly focused on childhood cancers or nervous system diseases from occupational exposure. It has been suggested that acute cognitive effects may occur from short-term exposure to intense EMF.

Children are more sensitive to EMF compared to adults because they are still in the physiological and psychological development period. The nervous system has bioelectric properties that make it more susceptible to the effects of EMF. Generally, children in developing countries experience more intensive EMF effects than children of more developed countries due to greater clustering of homes around very high voltage lines. Gaining a greater understanding of the effects of EMF on children, especially impact on early development, remains to be a primary challenge. Researchers aimed to explore the influence of EMF from 500 kV HVT lines on neurobehavioral function in children and first divided various homes near HVT lines by quartile.

| Min | $P_{25}$ | $P_{50}$ | $P_{75}$ | Max |
|-----|-----|-----|-----|-----|
| 0.016 | 0.108 | 0.417 | 0.949 | 2.919 |

**Table 1** Quartile ranges for electric field in homes near HVT lines

| Min | $P_{25}$ | $P_{50}$ | $P_{75}$ | Max |
|-----|-----|-----|-----|-----|
| 0.010 | 0.016 | 0.028 | 0.043 | 0.072 |

**Table 2** Quartile ranges for magnetic field in homes near HVT lines

This passage was adapted from "Association between Exposure to Electromagnetic Fields from High Voltage Transmission Lines and Neurobehavioral Function in Children." Huang J, Tang T, Hu G, Zheng J, Wang Y, et al. *PLoS ONE*. 2013. 8(7) doi:10.1371/journal.pone.0067284 for use under the terms of the Creative Commons CC BY 3.0 license (http://creativecommons.org/licenses/by/3.0/legalcode).

## Question 84

Current moves downward through a nerve, in a location where the magnetic field is directed rightward through the body. Which of the following is a characteristic of the force on the moving positive charges?

    I. Nonzero magnitude
    II. Direction perpendicular to current
    III. Direction perpendicular to the magnetic field

- **A.** I only
- **B.** III only
- **C.** II and III
- **D.** I, II, and III

## Question 85

A magnet is held vertically a meter to the right of a person, with the north end facing upwards. In what direction does the magnetic field pass through the person's body?

- **A.** Downward
- **B.** Upward
- **C.** Left
- **D.** Right

## Question 86

Which of the following could scientists use to measure the magnitude of the magnetic field at a certain point?

    I. Measure force on an electron when the electron is moving 1 m/s parallel to the field.
    II. Measure force on an electron when the electron is moving 1 m/s at a 45 degree angle to the field.
    III. Measure force on an electron when the electron is moving 1 m/s perpendicular to the field.

- **A.** I only
- **B.** II only
- **C.** I and II
- **D.** II and III

## Question 87

A +1 nC charge flows up the spine of a person towards the brain. Which of the following is true if there is a HVT line directly above the person and potential due to the line decreases as altitude decreases?

- **A.** The charge is slowed because positive charges are pushed from low to high potential.
- **B.** The charge is slowed because positive charges are pushed from high to low potential.
- **C.** The charge is sped up because positive charges are pushed from low to high potential.
- **D.** The charge is sped up because positive charges are pushed from high to low potential.

## Questions 88 through 92 are NOT based on a descriptive passage.

## Question 88

Which of the following changes to a cylindrical wire would cause the largest decrease in resistance?

- **A.** Doubling length and halving resistivity
- **B.** Quadrupling radius and doubling length
- **C.** Doubling radius and quadrupling length
- **D.** Tripling cross-sectional area

## Question 89

The capacitor shown below is fully charged. Both resistors have a 2Ω resistance. When the switch is opened, what is the initial current through resistor A?

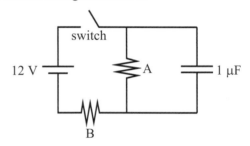

- **A.** 2 A
- **B.** 3 A
- **C.** 6 A
- **D.** 12 A

## Question 90

Capacitor A has dimensions of 3 cm × 4 cm and the plates are separated by a layer of air 5 cm wide. If capacitor B is 4 cm × 5 cm, and the plates are separated by a layer of air 4 cm wide, which of the following statements is true?

- **A.** A has a capacitance slightly less than twice that of B.
- **B.** B has a capacitance slightly less than twice that of A.
- **C.** B has a capacitance slightly over twice that of A.
- **D.** A and B have the same capacitance.

## Question 91

Charges A, B, C, and D are charged particles forming a square as shown. A and D each have a charge of +2 C; B and C each have a charge of –4 C. If $q$ is a particle with a charge of +1 C sitting directly in the middle of the square, what is the net force on $q$ due to the other particles?

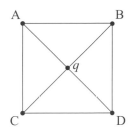

- ○ **A.** 0 N
- ○ **B.** 1 N
- ○ **C.** 1.4 N
- ○ **D.** 4 N

## Question 92

A particle possessing a charge of +2 C and a mass of 1 g is exposed to an electric field with strength 5 N/C. How far will the particle move in 10 s?

- ○ **A.** $1 \times 10^3$ m
- ○ **B.** $2 \times 10^5$ m
- ○ **C.** $5 \times 10^5$ m
- ○ **D.** $1 \times 10^6$ m

---

**STOP.** IF YOU FINISH BEFORE TIME IS CALLED, CHECK YOUR WORK. YOU MAY GO BACK TO ANY QUESTION IN THIS TEST BOOKLET.

---

STOP    203

# 30-MINUTE IN-CLASS EXAM FOR LECTURE 5

## Passage I (Questions 93-96)

Exposure to excessive noise is a major cause of hearing disorders worldwide; much disabling hearing loss (HL) in adults is attributed to occupational noise, but even outside of the workplace, millions of adolescents and young adults are potentially at risk of permanent hearing symptoms through listening to their favorite music. The risks of excessive music listening are most likely to result in hearing-related symptoms such as tinnitus – a perceived sound in the ears with no external source of sound being present, but other symptoms such as muffled sounds, distortion, or hyperacusis are also possible.

Sound waves with a sound pressure level of 85 dB can cause permanent hearing damage after long or repeated exposures. Sometimes, sound wave pressure levels are also described in A-weighted decibels (dBA). This unit is an attempt to better quantify the relative loudness of sounds, by taking into account the ear's poorer sensitivity for lower pitched tones. dBAs are defined the same way as decibels, with 0 dBA describing the threshold of hearing in a young healthy person. Table 1 summarizes the sound pressure levels of common noises.

| Sound pressure level (dB) | Common noise |
|---|---|
| 0 | Mosquito flying 3 m away |
| 45 | Refrigerator operation |
| 60 | Normal conversation |
| 85 | Rush hour traffic |
| 95 | Motorcycles |
| 105 | MP3 player at maximum volume |
| 120 | Police/fire/ambulance sirens |
| 150 | Fire crackers, hand guns |
| 160 | Shot gun discharge |

**Table 1** Sound pressure level of common noises

Increasing numbers of adolescents and young adults now experience permanent symptoms indicative of poor hearing due largely to listening to music at high volumes. The extent to which this demographic is exposed to loud music and suffers adverse health consequences was explored in a population-based study. The equivalent noise dosage participants experienced for 56 hours per week was calculated, and its relationship to hearing was explored. Some of the study's findings are summarized below in Table 2.

| Risk level | Self-reported hearing symptoms (% of population) | Likelihood of reporting hearing symptom after music exposure compared to baseline |
|---|---|---|
| Not at risk: 80 dBA | 24.6 | 1.00 |
| Low risk: 80-85 dBA | 73.2 | 8.84 |
| Moderate risk: 85-90 dBA | 74.2 | 8.69 |
| High risk: 90 dBA | 82.1 | 15.30 |

**Table 2** Prevalence of hearing symptoms among concert attending students

This passage was adapted from "Risky Music Listening, Permanent Tinnitus and Depression, Anxiety, Thoughts about Suicide and Adverse General Health." Vogel I, Looij-Jansen P, Mieloo C, Burdorf A, Waart F. *PLoS ONE.* 2014. 9(6) doi:10.1371/journal.pone.0098912 for use under the terms of the Creative Commons CCBY 4.0 Attribution license (http://creativecommons.org/licenses/by/4.0/legalcode).

## Question 93

Two identical hand guns are fired simultaneously. What is the combined sound pressure level?

- O **A.** 150 dB
- O **B.** 300 dB
- O **C.** 153 dB
- O **D.** 167 dB

## Question 94

If a motorcycle starts behind a stationary bystander and travels some distance past him, the bystander will perceive the pitch of the motorcycle to:

- O **A.** rise and then fall.
- O **B.** fall and then rise.
- O **C.** rise and remain at the new frequency
- O **D.** fall and remain at the new frequency.

## Question 95

A 86.4 cm bass guitar string is plucked at a concert, vibrating at its first harmonic. What is the wavelength of the sound it produces?

- O **A.** 345.6 cm
- O **B.** 259. 2 cm
- O **C.** 172.8 cm
- O **D.** 86.4 cm

## Question 96

What is the period of the car horn, whose wave form is shown below?

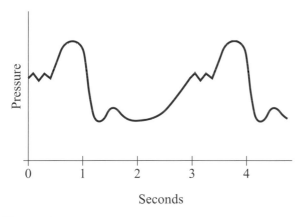

- O **A.** 0.33 sec
- O **B.** 4 sec
- O **C.** 1.5 sec
- O **D.** 3 sec

## Passage II (Questions 97-101)

Hyperopia is a condition where light focuses behind the retina. Myopia is the opposite condition. There are two major conflicting ideas in the management of hyperopia, which puts clinicians in a certain dilemma. One perspective concerns the theory that eye growth and emmetropization, the adaptation of the lens over time towards perfect vision, are controlled by visual input. This gives the idea that spectacle correction of hyperopia may interfere with emmetropization and leave the child with significant hyperopia. The other perspective is that refractive correction of hyperopia may improve visual acuity as well as the accuracy of accommodation. Consequently, the recommended guidelines regarding the threshold for hyperopic correction and optimal amount of correction vary.

Previous studies have found conflicting results of the effect of spectacle correction on emmetropization. One study found that consistently wearing glasses impeded emmetropization while another demonstrated that there was no overall difference between children who were treated and those who were not. However, these studies are limited to very young infants, lacking evidence on the changes observed throughout the later years of childhood.

In this study, researchers aimed to determine the effect of spectacle correction on the change in hyperopia throughout early and late childhood by comparing hyperopic children matched by age and refractive errors who received different amounts of spectacle correction.

| | Full correction | Undercorrection |
|---|---|---|
| Change in degree of hyperopia (diopters/year) | 0.03 | -0.43 |

**Figure 1** Change in hyperopia in fully corrected and undercorrected subjects

This passage was adapted from "Change in Refractive Errors Related to Spectacle Correction of Hyperopia." Yang HK, Choi JY, Kim DH and Hwang JM. *PLoS ONE*. 2014. 9(11) doi:10.1371/journal.pone.0110663 for use under the terms of the Creative Commons CC BY 4.0 license (http://creativecommons.org/licenses/by/4.0/legalcode).

## Question 97

Researchers constructed a lens with the same optical power as the change in power over 5 years in undercorrected hyperopia patients. What is the focal length and type of this lens?

- O **A.** Converging lens with a focal length of 2.15 cm
- O **B.** Converging lens with a focal length of 47 cm
- O **C.** Diverging lens with a focal length of 2.15 cm
- O **D.** Diverging lens with a focal length of 47 cm

## Question 98

Which of the following would increase the power of the eye by the greatest factor?

○ **A.** Quartering the focal length
○ **B.** Halving the focal length
○ **C.** Doubling the focal length
○ **D.** Quadrupling the focal length

## Question 99

A doctor sees a patient whose eye forms an image between the front of the eye and the retina. Which of the following is true of the image?

○ **A.** Virtual and inverted
○ **B.** Virtual and upright
○ **C.** Real and inverted
○ **D.** Real and upright

## Question 100

An eye with a power of 20 diopters views an object 10 cm in front of the eye. What is the focal length of the eye, and where does the image form?

○ **A.** Focal length of 5 cm, and the image forms 10 cm behind the eye
○ **B.** Focal length of 5 cm, and the image forms 10 cm in front of the eye
○ **C.** Focal length of 20 cm, and the image forms 10 cm behind the eye
○ **D.** Focal length of 20 cm, and the image forms 10 cm in front of the eye

## Question 101

Which of the following could occur if the human eye overcompensates for hyperopia?

○ **A.** Strabismus, resulting in the eye focusing light in front of the retina.
○ **B.** Strabismus, resulting in the eye focusing light behind the retina.
○ **C.** Myopia, resulting in the eye focusing light in front of the retina.
○ **D.** Myopia, resulting in the eye focusing light behind of the retina.

## Passage III (Questions 102-106)

In spite of an effective treatment, cataracts are the world-leading cause of poor vision, accounting for 20 million cases of bilateral blindness. Even in the industrialized world, cataracts are a significant health care problem that is expected to increase as the proportion of senior citizens rises. The subjective symptoms of cataracts range from a subtle impairment such as difficulties reading in the dark to overt blindness.

One major optical feature that leads to cataract symptoms is the scattering of light. Scattering is caused by accumulation of large protein aggregates but also by changes in protein-protein interaction due to changes in the tertiary structure of the proteins induced by a variety of degrading mechanisms.

Non-invasive photobleaching is a potential means of reducing the need for cataract surgery. This may be clinically relevant for the prevention or early treatment of cataracts, a disease of very slow and gradual onset, and can be made non-invasive using short infrared femtosecond laser pulses that can produce two-photon effects that are equivalent to single blue photons in a targeted area deep inside the lens. To determine the action spectrum for photobleaching, researchers irradiated several human donor lenses with continuous wave laser light at 375, 405, 420, 445, 457 or 473 nm. Photobleaching was monitored by photography and transmission measurements.

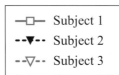

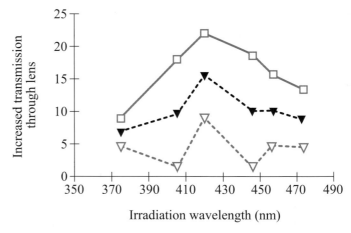

**Figure 1** Increased transmission through lens in 3 subjects following photobleaching at various wavelengths

This passage was adapted from "Action Spectrum for Photobleaching of Human Lenses by Short Wavelength Visible Irradiation." Kessel L and Larsen M. PLoS ONE. 2015. 10(4) doi:10.1371/journal.pone.0123732 for use under the terms of the Creative Commons CC BY 4.0 license (http://creativecommons.org/licenses/by/4.0/legalcode).

Next ▶

## Question 102

What is the frequency of the most effective photon treatment?

○ **A.** $7.1 \times 10^5$ Hz
○ **B.** $7.5 \times 10^5$ Hz
○ **C.** $7.1 \times 10^{14}$ Hz
○ **D.** $7.5 \times 10^{14}$ Hz

## Question 103

The 375 nm wavelength laser is closest to what section of the electromagnetic spectrum?

○ **A.** Violet
○ **B.** Yellow
○ **C.** Red
○ **D.** Infrared

## Question 104

Based on the results of the experiment, which of the following is most accurate?

○ **A.** The energy level of the laser did not affect the improvement in optical transmission.
○ **B.** An ultraviolet laser was most effective in improving optical transmission.
○ **C.** A laser emitting in the visible spectrum closest to violet was most effective in improving optical transmission.
○ **D.** A laser emitting in the visible spectrum closest to red was most effective in improving optical transmission.

## Question 105

The index of refraction of the lens is 1.35, while the index with a cataract changes to 1.5. Which of the following statements is true when light passes from lens to air?

○ **A.** With a cataract, the critical angle is smaller and TIR is more likely.
○ **B.** With a cataract, the critical angle is smaller and TIR is less likely.
○ **C.** With a cataract, the critical angle is bigger and TIR is more likely.
○ **D.** With a cataract, the critical angle is bigger and TIR is less likely.

## Question 106

The scattering observed in the lenses of cataract patients is most analogous to:

○ **A.** refraction.
○ **B.** TIR.
○ **C.** diffraction.
○ **D.** diffuse reflection.

## Passage IV (Questions 107-110)

The extraplacental fetal membranes which surround the amniotic cavity are composed of the amnion and the chorion. The chorion contains fluid and the amnion, which holds the developing fetus. The refractive index of chorionic fluid is 1.3, while the index of the amnion membrane is 1.4. These membranes form an adjustable container for a developing and moving fetus. They are genetically identical to the fetus but have a limited lifetime, existing only to the point of programmed rupture at term, which is a normal event during the first stage of labor. Preterm premature rupture precedes 30–40 per cent of preterm births and carries significant risks for the infant. An understanding of the basic structural components of the human fetal membranes, and how they adapt to changing needs as the uterine contents enlarge, is central to the eventual control of this major health problem.

The most structurally robust of the fetal membranes is the amnion. The amnion consists of a thin layer of epithelial cells and connective tissue. X-ray diffraction (XRD) has been used to great effect in studying collagen organization in relation to development and disease within structural tissues such as the cornea, breast, bone and cartilage. Low-angle XRD is a non-invasive technique which produces structural information on the average collagen fibril diameter, average spacing between fibrils and their arrangement within the tissue. XRD using light with a wavelength of 0.35 nm was used to study the collagen fibril characteristics in the amnion throughout pregnancy.

This passage was adapted from "The Biomechanics of Amnion Rupture: An X-Ray Diffraction Study." Connon CJ, Nakamura T, Hopkinson A, Quantock A, Yagi N et al. PLoS ONE. 2007. 2(11) doi:10.1371/journal.pone.0001147 for use under the terms of the Creative Commons CC BY 3.0 license (http://creativecommons.org/licenses/by/3.0/legalcode).

## Question 107

Light identical to that used in XRD is projected through two slits that are 1 nm apart and then onto a screen. Which of the following is true of the resulting band pattern?

    I. A maximum occurs on the screen directly across from the point between the two slits.

    II. The angle between the light rays going to the zeroth order and the second order maximum is 90°.

    III. Only maxima appear on the screen.

○ **A.** I only
○ **B.** II only
○ **C.** I and II
○ **D.** II and III

## Question 108

Which statement accurately describes the X-rays in the passage?

○ **A.** The X-rays always have a speed of $3 \times 10^8$ m/s.

○ **B.** The X-rays have a higher frequency than that of visible light.

○ **C.** The X-rays have a frequency of 0.09 Hz.

○ **D.** The X-rays have a higher wavelength than that of visible light.

## Question 109

In a certain stage of the experiment, the amnion was extracted and placed on a glass slide. Which of the following is true of light passing from glass (n = 1.5) to the amnion?

○ **A.** Light slows down and bends toward the normal.

○ **B.** Light slows down and bends away from normal.

○ **C.** Light speeds up and bends toward the normal.

○ **D.** Light speeds up and bends away from normal.

## Question 110

Which of the following is true when comparing ultraviolet (UV) rays and X-rays?

○ **A.** UV-rays have a higher amplitude.

○ **B.** X-rays have a higher amplitude.

○ **C.** UV rays bend more when passing from air to glass.

○ **D.** X-rays bend more when passing from air to glass.

## Questions 111 through 115 are NOT based on a descriptive passage.

## Question 111

When the pitch of a sound wave decreases, which of the following is true?

○ **A.** The period and wavelength both increase.

○ **B.** The period increases and the wavelength decreases.

○ **C.** The period decreases and the wavelength increases.

○ **D.** The period and wavelength both decrease.

## Question 112

A pipe of length $L$ open at both ends carries a standing wave at its third harmonic. Which expression is equivalent to the velocity of the wave, which has a frequency $f$?

○ **A.** $2L/f$

○ **B.** $L/2f$

○ **C.** $2Lf/3$

○ **D.** $2Lf$

## Question 113

Although waves in the open ocean usually propagate in all directions, waves washing into the shore usually move nearly perpendicular to the shore. Which of the following best explains the reason for this phenomenon?

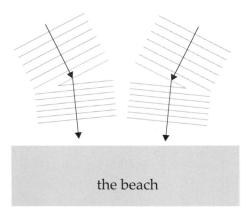

the beach

○ **A.** The shallow water decreases the speed of the waves, causing them to refract.

○ **B.** The shallow water increases the speed of the waves, causing them to refract.

○ **C.** The shallow water decreases the speed of the waves, causing them to diffract.

○ **D.** The shallow water increases the speed of the waves, causing them to diffract.

## Question 114

A mirror has a radius of curvature of 8 cm and makes a real, inverted image 20 cm from its surface. What is the object distance?

○ **A.** 4 cm

○ **B.** 5 cm

○ **C.** 10 cm

○ **D.** 20 cm

## Question 115

A 3 cm object is placed 15 cm in front of a convex mirror. The image forms 5 cm behind the mirror. How big is the image?

○ **A.** 1 cm

○ **B.** 3 cm

○ **C.** 5 cm

○ **D.** 9 cm

---

**STOP.** IF YOU FINISH BEFORE TIME IS CALLED, CHECK YOUR WORK. YOU MAY GO BACK TO ANY QUESTION IN THIS TEST BOOKLET.

---

# ANSWERS & EXPLANATIONS

## FOR

## 30-MINUTE IN-CLASS EXAMINATIONS

| Lecture 1 | Lecture 2 | Lecture 3 | Lecture 4 | Lecture 5 |
|-----------|-----------|-----------|-----------|-----------|
| 1. B | 24. A | 47. D | 70. A | 93. C |
| 2. B | 25. D | 48. A | 71. C | 94. A |
| 3. C | 26. B | 49. C | 72. D | 95. C |
| 4. D | 27. A | 50. D | 73. C | 96. D |
| 5. D | 28. D | 51. A | 74. C | 97. D |
| 6. B | 29. A | 52. A | 75. C | 98. A |
| 7. D | 30. B | 53. B | 76. C | 99. C |
| 8. C | 31. C | 54. D | 77. B | 100. A |
| 9. D | 32. B | 55. B | 78. C | 101. C |
| 10. A | 33. C | 56. B | 79. A | 102. C |
| 11. A | 34. C | 57. D | 80. C | 103. A |
| 12. C | 35. A | 58. B | 81. C | 104. C |
| 13. B | 36. B | 59. C | 82. D | 105. A |
| 14. B | 37. B | 60. D | 83. A | 106. D |
| 15. C | 38. D | 61. B | 84. D | 107. A |
| 16. A | 39. B | 62. D | 85. A | 108. B |
| 17. C | 40. B | 63. C | 86. D | 109. D |
| 18. D | 41. D | 64. C | 87. B | 110. D |
| 19. A | 42. A | 65. D | 88. B | 111. A |
| 20. D | 43. B | 66. A | 89. B | 112. C |
| 21. D | 44. C | 67. C | 90. C | 113. A |
| 22. C | 45. D | 68. B | 91. A | 114. B |
| 23. D | 46. B | 69. A | 92. C | 115. A |

# SCORING

Any attempt we could make at score correlation to the MCAT® would mislead. Unlike the AAMC MCAT® which includes easy questions, Examkrackers deliberately asks questions only of medium and high difficulty in order to optimize your practice time and maximize the increase to your MCAT® score. To accurately predict your MCAT® score, use an official AAMC MCAT® practice test.

Your goal is to see your raw score improve with each Examkrackers In-Class Exam and full-length EK-Test® you take. Look closely at each question you get wrong to find areas for review and to notice the habits that don't work. As you approach each new In-Class Exam or practice test, make commitments to replace what doesn't work with the approach you need to get questions right. Focus on the questions you get wrong to learn to think like the MCAT® and increase your score.

Toward your success!

# EXPLANATIONS TO IN-CLASS EXAM FOR LECTURE 1

## Passage I (Questions 1-5)

1. **B is the best answer.** Find the acceleration using $a = F/m$. With the original stimulus, the net force is the muscle force minus the force of gravity, 105 N – 100 N = 5 N. With the larger stimulus, the net force is 145 N – 100 N = 45 N. The difference in net force between the two stimuli is 45 N – 5 N = 40N. The difference in acceleration is therefore (40 N)/(10 kg) = 4 m/s$^2$.

2. **B is the best answer.** Use the equation $V_f^2 - V_0^2 = 2a\Delta y$, and the initial velocity is zero. Substitute $F/m$ for a. Therefore $V_f^2 = 2[(145\ N – 100\ N)/(10\ kg)](0.08m)$. Simplify the equation to $V_f^2 = 0.72\ m^2/s^2$. Then, estimate that the final velocity is therefore between 0.8 m/s and 0.9 m/s, since $0.8^2 = 0.64$ and $0.9^2 = 0.81$.

3. **C is the best answer.** To answer this question, first understand that muscle force during isometric contraction is equal to the force of gravity on the disc. Second, extrapolate the relationship between motor unit recruitment and muscle force to 100% recruitment, which will likely correlate to a force between 145 N and 200 N. The only disc mass among the answer choices that would experience a force of gravity in this range is the 16 kg disc.

4. **D is the best answer.** At this moment, the disc is not moving, so its kinetic energy is 0 (the minimum possible value). However, it has reached its maximal height, and therefore its maximal gravitational potential energy.

5. **D is the best answer.** The reduced force of gravity means that a reduced muscle force, and therefore a reduced stimulation level, are needed to achieve isometric contraction. If the stimulation is increased by the same amount, the muscle force will be less than that in the original experiment, but the net force (the vector sum of the muscle force and the force of gravity) will be the same as it was in the original experiment. Therefore, the disc acceleration will be unchanged.

## Passage II (Questions 6-10)

6. **B is the best answer.** The passage states that "RV isovolumetric acceleration (IVA) was calculated as the peak isometric myocardial velocity divided by time to peak velocity." In other words, $a = \Delta v/\Delta t$. Therefore, $\Delta t = \Delta v/a$. Once again, when in doubt, use units to confirm that this is the correct formula. $(m/s)/(m/s^2) = (m/s)(s^2/m) = (s)$. Do not be intimidated by the jargon used in this passage. The underlying concepts are very familiar. $\Delta t = (8\ cm/s)/(3.2\ m/s^2) = (8\ cm/s)/(320\ cm/s^2) = (1\ cm/s)/(40\ cm/s^2) = 0.025s$, which is choice B. Pay careful attention to units and simplify fractions whenever possible.

7. **D is the best answer.** If RVEF is positively correlated with right ventricle function, then healthy patients would be expected to have high RVEF values. Conversely, patients with pulmonary arterial hypertension (PAH) would be expected to have low RVEF values. To determine if patients with PAH should be expected to have higher or lower S' and IVA measurements, look at Table 1 and Figure 1. Table 1 shows that low RVEF values are associated with lower S' measurements. Therefore, patients with PAH would be expected to have lower S' measurements; choices A and B can be eliminated. According to Figure 1, low RVEF values are likewise associated with lower IVA measurements. Therefore, choice C can be eliminated and choice D is the best answer.

8. **C is the best answer.** As shown in Figure 1, RVEF is positively correlated with IVA. Therefore, if one increases, the other increases. The question stem states that RVEF increases, meaning that IVA also increases. Therefore, answer choices A and D, which state that IVA decreases, can be eliminated. To decide between choices B and C, determine whether force would increase or decrease as IVA increases. Recall that IVA stands for right ventricular isovolumetric acceleration. As stated in Newton's second law of motion, acceleration is directly proportional to force, $F = ma$. Therefore, the force with which the right ventricle contracts would increase as IVA increases. Choice B can be eliminated and choice C is the best answer. Intuitively, it makes sense that the greater the force of contraction, the greater the volume of blood ejected from the heart.

9.  **D is the best answer.** If the magnitude of blood flow velocity increases, then acceleration is in the same direction as velocity, that is, the positive direction. Therefore, choices A and C, which state that acceleration is in the negative direction, can be eliminated. Because acceleration is occurs in the direction of net force, net force must likewise be in the positive direction. Do not allow the statement "blood must flow against the force of gravity" to persuade you that net force is in the negative direction. The force of gravity is not the only force acting on the blood. It is the net force that the problem is concerned with, and the net force and acceleration are always in the same direction. Therefore, choice B can be eliminated and choice D is the best answer.

10. **A is the best answer.** The passage states, "During ventricular diastole, the leaflets of the tricuspid valve project into the right ventricle, allowing passage of blood from the right atrium to the right ventricle." Therefore, the net forces acting on the leaflets must be directed into the right ventricle. Choice A is the best answer. Choices C and D are not the best answers; the tricuspid valve is not continuous with either the pulmonary artery or the vena cavae. The net force on the leaflets would be directed into the right atrium (choice B) at the onset of ventricular systole (systole = "squeeze"), when the valve leaflets move to the closed position. Contraction of the papillary muscles attached to the leaflets by the chordae tendinae prevents the leaflets from being everted into the right atrium.

## Passage III (Questions 11-14)

11. **A is the best answer.** The passage states that the researchers measured the distance that the red blood cell was stretched, and then used the stiffness (force/distance) to find force. This suggests that the force = stiffness times distance. The relationship between force generated and stiffness is direct proportionality, so an overestimation of stiffness would also mean an overestimation of mechanical force. Choice B is the opposite of this conclusion. The stiffness of the red blood cell does not affect the antibodies that lead to T cell activation, eliminating choice C. Finally, the key results are the mechanical forces exerted by T cells on the red blood cells, so the results would definitely be affected by stiffness. The passage states that the stiffness was then used to calculate the force; choice D can be eliminated.

12. **C is the best answer.** The compression/elongation distance of the red blood cell and its stiffness were used to calculate the force generated. The proper equation can be determined based on units: distance times force/distance = force. This corresponds to $0.5 \times 50 = 25$, so 25 pN is the best answer. The other answers are all based on inaccurate relationships between force, stiffness, and distance. For example, 100 pN would be the answer if distance and force were multiplied to find stiffness.

13. **B is the best answer.** The passage states that actin polymerization is key to generation of forces by T cells. Stopping this process would have a negative effect on the magnitude of the force. Using a cell of a different stiffness would not impact the measured force generated because a change in stiffness would be compensated for by an opposite change in the distance of cell compression or elongation; choices A and D can be eliminated. Finally, the article does not mention pH at all, so this answer is likely irrelevant; choice C can be eliminated, and choice B is the best answer.

14. **B is the best answer.** According to the figure in the question stem, the pushing and pulling forces are equal in magnitude and opposite in direction. Between 0 s and 0.5 s, the APC is subject to a +10 pN force, and, therefore, accelerates in the positive direction. During this time, its velocity becomes increasingly positive. Therefore, choice A, which indicates that velocity is constant, can be eliminated. It is acceleration, not velocity, that is constant. Between 0.5 s and 1 s, the APC is subject to a −10 pN force and, therefore, accelerates in the negative direction. During this time, the magnitude of its velocity decreases, becoming less and less positive. Choice C, which, like choice A, depicts a discontinuous velocity function, should be eliminated. Both choices B and D depict a continuous velocity function. The difference is that D indicates that magnitude of acceleration is greater between 0.5 s and 1 s. Note that the magnitude of the positive slope of the left portion of the graph is less than the magnitude of the negative slope of the right portion of the graph. The figure in the question stem, however, indicates that the magnitude of the force, and, therefore, magnitude of acceleration acting between 0 s and 0.5 s is equal to the magnitude of force, and, therefore, magnitude of acceleration acting between 0.5 s and 1 s. Remember, $F = ma$. Choice D is eliminated and choice B is the best answer.

## Passage IV (Questions 15-18)

15. **C is the best answer.** The formula for friction is $F = \mu N$, where $\mu$ is the coefficient of friction and $N$ is the magnitude of the normal force. The normal force can be thought of as how much the bones push against each other, and the coefficient of friction is dependent on the texture of both interacting surfaces. Options II and III are accurate, so choices A and B can be eliminated. The area of contact between two substances does not actually affect the magnitude of friction, as shown in the previous equation. This eliminates option I, making choice C the best answer.

16. **A is the best answer.** Both mass and volume are given in the answer choices. Remember that mass is the quantitative measurement of inertia. This means the bone with the greatest inertia is the one with the largest mass. The volume values are given to suggest that density must be calculated, but this is extraneous information. The bone with the most density would be choice D. Since only mass is required to quantify inertia, the best answer must contain the highest mass. This makes choice A, 142 g, the best answer.

17. **C is the best answer.** Use Newton's Second Law to find the acceleration of the bone:

$$a = F/m = 0.004 / 0.03 = 0.133 \text{ m/s}^2.$$

This constant acceleration occurs for five seconds, and the bone starts from rest. When objects start from rest, $v_f = at$, so the final velocity is $0.133 \times 5 = 0.67$ m/s. Choice C is the best answer. Choice A mistakenly gives the acceleration. Choice B is a value that is half of the best answer. Choice D is the result of accidentally dividing mass by force to find acceleration.

18. **D is the best answer.** This question concerns Figure 2 because maximum load sustained is basically the same as the amount of force before fracture. This is directly related to the fracture point, which is the displacement at which an object will break. As force increases, the deformation in the bone increases up to the fracture point, at which the bone breaks. Bone area (Figure 1) may be related to this metric, but there is no evidence presented that implies a relationship between bone size and strength. Though it may be intuitive to assume larger bones are stronger, this is not a safe assumption based on the information given. There is one genotype that is clearly under the others in Figure 2, which is Osteoblast KO. The value for this group is about 6.0 N, while the other three genotypes have force values exceeding that. Choice D is the best answer.

## Stand-alones

19. **A is the best answer.** An ideal spring behaves according to Hooke's Law. Because $F = kx$, force varies directly with distance. The force line must be linear and positive, eliminating choices C and D. Now decide how potential energy varies with distance. According to the potential energy equation for springs, $U_s = \frac{1}{2}kx^2$, so $U_s \propto x^2$. The relationship between distance and potential energy is quadratic, which is reflected in the graph in choice A.

20. **D is the best answer.** Remember that acceleration and net force must be in the same direction according to Newton's Second Law. For that reason, the two forces shown in the figure are extraneous information. The best answer will state where the net force *must* lie. While it is possible the net force is in quadrant III, because a component of acceleration is in the –x direction, it is also possible that the net force lies in quadrant II. Choice A can be eliminated. It is impossible for the net force to lie in quadrant IV because then a component of acceleration would need to lie in the +x direction. Choice B can be eliminated. Choice C is the most specific. It is only possible if acceleration lies on the –x axis, which is not necessarily the case. Choice C can be eliminated. Because acceleration with a component on the –x axis must have net force pointing left of the origin, choice D is the best answer.

21. **D is the best answer.** The force that causes an object to accelerate down an inclined plane is equal to $mg \sin\theta$. Therefore, as $\theta$ increases, the force acting on the object increases. Because $F = ma$, the acceleration of the object also increases as $\theta$ increases. Thus the ball rolling down the ramp placed at an angle of 60° to the horizontal will experience a greater acceleration than the ball rolling down the ramp placed at an angle of 30° to the horizontal and will, by consequence, travel 1 m in a smaller amount of time. Therefore, both choices A and C can be eliminated. Because displacement is a vector, it is defined by both magnitude and direction. The two displacement vectors have the same magnitude (1 m) but different directions. Therefore, choice B can be eliminated and D, none of the above, is the best answer choice.

22. **C is the best answer.** Tension in a massless rope is constant and equal to the force acting on each body attached to the rope. As per Newton's Third Law of Motion, each group of men both exerts a 2000 N force in one direction and experiences a 2000 N force in the opposite direction. Because the force acting on each body attached to the rope has a magnitude of 2000 N, the tension in the rope is also said to have a magnitude of 2000 N.

23. **D is the best answer.** Recall that the magnitude of a spring force is described by the following equation: $F = kx$. Because $F = mg$, we can say that $kx = mg$. $k = (mg)/x = (5 \text{ kg} \cdot 10 \text{ m/s}^2)/(0.10 \text{ m}) = 500 \text{ kg/s}^2 = 500 \text{ N/m}$.

# EXPLANATIONS TO IN-CLASS EXAM FOR LECTURE 2

## Passage I (Questions 24-27)

24. **A is the best answer.** At first, the answer may be appear to be choice D, because $W = Fd = 10 \times 10 = 100$ J. However, work is actually equal to Fd cos θ. The force exerted is upwards, and the distance travelled is forwards (horizontal). Therefore, choice D can be eliminated. When the force and the distance are perpendicular, the work done is always 0 J, making choice A the best answer. Any nonzero values for work done, choices B and C, can be eliminated.

25. **D is the best answer.** The first part of the question is a roundabout way to describe a situation in which the torque is half of the original torque. The equation for torque is $\tau = Fr \sin \theta$. F is the force, r is the distance, and θ is the angle between the force and the plane of rotation. Increasing the force without a change in distance or angle, as in choices A and B, would never decrease the torque. Similarly, doubling the distance would double the torque, ruling out choice C. Choice D is the best answer because decreasing the angle from perpendicular to 30° would reduce the torque by half because sin 90° = 1 and sin 30° = 0.5.

26. **B is the best answer.** The relationship between velocity of shortening and load on the muscle is never exactly specified, but the passage does state that it is an inverse relationship. If load increases, then velocity has to decrease. Both choices A and B represent decreases. A decrease all the way to 0 rad/s would represent an isometric contraction, which was not tested in this experiment. Choice A can be eliminated. Choice B, 2.7 rad/s, is the best answer.

27. **A is the best answer.** The key distinction to make here is whether having a rotational velocity is a characteristic of dynamic equilibrium or not. Static equilibrium is when all velocities, including rotational, are zero. This is not the case, and option II is not true. The system is in dynamic equilibrium, so option I is included in the best answer. No specific information is given about a change in height, which would produce a change in gravitational potential energy, so option III is unknown and can be eliminated. The best answer is choice A, only option I.

## Passage II (Questions 28-32)

28. **D is the best answer.** This question is discussing the work performed by a test subject doing an exercise, so the first step is to identify where and how work is being performed. Remember, work refers to the amount of energy imparted into an object by an external force. In this case, work refers to the increase in gravitational potential energy, $U = mgh$, of the weight due to the force provided by the subject's leg muscles. The net amount of work performed by the subject can be found by identifying how the potential energy has changed over the course of the movement. Over the course of the knee extension, the 500 N weight has moved from its initial position to a position 0.3 m × (sin(90°) − sin(30°)) = 0.3 m × (1 − 0.5) = 0.15 m above its starting point. This means that the work performed by the subject is U = 500 N × 0.15 m = 75 J, making choice D the best answer. Choice A is a weak answer choice because it disregards the fact that the weight is only lifted 0.15 m rather than 0.3 m, the full length of the tibia. Choice B is a weak answer choice because the weight has a different amount of potential energy than what it started with, indicating that a net amount of work was performed. Choice C is also a weak answer because it sums all eight repetitions in one set, even though the net amount of work being done to lift the weight is negated by lowering the weight in each repetition. Choice D is the best answer choice.

29. **A is the best answer.** This question is asking about the force required to maintain a constant velocity knee extension. Remember, in order to maintain a dynamic equilibrium, there must be no net force and no net torque on the object. The force and torque counteracting the subject is provided by gravity. The force of gravity is constant in its magnitude and direction, but the torque that gravity applies on the tibia changes depending on the angle of the tibia relative to horizontal. The torque is maximal when the force is applied perpendicularly to the lever arm, so the highest torque experienced by the tibia from gravity will be when the tibia is at 30°, the end of the knee extension, and the closest angle to horizontal. If the highest torque is experienced at 30°, then the highest force is required from the subject at this point in order to directly counteract the torque, making choice A the best answer. Choices B and C are weak answer choices because the torque on the tibia from gravity is lower at these angles due to the smaller angle between the lever arm and the direction of force. Choice D is tempting, but in order to keep a constant velocity, the net forces and torques on the object must be zero. This means that the force the subject performs might not necessarily be constant, but it would always counteract the actions of gravity. Choice A is the best answer choice.

30. **B is the best answer.** Looking at the answer choices to this question, they differ in two ways—whether fatigued muscles experience a change in power or a change in energy, and whether this change was a positive or negative change. Of the two sets of data provided, the data from the 20th set of knee extensions reflects the fatigued muscle, while the data from the first set reflects non-fatigued muscle. Comparing the first and 20th sets of data, the 20th set has a lower RTD – represented by the slanted, dashed line – and a lower peak torque than the first set. Choice A is a weak answer choice because the total amount of energy the muscle has available was not directly measured by the experiment, nor was it shown directly or indirectly in the data. Choice C can also be eliminated because the energy of the muscle was not measured by the experiment. Choice D is a weak answer because the data shows that the 20th set has a lower RTD and lower peak torque than the first set, and choice D claims the opposite. Choice B is the best answer because it accurately identifies that the fatigued muscle showed lower RTD values. A decrease in the rate of torque development directly decreases the power, a measure of the rate at which work can be performed. Work performed by a torque is the magnitude of the torque multiplied by the angle of motion, so the power is the magnitude of the RTD multiplied by the angle of motion.

31. **C is the best answer.** This question is asking about mechanical advantage, as it is asking about what must be the case when the subject uses a machine to perform work. Machines reduce the force required to do a given amount of work, which is referred to as mechanical advantage. The use of a machine does not indicate how the rate of work performed, or power, changes, so choice A is a weak answer. It is unlikely that the subject is using the same force as in the knee extensions, or there would be no mechanical advantage to using the pulley. Choice B is a weak answer. Choice D is a weak answer because machines lower the force required while keeping the work performed constant. Choice C is the best answer because the pulley cannot reduce the amount of work performed—it can only decrease the required force.

32. **B is the best answer.** This question is asking about conservative forces, indicating to think about the balance of mechanical energy within the system. The two forms of mechanical energy are kinetic and potential energy. When trying to balance mechanical energy within the system, it is also important to identify the extent of the system. For the purposes of this question, the system is the weight and its position and motion in the space around it. Because the weight experiences an increase in potential energy, due to its increased height of the weight, and no change in kinetic energy, the force is not a conservative force, so choice A can be eliminated. Choice C is a weaker answer choice as well because the explanation is not sufficient to identify why the force applied by the patient on the weight is not conservative—there are many conservative forces that act against other conservative forces, such as buoyant force acting against gravity. Choice D may seem like a tempting answer choice, but the chemical energy of the muscle is not encompassed by the system we are concerned with, making it a weak answer choice, and the force is not a conservative force. Choice B, on the other hand, is the strongest answer choice because it accurately identifies that the total mechanical energy of the weight is not conserved.

33. **C is the best answer.** The kinetic energy generated during push-off is produced by the muscles of the legs, which contract and thereby generate a force that causes the individual to accelerate upward. Muscle contraction requires energy stored in the phosphate bonds of adenosine triphosphate and/or phosphocreatine. This bond energy is classified as chemical potential energy, making choice C the best answer. As stated in the question stem, this chemical potential energy is converted to kinetic energy, which is in turn converted to gravitational potential energy. During descent, this gravitational potential energy is converted back into kinetic energy. The gravitational potential energy is not, however, the source of the initial kinetic energy generated during push-off, eliminating choice A. Rest energy is the energy associated with mass, and is equal to $mc^2$, where $m$ is mass and $c$ is the speed of light. Because push-off is not associated with any significant change in mass, choice B can be eliminated. Thermal energy is the energy associated with the rotational, translational, and vibrational motion of molecules. Differences in thermal energy result in differences in temperature, which in turn prompt transfers of energy as heat. While it may be true that the breaking of intramolecular phosphate bonds prompts changes in motion of molecules, including actin and myosin, associated changes in thermal energy are an effect rather than a cause of muscle contraction; choice D can be eliminated.

34. **C is the best answer.** As indicated in Figures 1 and 2, negative work is done during collision and positive work is done during recovery. Because this question does not ask about positive or net work done, the focus should be on the bottom portion of Figure 2, which shows negative muscle work done during collision. Choice A can be eliminated, as it states that positive work is done during collision. Choices B and D, which discuss work done during recovery, can also be eliminated. Choice C is the best answer. Each of the three lines on the bottom portion of Figure 2 corresponds to one of the three landing strategies. The graph indicates that work done by muscles is minimized when a stiff landing strategy is selected. For a given displacement of center of mass, negative muscle work associated with staff landings is less than work associated with either preferred or soft landings.

35. **A is the best answer.** As shown in Figure 1, assuming a constant vertical posture, work done by the forces generated by muscle contractions is negligible during the aerial phase. $P = 0$ $W = 0$ J/s. Therefore, choices B and C can be eliminated. Nonetheless, work is done to return the individual to the ground. It is done by the force of gravity ($F_G$), which completes work equal to $F_G d = -\Delta U$.

36. **B is the best answer.** Figure 1 shows power as a function of time. Recall that power is equal to work per unit time, $P = W/\Delta t$. Therefore, $W = P\Delta t$. The $y$-coordinates in Figure 1 correspond to power and the $x$-coordinates correspond to time. Therefore, work done is equal to the area under the portion of the graph depicting push-off. Note this area is in the shape of a triangle. Area of a triangle is equal to $\frac{1}{2}bh$, where $b$ is the base of the triangle and $h$ is the height of the triangle. The base of the triangle is equal to $\Delta t = 1.8$ s $- 0.8$ s $= 1$ s. The height of the triangle is the perpendicular distance from the apex of the triangle to it base, which is equal to $P = 2$ kW $= 2 \times 10^3$ W $= 2 \times 10^3$ J/s. Be sure to pay careful attention to SI prefixes. Otherwise, it may be tempting to select answer choice D. $W = \frac{1}{2} (2 \times 10^3$ J/s$)(1$ s$) = 1 \times 10^3$ J, so choice B is the best answer. Remember to multiply by $\frac{1}{2}$, or else this may lead to picking choice A.

37. **B is the best answer.** Recall that power is equal to work done per unit time. $P = W/\Delta t$, and $W = P\Delta t$ meaning work and time are directly proportional to one another. Assuming constant power, work decreases by the same factor that time decreases. The question stem assumes that collision time was underestimated (decreased) by a factor of 4. Choice A, which suggests work would be underestimated (decreased) by a factor of 2, and choices C and D, which suggest that work would be overestimated (increased), can be eliminated. Choice B is the best answer.

## Passage IV (Questions 38-41)

38. **D is the best answer.** The equation for kinetic energy is $KE = \frac{1}{2} mv^2$. The mass of P1 is $\frac{1}{3}$ that of P2, while the velocity of P2 is double that of P1. Plugging these ratios into the kinetic energy equation gives a ratio of $\frac{1}{3} \times \frac{1}{4} = \frac{1}{3}$, making choice D the best answer. Choice B is the result when only considering the effect of speed on KE, and choice A only considers mass. Lastly, choice C is the opposite of the best answer. One way to do a "common-sense" check between choices C and D is to consider whether mass or velocity matters more. Mass is to the 1st power in the KE equation, while velocity is squared. It is likely that the subject with less mass but twice the velocity has a higher KE. P2 has the higher KE in this question, so the larger number should be in the denominator.

39. **B is the best answer.** Each answer is some mathematical combination of the three numbers provided in the question stem. Choice A is distance times time over force. Choice B is force times distance over time. Choice D is force times time over distance. The calculation of power can be determined by figuring out how to get to the proper unit of watts, or joules per second. Force times distance gives work in J. Force times distance over time, choice B, yields the appropriate units. The calculation for power in this question would be $(17 \text{ N})(8 \text{ m})/(10 \text{ s}) = 13.6$ W. Choice C is just a rearranged version of the best answer, and is meant to be chosen as the result of a careless error. Rather than 13.6 W, it is 16.3 W, with the ones and tenths digit swapped.

40. **B is the best answer.** Energy in this scenario begins as chemical potential energy through the use of ATP in the muscles of the test subject. This is converted to kinetic energy, causing the body and bike pedals to move. Kinetic energy is then stored as electric potential energy through the power generator. Choice B is the best answer. Choice C implies that power is flowing from the power generator into the subject, which does not make sense. Electrical potential energy cannot be the start, as in choice D, because the power generator comes in once the subject is pedaling and charging it up. Choice A is not the best answer because the kinetic energy had to start from somewhere, and that source is the chemical potential energy in the bonds of ATP molecules in the biker.

41. **D is the best answer.** Figure 1 provides the maximum force exerted on the VBR and the power at that point. None of this information allows for calculation of the total work done during the test. This would require power and time, or force and distance. Not only is there not enough information, but also the force shown is not even the force exerted on the pedals of the bicycle. It is the force exerted on the VBR. Even more importantly, no time is given. Choice D, cannot be determined, is the best answer.

## Stand-alones

42. **A is the best answer.** Multiply fuel used by efficiency to find work done. $600 \text{ J} \times 0.8 = 480 \text{ J}$ of work. This work occurs over 15 s. To find power, divide work by time: $480 \text{ J}/15 \text{ s} = 32$ W. Choice A is the best answer. Choice B is not the best answer because it ignores efficiency. Choices C and D mistakenly multiply work or fuel used by time.

43. **B is the best answer.** Terminal velocity means that the force of air resistance is equal to the force of gravity. When those two forces are balanced, an object is in equilibrium even though it is in motion. This makes choice B the best answer. An object in projectile motion constantly experiences the force of gravity. Even at the top of its arc it is accelerating downwards because of gravity, so choice A is a weak answer. A pendulum constantly changes speed and direction, so its velocity is constantly changing. This means it is never in equilibrium, so choice C is a weak answer. An object experiencing a single non-zero force will accelerate in the direction of that force and will not be in equilibrium, so choice D is not a strong answer.

44. **C is the best answer.** There are two forces acting on the forearm: gravity ($F_g$) acting at the center of mass of the forearm and the force exerted by the biceps muscle ($F_b$), acting at a point close to the elbow. Assume the biceps tendon inserts at a distance of $x_1$ from the elbow and the center of mass lies at a distance of $x_2$ from the elbow. The net torque is $F_b \times x_1 - F_g \times x_2$. It is important to observe that net torque is positive in the direction the biceps tendon is pulling because the arm is in a lifting motion. Increasing the weight of the forearm makes $F_g$ larger which decreases net torque, so choice A is not a strong answer. Redistributing forearm mass so more of it is in the hand makes $x_2$ larger because it puts the center of mass closer to the hand, so choice B is a weak answer. Decreasing mass of the biceps muscle would decrease the force it can pull with, so $F_b$ would be lower. This makes choice D a weak answer. Inserting the biceps tendon further from the elbow increases $x_1$, which would increase net torque, making choice C the best answer.

45. **D is the best answer.** $\tau = Fl$. In order for the meter stick to be in rotational equilibrium, $\tau_{clockwise}$ must equal $\tau_{counterclockwise}$. The point of rotation is the attachment point of the string. The mass on the right exerts a clockwise torque equal to (5 kg · 10 m/s²)(0.80 m) = 50 N · 0.80 m. The mass on the left must exert a counterclockwise torque of equal magnitude. Because the lever arm for the mass on the left, $l = 0.20$ m, is ¼ that of the lever arm for the mass on the right, $l = 0.80$ m, the force it exerts must be 4 times that exerted by the mass on the right. The mass on the right exerts a force of 50 N. Therefore, the mass on the left must exert a force of 200 N.

46. **B is the best answer.** This problem is best solved by avoiding lengthy calculations. Recall that a pulley halves the force required to do a given amount of work. In the absence of a pulley, a force of 10 kg × 10 m/s² = 100 N would be required to lift the 10 kg mass. With the pulley, just 50 N is required. Depending on the placement of the force and load relative to the pivot point, a lever can likewise reduce the force required to do a given amount of work. Because the distance of the force from the pivot point is twice that of the load from the pivot point, the lever likewise halves the force required, this time from 50 N to 25 N.

# EXPLANATIONS TO IN-CLASS EXAM FOR LECTURE 3

## Passage I (Questions 47-51)

47. **D is the best answer.** Consider the equation for pressure: $P = \rho gy$. Pressure is equal to density times gravity times depth. Since density of water is constant throughout the pool, as is the gravity constant, only the pressure varies directly with depth. For this reason, the deepest or lowest body part listed among the answer choices is the best answer. This is choice D, the foot. All other choices are above the foot. Additionally, it would only make sense for the best answer to be an extreme of the body, either the highest or lowest. The question asks where pressure will be highest, which automatically rules out choices B and C since they occupy intermediate positions.

48. **A is the best answer.** Density is mass/volume, so consider differences in mass and volume when finding the answer to this question. 0.5 ng is the mass of an RBC, and 2 ng is the mass of a leukocyte. A leukocyte has twice the size of an RBC according to the question stem and four times the mass according to the passage. Dividing the ratio of the masses by the ratio of the volumes gives the ratio of the densities. This is ²⁄₄ = ½, so an RBC is half as dense as a leukocyte. Choice A is the best answer, and choice C is the reverse of this. Choices B and D only consider the difference in mass from 0.5 to 2. This ratio is ¼ or 4, depending on the order of comparison, but density involves volume as well, so these answers can be eliminated.

49. **C is the best answer.** The key impact of the blockage is that velocity is increased based on the continuity equation: $Q = Av =$ constant. If area is decreased, velocity is increased. Since the question stem assumes real flow, choice A presents the opposite effect and can be eliminated. Blood in the blocked area has the same potential energy as other areas of the vessel since the artery is horizontal. Blood in the blocked area has the same potential energy as other areas of the vessel since the artery is horizontal. Blood in the blocked area will have a lower pressure, choice C, according to Bernoulli's equation: $P + ½ \rho v^2 + \rho gy =$ constant. Potential energy density is constant, and velocity is increased in the blockage. If velocity is increased, then pressure must be decreased in the blockage to compensate and maintain Bernoulli's equation. Choice C is the best answer.

50. **D is the best answer.** This question tests the concept of surface tension. An upward meniscus means that cohesive forces are greater than adhesive forces. This is because cohesive forces are between blood molecules and adhesive forces are between blood and the tube. If the meniscus is upwards, this means that blood preferentially interacts with itself. A downward meniscus is the opposite. Adhesive forces are higher than cohesive forces, so the most likely change is that cohesive forces decrease and adhesive forces increase relative to regular blood, which is described by choice D.

51. **A is the best answer.** Based on the passage, severe infection involves a large number of parasites in the bloodstream. The question states that these parasites increase viscosity. Lack of viscosity is one of the assumptions of ideal flow, so an increase in viscosity makes blood flow less ideally. Choice B can be eliminated and choice A is the best answer. Next, choices C and D concern the number of blood vessels in infected individuals. No evidence in the passage suggests that this would change, so these answers can be ruled out.

## Passage II (Questions 52-55)

52. **A is the best answer.** The density of water is 1000 kg/m$^3$. Volume flow rate (Q) is found by multiplying cross-sectional area (A) and velocity (v). It is important to note the inverse relationship between velocity and area here. Mass flow rate is found by multiplying density $\rho$ by volume flow rate, $I = \rho \times Q = \rho \times Av$. Velocity from the passage is 0.1 mm/s which is the same as $1 \times 10^{-4}$ m/s. Area is found using $A = \pi \times r^2$ and $r = d/2$, where diameter from the question stem is given as $10 \times 10^{-6}$ m, so $A = \pi \times (5 \times 10^{-6})^2$ m$^2$. Multiplying by velocity, $1 \times 10^{-4}$ m/s, gives $Q = 7.85 \times 10^{-15}$ m$^3$/s. Multiply by the density, 1000 kg/m$^3$, to get choice A in the proper units of kg/s given for mass flow rate.

53. **B is the best answer.** This question can be answered using information from Figures 1 and 2. Figure 1 shows that interstitial hydrostatic pressure is a force pushing in against the outside of a vessel. It should oppose filtration, which is movement of something out of the vessel. Figure 2 shows that at small distances from the center of a tumor, increases in the tumor's necrotic core size are associated with higher interstitial pressure. This means the capillary near the tumor with the smaller core will experience less force opposing filtration, and filtration should be higher. Choice B is a strong answer. Choice A states the exact opposite and can be eliminated. Figure 2 demonstrates that the pressures will not be the same, making choice C a weak answer. All passage information indicates that pressure changes affect filtration in a predictable way, making choice D highly unlikely. Tumors often display rapid, disorganized growth that leads to poor blood perfusion in the center of the mass. To maintain this high replication rate, tumors require blood flow. Eventually the metabolic demands of the cells at the center of the tumor exceed the energy available to them, and cell death, or necrosis, occurs. Blood flow to the necrotic centers of tumors ceases. Note that none of this information is necessary to answer the question – just recognize from Figure 2 that necrotic core size is a variable linked to increased interstitial pressure. Figure 1 also contains more information than what is needed to answer this question. To calculate the direction and rate of filtration, four types of pressure are taken into account: hydrostatic pressure within a capillary (blood pressure) and oncotic pressure (a type of osmotic pressure) in the interstitial space both favor filtration, while interstitial hydrostatic pressure and capillary oncotic pressure oppose it. The sum of all four pressures determines filtration.

54. **D is the best answer.** The Venturi effect states that as a pipe or vessel narrows, fluid velocity will increase and its hydrostatic pressure will decrease. A decrease in the capillary hydrostatic pressure, according to Figure 1, will inhibit drug delivery, so choice D is a strong answer. Smaller drug concentrations in the tumor center would not change or reduce interstitial fluid static pressures and would increase the diffusion gradient, allowing more drug delivery, so choice A is a weak answer. A smaller interstitial hydrostatic pressure in the center would also increase drug delivery because it would allow more drug diffusion out of capillaries and into the interstitial fluid, so choice B can be eliminated. Larger drug plasma concentrations would likely have no effect on viscosity. They would change the osmotic pressure in favor of drug flow out of the capillaries as shown in Figure 1, so choice C is not true.

55. **B is the best answer.** Pascal's law states that $P = \rho gy = mg/A$ where $y$ is the depth of the fluid. The passage states that pressure is the primary factor affecting drug delivery. Choosing a location higher in the leg would decrease the fluid depth, so this would decrease pressure, making Choice A not true. Pascal's law is the same regardless of cross-sectional area, so choice C is not true. According to Pascal's law, increasing density would increase pressure, so choice D is not true. According to Pascal's law, increasing density would increase pressure because density is equal to mass divided by volume, so choice B is a true statement.

## Passage III (Questions 56-60)

56. **B is the best answer.** Know the general characteristics of an ideal fluid. An ideal fluid is not viscous, does not have turbulent flow, and has uniform density. Choice D can be eliminated because blood is an example of a real fluid, and no real fluid actually acts like an ideal fluid. Just like an ideal gas, an ideal fluid is a simplifying model that can be used to predict the behavior of a more complex real substance. Choice C can also be eliminated, since the whole point of the ideal fluid model is to predict the behavior of real fluids. Poiseuille's Law even provides a way to make quantitative predictions that are specific to real fluids. Choice A flips real and ideal fluids; ideal fluids, not real fluids, are expected to always have laminar flow. In fact, the transition from laminar to turbulent flow when an artery is compressed allows the measurement of blood pressure. This leaves B as the best answer. It is assumed that an ideal fluid has no viscosity, but viscosity does play a role in the flow of blood.

57. **D is the best answer.** Although Bernoulli's equation indicates that the sum of pressure, kinetic energy per unit volume, and potential energy per unit volume remain constant, this equation is only strictly true for an ideal fluid. Blood is a real fluid, and the question stem does not indicate any simplifying assumptions that would lead to treating blood as an ideal fluid. In a real fluid, energy is lost due to drag against the walls of the blood vessels. Since fluid pressure is created by the movement of molecules within the fluid (kinetic energy), the loss of energy results in decreased pressure. Choice D is the best answer.

58. **B is the best answer.** Fluids generally flow from high to low pressure, and atmospheric pressure can be expected to remain constant over the course of respiration. Expiration (air leaving the lungs) must reflect *increased* pressure in the intrathoracic cavity, eliminating choice C. Conversely, inspiration (air flowing into the lungs) must reflect *decreased* pressure in the intrathoracic cavity. Recall that pressure in the chest cavity becomes lower than atmospheric pressure during inspiration, eliminating choice D. Choices A and B both accurately describe changes in intrathoracic pressure that occur during inspiration. However, Figure 1 shows that decreased pulmonary artery pressure occurs during expiration, not inspiration. Presumably, decreased pulmonary artery pressure would be the result of decreased venous return, so it must be the case that the decrease in venous return occurs during expiration, making choice B the best answer. This also makes sense given how differences in pressure affect fluid flow. In the simple case of fluid flowing through a pipe, the higher the pressure is at the beginning of the pipe compared to the end, the greater the fluid flow will be. Although the circulatory system is far more complex than a simple pipe, the principle is the same: fluid flows from higher to lower pressure. Since increased intrathoracic pressure increases the pressure at the end of the "pipe" of a vein returning to the heart, flow to the heart is decreased, as indicated by choice B.

59. **C is the best answer.** Whenever pressure and velocity of a fluid is involved, think of Bernoulli's equation and the trade-off between uniform and translational kinetic energy. According to Bernoulli's equation, assuming that other factors (such as height) are held constant, a decrease in velocity must be accompanied by an increase in pressure. For this reason, choices A and D can be eliminated. Recall that two types of motion occur in a moving fluid: random translational motion and uniform translational motion. However, only random translational motion contributes to fluid pressure. Choice C both accurately indicates higher pressure in the vessel with the slower-moving fluid and points to random translational motion as a contributor to the fluid pressure, so C is the best answer. Choice B could be tempting because it posits higher pressure; further, we know that the greater the surface area, the slower the velocity of a real fluid, due to the effect of drag. However, the information given in the question stem does not allow the conclusion that the slower velocity must be due to higher surface area. In addition, the question stem states that other factors are constant between the blood vessels. For these reasons, choice B is not the best answer.

60. **D is the best answer.** This question is asking about the flow rate of a real fluid through the airway, which can be approximated as a tube or pipe. Remember Poiseuille's Law:

$$Q = \Delta P \frac{\pi r^4}{8\eta L}$$

Poiseuille's Law is more likely to be seen applied to liquids, but it is valid for all fluids, including gases such as air. It is not necessary to have Poiseuille's Law memorized for the MCAT®, but know the proportional relationships. In particular, know that flow rate is directly proportional to $\Delta P$ and $r^4$. The exponential relationship with radius is the reason that a small change in radius leads to a substantial change in flow rate. No information is given in the question stem to indicate that any other variables involved in Poiseuille's Law are different between the airways, so radius can be assumed to be the only factor that changes. Since the average radius in COPD patients is ½ of the average radius in non-COPD patients, the flow must be $(½)^4$ as large, which is $1^4/2^4$ or $\frac{1}{16}$ as large. Choice D is the best answer.

Note that even without knowing what exponent is assigned to radius in the equation, the answers can be narrowed down to choices B or D with a general understanding of the relationships between variables in Poiseuille's Law. Since radius decreases, flow rate must also decrease, and choice C can be eliminated. Remember that radius is associated with an exponent in the equation. The flow rate would change by the same factor as the radius only if flow rate and radius were directly proportional, with no exponent involved. Even without knowing what the exponent is, choice A can be eliminated. Choice B would be the answer if the radius was squared in Poiseuille's Law, rather than being raised to the fourth power.

## Passage IV (Questions 61-64)

61. **B is the best answer.** The specific gravity is the ratio of the density of a substance to that of a reference, in this case water. Water's density is 1000 kg/m³. To find the specific gravity of air, divide 1.225 by 1000 to get 0.001225. Choice B is the best answer. The main difficulty in this question is determining where to place the decimal point, and keeping track of zeroes.

62. **D is the best answer.** The buoyant force depends on the volume as well as the density of the liquid that the object is submerged in. A key point to notice is that all answer options have 1 L of liquid displaced since all scenarios have fully submerged 1 L objects. Thus, the factor of volume is taken out. When only considering density, choice D has the highest value. A specific gravity of 6.0 is higher than 3.0, 1.5, and water, which has a specific gravity of 1.0.

63. **C is the best answer.** 1200 $cm^3$ passes through the trachea in 1 s. This means that the volumetric flow rate, $Q$, is 1200 $cm^3$/s. $Q = Av$, so to find $v$, A needs to be calculated. The question states that the trachea is a circle with diameter of 4 cm, and radius of 2 cm. The area of the trachea is $\pi r^2 = 3.14 \times 2 \times 2 = 12.57$ $cm^2$. $Q/A$ is 1200 / 12.57, which should be slightly less than one hundred. No calculation is necessary to find that choice C is the right answer. Choice D is exactly one hundred, and is not the best answer. Choices A and B are close to the answer when volume is not first converted to $cm^3$.

64. **C is the best answer.** Option I states that there is a bigger difference in pressure at a higher altitude. This is not the best answer because pressure within the closed circulatory system is not significantly affected by the outside conditions. The head is still the same distance from the feet. This rules out choices A, B, and D. Next, Figure 1 indicates that velocity is increased in the middle cerebral artery in hypoxic conditions, which mimic high altitude. Option II is most likely true. Because there is only one answer including option II and excluding option I, choice C must be the best answer. Option III is unlikely to be true because volumetric flow rate will not decrease when the only clear change is an increase in velocity. This is based on the continuity equation: $Q = Av$.

## Stand-alones

65. **D is the best answer.** Because the object is fully submerged, it displaces a volume equal to its own. This is 1 L of water, or 1 kg. This amount of water leads to a buoyant force of 9.8 N. The force of gravity on the object is equal to mg, 5 × 9.8 = 49 N. However, these are not the only two forces acting on the object. There is also the normal force from the bottom of the pool. The net force is 0 N because the object is just sitting at the bottom of the pool (choice D). Choices A, B, and C are just the magnitudes of each individual force.

66. **A is the best answer.** Any points in a container of water that are open to the atmosphere will be at atmospheric pressure. Since the top of the container is open, and the opening below is also exposed to the atmosphere, the pressure at both locations is 101,325 Pa. Therefore, the difference is 0 Pa, choice A. Choices B and C are based on pressure differences from height, but because the water is not stationary, other factors must be considered. Next, choice D only provides atmospheric pressure, not the difference in pressure between the two points.

67. **C is the best answer.** This problem is best solved by avoiding lengthy calculations. Recall that the fraction of an object submerged in a fluid is equal to the density of the object divided by the density of the fluid. Therefore, the percentage of the container that floats above the water is equal to 100% - ($\rho_{object}/\rho_{fluid}$) × 100%. The density of the object is 2 kg/5 L = 0.4 kg/L and the density of the lake water is 1 kg/L. Therefore, 40% of the container is submerged and 60% of the container floats above the water.

68. **B is the best answer.** When the brick floats on the Styrofoam, it displaces a volume of water with mass equivalent to its mass. Because the brick is denser than the water, the volume of water displaced is greater than the volume of the brick. If the brick were to sink, however, it would displace a volume of water equal to its own volume. Therefore, if the brick were allowed to sink to the bottom, the water level would fall.

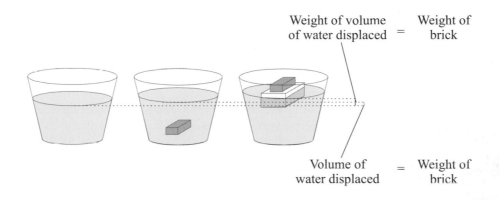

Weight of volume of water displaced = Weight of brick

Volume of water displaced = Weight of brick

**69. A is the best answer.** Bernoulli's equation states:

$$P + \rho g h + \frac{1}{2}\rho v^2 = K$$

Assume that $P_1$, $h_1$, and $v_1$ describe the pressure, height, and velocity of the water at the top of the tower and that $P_2$, $h_2$, and $v_2$ describe the pressure, height, and velocity of the water at the leak. If (1) $P_1 = P_2 = P_{atm}$, (2) $v_1$ is assumed to be 0, and (3) $h_2$ is assigned an arbitrary value of 0, then:

$$v = \sqrt{2gh}$$

If $h_2$, the height of the water at the leak, is assigned a value of 0, then $h_1$, the height of the water at the top of the tower, has a value of 5 m, and $v = \sqrt{2 \times 10 \frac{m}{s^2} \times 5\ m} = 10$ m/s.

# EXPLANATIONS TO IN-CLASS EXAM FOR LECTURE 4

## Passage I (Questions 70-74)

**70. A is the best answer.** The question stem asks for the assumption that fat tissue functions as an Ohmic device, that is, a device that follows Ohm's law, $\Delta V = iR$, where $V$ is potential (and $\Delta V$ is voltage), $i$ is current, and $R$ is resistance. According to Ohm's law, voltage is directly proportional to resistance. Therefore, assuming current remains constant, voltage should increase as resistance increases and decrease as resistance decreases. Choices B and C can be eliminated. According to the passage, "BIA makes use of the fact that electrical conductivity of lean tissue is greater than that of fat." Because fat tissue has a lower conductivity than lean tissue, it can be inferred that resistance increases as the fraction of fat tissue increases. Resistivity, $\rho$, increases as conductivity, $\sigma$ decreases. $\rho = 1/\sigma$ and $R \propto \rho$. As conductivity decreases, resistance increases. Choice D is eliminated and choice A is the best answer.

**71. C is the best answer.** Use the definition of current, $i = Q/\Delta t$. So $\Delta t = Q/i = (20\ \text{C})/(10{,}000\ \text{A}) = (20\ \text{C})/(10{,}000\ \text{C/s}) = 2 \times 10^{-3}$ s.

**72. D is the best answer.** $V = IR$: From the passage we know that the potential difference, voltage, between the ground and the top of the atmosphere is 400,000 V. The current, $10^{-12}$ A/m$^2$, is also given.

$$V = iR$$
$$4 \times 10^5\ \text{V} = (10^{-12}\ \text{A/m}^2) \times R.$$
$$R = 4 \times 10^{17}\ \Omega\ (\text{m}^2)$$

**73. C is the best answer.** This question concerns the rate of energy transfer, or power, $P = iV$. Again the potential difference of the atmosphere is 400,000 V. The current, 1800 A, is given in the question stem.

$$P = iV$$
$$P = (1.8 \times 10^3\ \text{A})(4 \times 10^5\ \text{V}) = 7.2 \times 10^8\ \text{J}$$

**74. C is the best answer.** Current always flows from high potential to low potential, so choices B and D are wrong. During a lightning strike, electrons flow from the cloud to the ground, so current must flow in the opposite direction: from the ground to the cloud.

## Passage II (Questions 75-79)

**75. C is the best answer.** $P = iV = V^2/R = i^2R$. In order to maximize power at the tissue, current in the circuit needs to be maximized. This can be achieved by decreasing the internal resistance and tissue resistance because current and resistance are inversely proportional ($V = iR$), eliminating choices A and B. Decreasing the battery voltage will decrease the total available power to the circuit ($P = iV$), eliminating choice D. Note that increasing the tissue resistance appears to increase the power, $P = i^2R$, but current will be decreased by the same factor due to Ohm's Law, actually reducing the power since current is squared.

76. **C is the best answer.** Rearranging Ohm's Law, $V = iR$, for current yields $i = V/R$. The internal resistor and tissue are in series, so the resistances may be added, making the current equal $V/(R_t+R_i)$. Choice D would be the best answer if the resistors were in parallel.

77. **B is the best answer.** Two identical resistors in parallel will have an equivalent resistance of half of a single resistor. This is demonstrated by $1/R_{parallel} = 1/R + 1/R = 2/R$. Therefore, $R_{parallel} = R/2$. If resistance is halved, then current is doubled.

78. **C is the best answer.** Work is equal to the electric potential energy, $qEd$, where $d$, displacement, is parallel to the lines of force. Any movement perpendicular to the lines of force (equipotential lines) requires no work. Therefore, only the movement in the direction of the lines of force are contributory. In this case, that would be $x \cos(30°)$. The work done then is $qEx \cos(30°)$.

79. **A is the best answer.** The resistance of a wire is given by Equation 1. It is independent of the voltage or current within the circuit, eliminating choices B and C. In order to minimize resistance, the length of the axon should be decreased and the diameter should be increased. This eliminates choice D, leaving choice A as the best answer.

## Passage III (Questions 80-83)

80. **C is the best answer.** The passage states that the total number of vesicles is calculated based on the number of vesicles secreted from the footprint, and the fraction of the membrane that the footprint represents. The ratio of 5 vesicles in footprint to 25 vesicles total should be equal to the ratio of the area of the footprint to the area of whole membrane. The ratio 5/25 simplified is ⅕, and ⅕ is equivalent to 20%. The footprint is stated to be a subset of the membrane, so it is not 100% of the membrane, so choice A is not the best answer. Choices B and D, 50% and 10%, are possible results from misinterpreting the relationship between the footprint vesicle exocytosis and total vesicle exocytosis.

81. **C is the best answer.** The calculation of the total number of vesicles secreted is entirely based on the assumption that the area of the membrane that can be accurately observed, the footprint, is representative of the entire membrane. If this is not the case (if the TIRF-Microscopy somehow disturbs the footprint, for instance) then the results are not applicable to the whole cell. Another cell growth medium for a different adrenal cell type would probably be similar, as many cells need similar resources, especially two cell types within the same organ. Either overestimation or underestimation on all trials would not affect the results as heavily as the footprint being inaccurate would. This is tricky, because when two opposite answers are presented, the best answer is often one of them. However, both choices B and D would still show a correlation between change in capacitance and number of vesicles secreted, and that is the main result.

82. **D is the best answer.** Based on the passage, the chromaffin cell membrane acts as a capacitor, separating the cytoplasmic and extracellular charges. For this reason, laws like the parallel plate capacitor equation, $C = \kappa\varepsilon A/d$, apply to the cell. $\kappa$ is the dielectric constant, $A$ is the area of the plate, and $d$ is the distance between the plates. In this case, $A$ is the surface area of the cell, and $d$ is the width of the membrane. Decreasing $A$ would decrease $C$, as they are directly proportional. Increasing $\kappa$ (choice A) or decreasing $d$ (choice C) would both cause increases in capacitance based on the equation. Lastly, vesicle exocytosis (choice B) has a positive correlation with change in capacitance, meaning secretion would lead to an increase in membrane capacitance.

83. **A is the best answer.** The electric field between the plates of a parallel plate capacitor can be calculated with the equation $E = V/d$. The membrane potential is the potential difference between the two 'plates.' The membrane thickness is the distance between the plates. When the two numbers from the question are plugged in, the equation becomes $E = (70 \times 10^{-3})/(8 \times 10^{-9})$, resulting in choice A. The other answers could result from using the wrong equation and calculating $d/V$, or mistakes in scientific notation and division of powers of 10.

## Passage IV (Questions 84-87)

84. **D is the best answer.** When a magnetic field acts on a charge, the force is perpendicular both to the velocity of the charge and the direction of the field. In this question, the positive charge velocity is in the same direction as the current, so options II and III are true. Next, the only case when the magnitude of the force is zero is when the current is parallel or antiparallel to the magnetic field. This is not the case here, as the two directions are perpendicular. Therefore, option I is also true. The best answer is choice D.

85. **A is the best answer.** Magnetic fields point from the north pole to the south pole around the magnet. Because the body is to the left of the magnet, and the north end is facing up, the magnetic field lines pass from above the person to below. The best answer is choice A, downwards.

86. **D is the best answer.** Magnetic force on a moving charge is governed by the equation: $F = qvB \sin\theta$. When the velocity is parallel to the field, $\sin 0° = 0$. This means no force will be felt by the electron, so nothing is revealed about the field. Option I is unlikely, and choices A and C can be eliminated. When the angle is nonzero, a nonzero force can be found and the magnitude of the field can be determined, since $q$ and $v$ are also known. Options II and III are correct, and choice D is the best answer.

87. **B is the best answer.** The charge is flowing upwards, going from low to high potential with respect to the line, as the potential due to the line decreases with altitude. As a rule, positive charges experience a force that pushes them from high to low potential, and negative charges preferentially move from low to high potential. Choices A and C get this rule wrong, so they can be eliminated. Next, the charge is slowed down because, based on the charge's movement from low to high voltage, the force exerted on the charge by the HVT line is downward. This force opposes the direction of its motion, so the charge is slowed relative to its speed far away from the HVT line. Choice D misstates the effect of force on the charge's motion, so choice B is the best answer.

## Stand-alones

88. **B is the best answer.** Consider each set of changes separately to find which changes the resistance by the largest ratio. $R = \rho L/A$, where R is resistance, $\rho$ is resistivity, L is length, and A is area. Doubling the length and halving resistivity ends up canceling in the resistance equation. The resistance does not change at all. Choice A is unlikely to be the best answer. Quadrupling the radius increases the area by a factor of 16. Doubling the length doubles resistance, but increasing area decreases resistance by a factor of 16, so the resistance is reduced by a factor of 8. This change is substantial, so choice B is a strong answer. If the radius doubles, the area quadruples. If the length also quadruples, these changes cancel, as in choice A. Choice D cuts the resistance to ⅓ of its original value by tripling area. This is less than the change in choice B, so choice B is the best answer.

89. **B is the best answer.** When the capacitor is fully charged, it functions as a break in the circuit. When the switch is closed and the capacitor is fully charged, current flows only from the battery, across resistors A and B, and back to the battery. Because the resistance of resistors in series are additive, $R_{\text{eff}} = 2\Omega + 2\Omega = 4\Omega$. $i$, current across resistors A and B, equals $\Delta V/R = 12\ V/4\Omega = 3\ A$. Since 3 A runs across each resistor, the voltage drop across each resistor, $\Delta V$, equals $iR = (3\ A)(2\ \Omega) = 6\ V$. Because two paths in parallel always have the same voltage drop across them, the voltage drop across the capacitor must also be 6 V. When the switch is closed and the capacitor is fully charged, current across the capacitor is 0 A.

However, the moment the switch is opened, it becomes a break in the circuit, and current instead flows from the capacitor, across resistor A, and back to the capacitor. In this instance, $i = \Delta V/R = (6\ V)/(2\Omega) = 3\ A$.

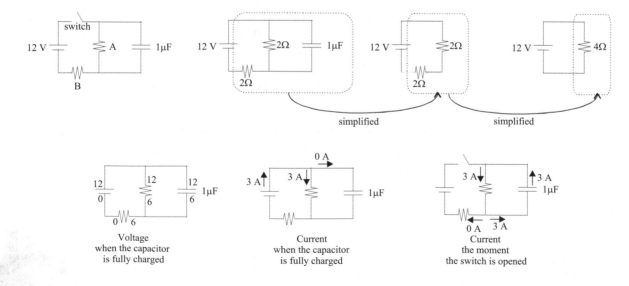

90. **C is the best answer.** Capacitance is directly proportional to area and inversely proportional to distance between plates. Since both A and B are separated by air, the dielectric constant is 1 for both and will not cause a difference between them. The area of A is 12 cm$^2$, while the area of B is 20 cm$^2$. The area over distance for A is 12/5 = 2.4, while this same value for B is 20/4 = 5. 5 is slightly more than double of 2.4, so choice C is a strong answer. The capacitance of capacitor A is not greater than that of capacitor B, and they do not have the same capacitance, so choices A and D can be eliminated. Notice that choice B is the opposite of choice C, and both cannot be selected, making choice C is the best answer.

91. **A is the best answer.** According to Coulomb's law ($F = kqq/r^2$), A and D apply equal and opposite forces on $q$, and so do C and B.

92. **C is the best answer.** The electric force exerted on the particle is equal to the product of field (force per unit charge) and charge. $F = (5 \text{ N/C})(2 \text{ C}) = 10$ N. Because $F = ma$, $a = F/m - (10 \text{ N})/(1 \text{ g}) = (10 \text{ N})/(10^{-3} \text{ kg}) = 10^4 \text{ m/s}^2$. Distance traveled, $x$, equals ½$at^2$. Therefore, $x = ½(10^4 \text{ m/s}^2)(10 \text{ s})^2 = 0.5 \times 10^6 \text{ m} = 5 \times 10^5$ m.

# EXPLANATIONS TO IN-CLASS EXAM FOR LECTURE 5

## Passage I (Questions 93-96)

93. **C is the best answer.** Decibels are not an additive unit, since they reflect a logarithmic scale of sound pressure. 150 dB means that the sound of a gun firing is $10^{15}$ times more powerful than a sound at the threshold of human hearing. Two identical hand guns firing would be twice as powerful as the sound of one hand gun firing because in-phase sound waves are additive. This new sound would be $2 \times 10^{15}$ times more powerful than a sound at the threshold of human hearing.

Expressed in decibels, this new sound is $(10)\log_{10}(2 \times 10^{15}) = 10 \times (15 + \log_{10}(2)) - 10 \times (15 + 0.3) = 153$ dB. Select the best answer, choice C.

Choice A assumes that there is no volume increase whatsoever, despite adding a new and identical sound source. This contradicts physical intuition, and can be eliminated. Choice B assumes that decibels are an additive unit, when they are not. Logarithmic units are rarely additive. If a 1 L solution with a pH of 5 were mixed with a 1L solution with a pH of 4, the new pH of the 2 L would not be 9! The same way pH cannot be added, neither can decibels. Eliminate choice B. Choice D is a distractor that appears to be a plausible calculation, but it is bogus.

94. **A is the best answer.** This is a classic qualitative Doppler effect problem. As the motorcycle approaches the bystander, more sound waves will leave the motorcycle and strike the bystander in a given time interval. This results in a greater frequency and is perceived as a higher pitch. As the motorcycle drives past the bystander, the sound waves leaving the motorcycle become further apart in space, and less sound waves strike the bystander in a given time interval—this results in a lower frequency. Lower frequencies are perceived as lower pitches. Choice A best describes what will happen in this scenario. Choice B is the opposite of the best answer and can be eliminated. So long as the object travels with a non-zero velocity relative to the observer, the sound waves leaving it will either be moving further apart or closer together to each other as they strike the observer. The pitch from the moving object will change throughout the entirety of its motion. Choices C and D imply that sounds which leave the moving object stabilize at a given pitch, but they will not stabilize until the object stops moving. For that reason, choices C and D can be eliminated.

95. **C is the best answer.** Use the equation $L = \frac{n}{2}\lambda$. This equation relates the length of a string to the sound wave it produces. When a string is plucked as is, and not stopped at any point along its length, it will produce the lowest sound possible. This standing wave pattern, which only has 1 antinode, is the 1$^{st}$ harmonic and has $n = 1$.

$$\lambda = \frac{2L}{n}$$
$$\lambda = 2 \times 86.4 = 172.8 \text{ cm}$$

The other answer choices come from using the wrong harmonic in this equation. The first harmonic of a simple vibrating string is the harmonic which has one antinode, and produces the lowest pitch.

96. **D is the best answer.** A period is the time interval that a wave lasts. It can be found either directly from the graph, or by calculating the reciprocal of the frequency. In this case, it is easier to find it directly from the graph. Find a part of the wave structure which repeats itself. It is easiest to start with the jagged portion at the far left. The interval it takes for this structure to reappear is the duration of the wave. It starts at 0 seconds, and reappears at 3 second. This wave has a period of 3 seconds.

Watch out for the distractors here. Choice A is the frequency, not the period, so it can be eliminated. Choice B is the duration of the graph, but is not any value relevant to the period, so it can be eliminated. Choice C is the time period it takes to reach the trough of a wave. This is not what the question asked for. Eliminate it.

## Passage II (Questions 97-101)

97. **D is the best answer.** Based on Figure 1, the change in power each year in undercorrected subjects is -0.43 diopters, so over 5 years, there is a total change of -2.15 diopters. The focal length is the inverse of the power, so the focal length is $1/-2.15 = -0.47$ m, or -47 cm. The negative indicates that this is a diverging lens, meaning choice D is the best answer.

98. **A is the best answer.** Power is inversely related to focal length, as shown by the following equation: $P = 1/f$. The biggest decrease in focal length will cause the greatest increase in lens power. Choices C and D show increases in focal length, which would decrease the power. Choice A decreases the focal length more than choice B does, so choice A is the best answer. Another way to approach this question is that the strongest lens focuses light as close to itself as possible. This is synonymous with a great reduction in focal length.

99. **C is the best answer.** The eye is a converging lens, and for any lens, an image that forms behind the lens is real. Images that form where light is expected to be are real. This convention is based on the function of each optical device. Mirrors reflect light, so images in front of the mirror are real. Because light passes through lenses, real images form behind them. This is the situation describes in the question, so the image is real. This makes choices A and B unlikely. All real images are inverted, so the best answer is choice C. Remember that "I (eye) am positive that the real is inverted."

100. **A is the best answer.** The thin lens equation is the go-to equation when image distances, object distances, and focal length are provided. The focal length is not directly given, but because $f = 1/P$, the focal length can be calculated as 0.05 m or 5 cm. This rules out choices C and D. Next, these values can be plugged into the thin lens equation to calculate image distance: $1/5 = 1/10 + 1/d_i \times d_i = 10$ cm, and this positive value indicates that the image is real and behind the eye. Remember that positive image distances indicate real images, and this results in images behind lenses and in front of mirrors. Choice A is the best answer.

101. **C is the best answer.** Strabismus is a distractor and is neither necessary material nor described in the passage. This makes choices A and B unlikely. As the eye compensates for hyperopia, it becomes closer and closer to normal vision. Then, if it goes any further, it will fully shift to the opposite of hyperopia, which is myopia. In myopia, the eye focuses light in front of the retina. This is choice C.

## Passage III (Questions 102-106)

102. **C is the best answer.** 420 nm is the wavelength of the highest point for all 3 subjects in Figure 1. $v = f\lambda$, so $3 \times 10^8 = f \times 420 \times 10^{-9}$. $f = 3 \times 10^8/(420 \times 10^{-9}) = 7.1 \times 10^{14}$ Hz, choice C. Choice A is the result of directly using the 420 without converting to meters. Choices B and D are the result of incorrectly using 400 nm, one of the overall low points and weakest treatments.

103. **A is the best answer.** It is important to remember that the visual spectrum, colored light, ranges from approximately 400 nm to 700 nm. In order of decreasing wavelength, the order is ROY G BIV. The lowest wavelength is violet at around 400 nm. All other options – including infrared, which has a wavelength higher than red – are farther from the 375 nm wavelength. Choice A is the best answer.

104. **C is the best answer.** Based on Figure 1, there is a clear trend with a peak centered near a wavelength of about 420 nm. Wavelength is inversely proportional to energy, so lower wavelengths of light are associated with greater energy. Choice A can be eliminated because there is a trend relating the energy of light to improvement in optical transmission. The peak falls within the visible spectrum, which is about 400-700 nm. Because the peak is not in the ultraviolet range, choice B can be eliminated. 400 nm is closer to violet than red light, which is centered near 700 nm, so choice C is a stronger answer than choice B.

**105. A is the best answer.** Consider the relationship between TIR and critical angle. The smaller the critical angle gets, the larger range there exists for TIR to occur. This rules out choices B and C. The index increases, which means the critical angle for light going from lens into air decreases. This matches exactly with choice A.

**106. D is the best answer.** Refraction occurs when light bends as a result of changing medium. This does not generally scatter the light, so choice A is a weak answer. TIR is fairly similar to reflection off a plane surface, where light stays parallel. Choice B is unlikely. Diffraction is the bending of light as a result of there being a boundary in the light's path that is close in size to the wavelength of the light. Lastly, diffuse reflection is reflection off a nonplanar surface, leading to scattering of light rays. Choice D is the best answer.

## Passage IV (Questions 107-110)

**107. A is the best answer.** This question sets up a double-slit diffraction scenario. The light used has a wavelength of 0.35 nm based on the information in the passage. Next, the distance between the slits is 1 nm. Double-slit diffraction is governed by the equation: $d \sin \theta = m\lambda$, where $d$ is the distance between the two slits, $\theta$ is the angle between the 0th and $m$th order maxima, $m$ is the order, and $\lambda$ is the wavelength of light used. For all double-slit diffraction, there is a maximum called the 0th order maximum directly across from the middle of the two slits. This makes option I likely to be included in the best answer. Choices B and D can be eliminated. The zeroth order maximum is directly across on the screen, so those light rays are basically traveling horizontally to the screen. For the angle to be perpendicular, the second order maximum would have to be on the side with the slits, which is not the case. All maxima form on the screen across from the light source and the slits. This means option II is unlikely. This eliminates choice C, likely making choice A the best answer. However, confirm by reviewing option III. As double-slit diffraction results in a series of alternating bright bands, or maxima, and dark bands, or minima, both maxima and minima appear. Additionally, there is some destructive interference that occurs between the maximum and the minimum for each order as the light rays from each slit sum. Thus, option III is not a component of the best answer. Choice A is the best answer.

**108. B is the best answer.** Choice A states that the speed of the X-rays in the experiment do not change. This is not accurate, as they pass through several media that are not air, including fluid and membranes within the womb. These substances have refractive indices that are greater than 1, meaning they slow light down from its speed of $3 \times 10^8$ m/s. Choice A can be eliminated. Choice B is a good answer since X-rays do in fact have a higher frequency than visible light. It is important to know the relative position of each type of light within the electromagnetic spectrum. Visible light has a higher wavelength and a lower frequency than X-rays. Choice C is unlikely because it miscalculates the frequency of the X-rays in the question. $v = f\lambda$, so $f = v/\lambda$. The 0.09 Hz is miscalculated by multiplying velocity and wavelength. Choice D is not the best answer because it implies the opposite of choice B, the best answer. X-rays have a lower wavelength and higher frequency than visible light.

**109. D is the best answer.** This question discusses light that passes from one medium to another. Glass has an index of refraction of 1.5, while the passage states that the amnion has an index of 1.4. Refraction happens in accordance with Snell's law, which states that $n_1 \sin\theta_1 = n_2 \sin\theta_2$. The angles are angles from the normal line, and the indices of refraction are inversely related to the angles on either side of the interface. To determine the speed of light in each medium, consider what index of refraction means. $n = c/v$ where $c$ is the speed of light in vacuum and $v$ is the speed of light in the given medium. $n$ is inversely related to the speed of light in that medium. Because light passes from a medium of higher index to one of lower index, light speeds up. This rules out choices A and B. Because the index of refraction decreases from the first medium to the second, the angle to the normal should increase. This means that light is bending away from the normal. Choice C can be eliminated and choice D is the best answer.

**110. D is the best answer.** Amplitude of a light wave is based on quantity, not quality. It is not entirely dependent on the type of light, as in UV versus X-ray, but rather on the quantity and energy carried by the light. Simply knowing the type of light gives nothing away regarding amplitude, so choices A and B are unlikely. Different types of light refract differently at the same interface, so choices C and D are both possible. Higher frequencies of light are refracted more because objects are more likely to absorb higher frequency light. This causes those frequencies of light to travel more slowly and be refracted more. To complete this question, it is important to know the electromagnetic spectrum and how different types of light bend at the same interface. UV rays have lower frequencies than X-rays, so they bend less at an air-glass interface. Choice C is can be eliminated. Choice D is the best answer because X-rays have higher frequency and undergo greater refraction.

**111. A is the best answer.** Pitch and frequency of sound waves are directly related. This means that the frequency of this wave decreases and the period increases, because $T = 1/f$, period increases. This rules out choices C and D. Frequency and wavelength are inversely related, so wavelength also increases. Remember that velocity of a wave is determined by properties of the medium, so velocity must remain constant. Choice A is the only accurate pairing of changes to period and wavelength.

**112. C is the best answer.** The velocity of all waves is a product of their wavelength and frequency, $v = \lambda f$. This question incorporates $L$, the length of the pipe, so it may be helpful to draw an open pipe resonating at its third harmonic. The picture will have three nodes and four antinodes, and the antinodes will occur at the open ends. Count the wavelengths. Inside this pipe of length $L$ there are one and a half wavelengths, so $L = 3/2 \times \lambda$. Now solve for $\lambda$ and incorporate it into the wave velocity equation. $\lambda = 2/3 \times L$, so $v = (2/3 \times L)f = 2Lf/3$. Choice C is the best answer. Choices A and B are algebraic distractors. Choice D would be the answer if the pipe resonated at its first harmonic.

**113. A is the best answer.** The answer choices ask first, whether the speed of the waves increases or decreases and, second, whether they diffract or refract. As the waves move to be perpendicular to the shore, they turn towards the normal. Waves turn towards the normal as their speed decreases. For this reason, waves turn towards the normal as they move from a medium with a lower index of refraction to a medium with a higher index of refraction ($n = c/v$, where $c$ is the speed of light in a vacuum and $v$ is the speed of light in the medium.) Therefore, the speed of the waves decreases, and choices B and D, which state that the speed of the waves increases, can be eliminated.

Waves refract when they transition from one medium to another and diffract when they encounter obstacles or apertures. Movement from deeper water to shallower water constitutes a change in medium. Therefore, the waves refract, and choice C, which states that the waves diffract, can be eliminated.

**114. B is the best answer.** In order to solve this problem, remember the thin lens equation and the sign conventions associated with it. The thin lens equation states that $1/f = 1/d_i + 1/d_o$. The question gives the radius of curvature and image distance and asks for the object distance, $d_o$. As per the thin lens equation. $1/d_o = 1/f - 1/d_i$.

In order to calculate the focal distance, remember that its magnitude is one half of the radius of curvature. Therefore, the magnitude of the focal distance is (8 cm)/2 = 4 cm. Know whether the mirror is converging or diverging to determine the sign of the focal distance. Remember that the focal distances of converging mirrors are positive, whereas the focal distances of diverging mirrors are negative. Because only converging mirrors can form real, inverted images, the mirror must be a converging one. Therefore, $f = +4$ cm.

The question stem indicates that the magnitude of the image distance is 20 cm. Recall that the image distances of real images are positive ("I (Eye) am positive that the real is inverted"), whereas the image distances of virtual images are negative. The question stem states that the image is real, so $d_i = +20$ cm.
Therefore $1/d_o = (1/4)$ cm $- (1/20)$ cm = 0.25 cm $-$ 0.05 cm = 0.20 cm. $d_o = 1/0.20$ cm = 5 cm.

**115. A is the best answer.** Whenever there is a problem that relates object and image heights and distances, consider using the magnification equation. It states that magnification, $m = -(d_i/d_o) = (h_i/h_o)$. The question stem gives the magnitudes of $d_i$, $d_o$, and $h_o$ and asks for the value of $h_i$. The sign conventions used in the thin lens equation similarly apply to the magnification equation. Because the image forms behind the mirror where the light is not, it must be a virtual image. The image distances of virtual images are negative, so $d_i = -5$ cm. Because the object is "where it belongs," that is, in front of the mirror the object distance is positive. Therefore, $d_o = +15$ cm. The object is assumed to be upright so $h_o = +3$ cm.

As per the magnification equation, $h_i = -(d_i/d_o)(h_o) = -((-5 \text{ cm})/(+15 \text{ cm}))(+3 \text{ cm}) = (1/3)(3 \text{ cm}) = 1$ cm

# ANSWERS & EXPLANATIONS

## FOR
## QUESTIONS IN THE LECTURES

# ANSWERS TO THE LECTURE QUESTIONS

| Lecture 1 | Lecture 2 | Lecture 3 | Lecture 4 | Lecture 5 |
|-----------|-----------|-----------|-----------|-----------|
| 1. C | 25. C | 49. D | 73. C | 97. C |
| 2. D | 26. A | 50. C | 74. B | 98. B |
| 3. C | 27. D | 51. C | 75. A | 99. C |
| 4. C | 28. B | 52. D | 76. B | 100. A |
| 5. B | 29. A | 53. C | 77. C | 101. D |
| 6. B | 30. A | 54. B | 78. A | 102. C |
| 7. A | 31. B | 55. A | 79. D | 103. D |
| 8. C | 32. C | 56. D | 80. B | 104. D |
| 9. C | 33. A | 57. D | 81. A | 105. A |
| 10. C | 34. A | 58. B | 82. B | 106. D |
| 11. B | 35. C | 59. D | 83. D | 107. C |
| 12. A | 36. A | 60. D | 84. B | 108. D |
| 13. D | 37. C | 61. C | 85. C | 109. C |
| 14. A | 38. D | 62. B | 86. C | 110. D |
| 15. D | 39. C | 63. C | 87. A | 111. B |
| 16. A | 40. B | 64. C | 88. A | 112. A |
| 17. C | 41. B | 65. A | 89. A | 113. B |
| 18. A | 42. B | 66. D | 90. C | 114. A |
| 19. C | 43. B | 67. B | 91. C | 115. A |
| 20. B | 44. A | 68. C | 92. B | 116. D |
| 21. B | 45. C | 69. A | 93. D | 117. B |
| 22. A | 46. C | 70. D | 94. A | 118. A |
| 23. A | 47. B | 71. D | 95. C | 119. D |
| 24. C | 48. C | 72. A | 96. D | 120. C |

# EXPLANATIONS TO QUESTIONS IN LECTURE 1

1.  **C is the best answer.** The balloon travels in three perpendicular directions. These can be considered three displacement vectors. The total displacement is the vector sum of the three. Notice that two of the vectors have lengths of 8 and 6, which are multiples of 4 and 3, respectively. These are the components of a 3-4-5 triangle, so the displacement from the tail of the 6 km vector to the head of the 8 km vector is 10 km. This 10 km vector is perpendicular to the other 10 km vector. Using the Pythagorean theorem with the two 10 km vectors results in a total displacement of approximately 14 km.

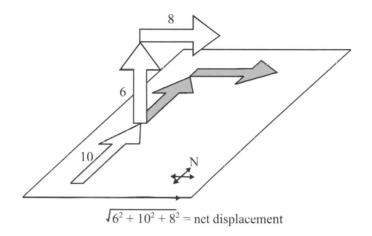

$$\sqrt{6^2 + 10^2 + 8^2} = \text{net displacement}$$

2.  **D is the best answer.** Acceleration is the rate of change of velocity. Since velocity is a vector, it specifies magnitude and direction. Even if speed stays constant, the direction of the Earth's motion is constantly changing. Therefore, the Earth is accelerating; choices B and C are not the best choices. Choice A makes a true statement, but does not answer the question.

3.  **C is the best answer.** Because the start and end points of the trip do not change regardless of the path taken, the displacement for the trip does not change. Displacement is not the same as total distance. By following a curved trajectory, the plane will travel a farther *distance*.

4.  **C is the best answer.** Because the car is slowing down, the velocity and the acceleration are in opposite directions and must have opposite signs. The positive and negative refer to the direction are arbitrary as long as they are opposite. Only choice C meets this requirement.

5.  **B is the best answer.** The direction for a vector must specify a straight path. A straight arrow cannot be drawn to represent a circle; choice B is not a vector. Choice A is a velocity vector, and choices C and D are displacement vectors.

6.  **B is the best answer.** This problem may be tricky because the question only implies a necessary variable. That variable is initial velocity. The initial velocity is zero. The average velocity of any constantly accelerating object that starts with zero velocity is the final velocity divided by two. This is from $v_{avg} = (v + v_0)/2$. In our case, $v_{avg} = (25 \text{ m/s} + 0 \text{ m/s})/2 = 12.5$ m/s. Then the average velocity times time equals displacement, $v_{avg}t = x$. Here, (25 m)/(12.5 m/s) = 2s. Or, by Salty's method:

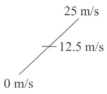

Average velocity times time equals distance: 12.5 m/s × 2 s = 25 m.

7.  **A is the best answer.** This is a plug-and-chug problem using the formula $v = v_0 + at$, which results in 25 m/s = 50 m/s + $a$(2 s). Therefore $a = -12.5$ m/s$^2$. If it had taken only one second to slow from 50 to 25 m/s, the acceleration would have been $-25$ m/s$^2$, but it took two seconds, so acceleration is smaller in magnitude. The answer is negative because the particle is slowing down, eliminating choices C and D.

8.  **C is the best answer.** The deceleration is 5 m/s$^2$, so the velocity is reduced by 5 m/s each second. After 1 second the velocity is 15 m/s; after 2 seconds, 10 m/s; after 3 seconds, 5 m/s; and after four seconds, 0 m/s. So the car stops in 4 seconds. The average velocity for motion with constant acceleration is the midpoint between the starting and ending velocities. The midpoint between 20 m/s and 0 m/s is 10 m/s. The average velocity times the time is 10 m/s × 4 s = 40 m.

    Or via the linear motion equations:

    $$v_f^2 = v_0^2 + 2ax$$

    The car comes to a stop, so $v_f = 0$.

    $$(0 \text{ m/s})^2 = (20 \text{ m/s})^2 + 2(-5\text{m/s}^2)x$$

    $$x = 40 \text{ m}.$$

9.  **C is the best answer.** Velocity is the slope of a displacement vs. time graph. Constant velocity requires only a straight line on a displacement vs. time graph. In choice A, the slope of the displacement vs. time graph is changing at every time point, so the velocity is not constant. To have constant velocity the acceleration must be zero. Any non-zero acceleration, as shown in choices B and D, indicates a changing velocity.

10. **C is the best answer.** To find the total distance traveled, solve for the total area between the line and the $x$-axis (area under the graph). From 0 to 5 seconds, the area under the graph is ½(20 m/s)(5s) = 50m. From 5 to 10 seconds, the area is ½ (20 m/s)(5s) = 50 m. Therefore, the total distance is 50m + 50m = 100m.

11. **B is the best answer.** The graph shows an object moving at a constant velocity and suddenly changing direction. The baseball is the only object that suddenly changes direction. Choice A is not the best answer because it describes gradual acceleration, and does not indicate a change of direction. Choice C represents constantly changing velocity; the speed may stay the same, but the direction constantly changes. Choice D describes a gradual change in velocity.

12. **A is the best answer.** The graph shows that displacement increases with time. Since the displacement graph is a straight line, the particle must be moving at constant velocity, so neither velocity nor acceleration are increasing.

13. **D is the best answer.** In order for the particle to move backwards, the velocity graph would have to dip below zero. Between 10 and 15 seconds, the particle slows down, but does not go backwards. The particle moves at constant acceleration with an average velocity of 5 m/s (10 m/s + 0 m/s / 2) from 0 to 5 seconds, for a displacement of (5 m/s) (5 s) = 25 m. Then from 5 to 10 seconds, it moves at a constant velocity of 10 m/s, so choice C is a true statement; displacement is (10m/s)(5s) = 50 m. For the final 5 seconds, it moves with an average velocity of 5 m/s; displacement is 25 m again. Therefore, the total displacement is 25m + 50m + 25m = 100m and choice A is a true statement. Choice B is a true statement, a constant slope on the velocity vs. time graph represents constant acceleration. Choice D is the only false statement, and is therefore the best answer.

14. **A is the best answer.** Horizontal speed has no effect on the length of time that a projectile is in the air, so the 30 m/s of initial horizontal speed can be ignored while solving this problem. Because the initial vertical speed is zero, use the equation $x = \frac{1}{2}gt^2$ to solve for time with $x = 40$ m and $g = 10$ m/s$^2$. Another quick approach is to reason that the rock will gain 10 m/s of vertical velocity every second. In this case, the rock goes from 0 m/s to 30 m/s of vertical velocity over 3 seconds. This gives an average vertical velocity of 15 m/s over 3 s, meaning it travels about 45 m downward. This is closest to 40 m, making answer choice A the best answer. Choices B, C, and D would all give huge overestimations using this quick method.

15. **D is the best answer.** The downward force is $mg = 100$ N. The first 100 N upward counters this to give a net force of zero and therefore a constant velocity. The question asks for a net force of $mg = 100$ N upwards. This requires adding another 100 N for a total of 200 N. Choice A is not the best answer; without applying an upward force, the net force on the mass will not change. Answer choice B is too small. Choice C will balance the object's weight, give it a net force of 0N, and therefore an acceleration of zero.

16. **A is the best answer.** Since both skydivers are at constant velocity, their acceleration is zero, and by Newton's Second Law they must both experience a net force of zero.

17. **C is the best answer.** The force parallel to the incline is $mg \sin\theta$. Use Newton's Second Law to calculate the acceleration down the incline:

$$F = ma$$
$$mg \sin\theta = ma \rightarrow a = g \sin\theta$$

The sine of $\theta$ is opposite over hypotenuse which is $20/40 = \frac{1}{2}$. Therefore the acceleration is $\frac{1}{2} g$ or $5 \text{ m/s}^2$. Substitute this into the linear motion equation and solve for time:

$$x = v_0 t + \frac{1}{2}at^2$$
$$40 \text{ m} = (0\text{m/s})t + \frac{1}{2}(5\text{m/s}^2)t^2$$
$$16 \text{ s}^2 = t^2 \text{ and } t = 4 \text{ s}.$$

18. **A is the best answer.** The force parallel to the ramp is the force down the incline, $mg \sin\theta$. As the angle of inclination, $\theta$, increases, $\sin\theta$ increases and so does the force parallel to the ramp. The force perpendicular to the ramp is the same as the normal force, $mg \cos\theta$. As $\theta$ increases, $\cos\theta$ decreases, and so does the normal force. Another approach is to imagine the most extreme situation where the angle is 90° and the box is sitting against a wall. In this case the force parallel to the ramp would be large and the box would be in free fall.

19. **C is the best answer.** Since the tires follow Hooke's law, the force changes with the displacement of the tires. The greater the displacement, the greater the force, $F = -k\Delta x$. The greater the force, the greater the acceleration, $F = -k\Delta x = ma$. Recall that the negative sign indicates direction, so compressing a spring results in a force in the opposite direction.

20. **B is the best answer.** The initial displacements of the springs are unknown, but it can be assumed that they were the same for both masses. The spring displaces an extra 1 cm when an additional 5 N of force is added. To solve for the spring constant, these numbers can be substituted into Hooke's law. $k = F/x = (5 \text{ N})/(1 \text{ cm}) = 5 \text{ N/cm}$.

21. **B is the best answer.** Newton's Third Law refers to the same type of force acting between two objects. In this case the Earth exerts a force of gravity on an object and the object exerts an equal and opposite force on the Earth. Choice A is not the best answer because the normal force is not always equal in magnitude to the force of gravity; for example, the normal force on an inclined plane. Choices C and D are not the best answers because the reaction force would be exerted by the object on the Earth. Choice D also restates the same force that is acting in the question stem.

22. **A is the best answer.** These choices each have two parts. To answer the question, decide which particles elute first, and then determine why. As molecules move through the columns, only the smaller molecules will pass into the beads. Larger molecules pass around the beads and will be less subject to friction. Choice A appears to describe that phenomenon, so keep that answer for now. It is true that large particles have greater weight and that they elute first, but choice B ignores the presence of the beads and the effect they may have on elution. Choice B is weaker than choice A because it does not address the cause of varying rates of elution. Even in the absence of the beads, particles with more weight would not necessarily elute first. All objects accelerate downward at the same rate regardless of weight. Smaller particles do not elute first, so choices C and D can be eliminated. Choice A is the best answer.

23. **A is the best answer.** Draw the free body diagram for the box. There are two forces acting on the box: the force of gravity, $10\text{kg} \times 10\text{m/s}^2 = 100\text{N}$ downwards, and the force lifting the box upwards, $F_{lift}$. In order to accelerate the box upward, the upward force must be greater than the downward force. Choice A is the only option greater in magnitude than the downward force of gravity. To solve for the exact value, use kinematics and force equations. The acceleration of the box is $v_f - v_i/\text{time} = 5 \text{ m/s} - 0 \text{ m/s} / 1 \text{ s} = 5 \text{ m/s}^2$. Since the box is accelerating upward, we set the upward and downward forces equal to each other and add $ma$ to the downward force:

$$F_{up} = F_{down} + ma$$
$$F_{lift} = 100\text{N} + (10 \text{ kg})(5 \text{ m/s}^2) = 100\text{N} + 50\text{N} = 150\text{N}$$

24. **C is the best answer.** The force of air resistance is dependent on the surface area, the shape, and the velocity of an object; the object's mass does not affect it. Surface area is directly proportional to air resistance. The feather has a larger surface area and experiences greater resistance, or upward force. This results in smaller net force and smaller acceleration downward; choice B is not the best answer. Acceleration due to gravity, $g$, is the same for all objects near the Earth's surface regardless of mass; choices A and D are not the best answers.

# EXPLANATIONS TO QUESTIONS IN LECTURE 2

25. **C is the best answer.** The net force on the rock climber is equal to the mass of the rock climber multiplied by her net acceleration, or $F_{net} = ma = (50 \text{ kg})(5 \text{ m/s}) = 250 \text{ N}$. The net force is equal to the vector sum of all of the forces acting on the rock climber. The two forces are tension (in the rope) and gravity, and they act in opposite directions, $F_{net} = F_T - F_g$. The force of gravity is $F_g = mg = (50 \text{ kg})(10 \text{ m/s}) = 500 \text{ N}$ directed downwards. The force of the tension in the rope is pointed up towards the helicopter, and is $F_T = F_{net} + F_g = 250 \text{ N} + 500 \text{ N} = 750 \text{ N}$.

26. **A is the best answer.** The question stem indicates that the skydiver has reached a constant, terminal velocity. Therefore, the skydiver experiences no acceleration. Remember that, in the absence of acceleration, there can be no net force. Therefore, the net force is zero and answer choices C and D can be eliminated. To decide between choices A and B, recall that equilibrium can be either static or dynamic. That is, equilibrium requires constant velocity, not necessarily zero velocity. The skydiver is in dynamic equilibrium, meaning that choice A is the best choice.

27. **D is the best answer.** The question stem states that "the object undergoes no acceleration." Therefore, net force acting on the object must be equal to zero. If two forces of equal magnitude pull to the north and east, respectively, then the net force due to these two forces must be directed northeast. In order for net force to equal zero, the third force must be directed opposite to the vector sum of the first two. Therefore, it must be directed in the southwest direction; choice D is the best answer.

28. **B is the best answer.** Acceleration requires net force. The answer is the one that describes movement in the absence of acceleration. In the absence of acceleration, velocity is constant. Choices A and C explicitly describe changes in velocity, so they can be eliminated. Choice D describes the movement of a pendulum at constant frequency. Recall that the force of gravity acts on a pendulum during its motion, causing it to accelerate such that its potential energy is converted into kinetic energy. As the pendulum approaches its equilibrium position, its velocity increases to a maximum before once again decreasing to zero. Since the pendulum experiences acceleration, it must experience a non-zero net force; choice D can be eliminated. A bucket lowered at a constant speed of 2 m/s experiences no acceleration, and, therefore, no net force; choice B is the best answer.

29. **A is the best answer.** Because the pole is not experiencing rotational motion, it can be inferred that the pole is not experiencing any net torque. If the tensions in lines A and B were the only forces acting on the pole, it would experience a net torque equal to the difference between the torque exerted by line B and the torque exerted by line A. $\tau_{net} = (400 \text{ N})(3 \text{ m}) - (200 \text{ N})(4 \text{ m}) = 1200 \text{ N m} - 800 \text{ N} = 400 \text{ N m}$ in the counterclockwise direction. However, because the pole "stands" and does not move, it can be inferred that the ground is exerting a force on the pole such that it experiences a net torque of 0 N m.

30. **A is the best answer.** Torque is the product of distance and force. The distance is measured from the axis of rotation to the point of application of the force (from one end of the wrench to the other in figure A), and is called the lever arm. The lever arm in choice C is shorter than that in the other choices, so choice C is eliminated. The force multiplied is the component of the force that acts in the direction perpendicular to the lever arm. The forces in choices B and D are not directly perpendicular to the lever arm, so the component acting in that direction is less than in choice A. Therefore, the torque is greatest in choice A.

31. **B is the best answer.** The axis of rotation is the point where the rope attached to the board. The hanging weight creates a counter-clockwise torque equal to 3 kg × 0.2 m. The weight of the board creates a clockwise torque at the distance from the rope attachment to the board's center of mass, which is 0.3 m. The net torque is zero, so the clockwise torque equals the counterclockwise torque, so 3 kg × 0.2 m = 0.3 m times the weight of the board. Therefore, the weight of the board is 2 kg.

32. **C is the best answer.** To balance the seesaw, the torque exerted by the 50 kg student should be equal to the force exerted by the 40 kg student. (400 N)(5 m) = (500 N)($x$). So, $x$ = 4, and the student should sit 4 m to the right of the seesaw center.

33. **A is the best answer.** The question stem indicates that, at disintegration, the velocity of the meteor is 0 m/s. The frictional force acts on the meteor such that its velocity decreases from 20 km/s to 0 m/s. That is, the force does work equal to $\Delta KE$ of the meteor. $W = Fd = F(100 \text{ km}) = \frac{1}{2}mv_f^2 - \frac{1}{2}mv_i^2 = \frac{1}{2}(1 \text{ kg})(20 \text{ km/s})^2 - \frac{1}{2}(1 \text{ kg})(0 \text{ km/s})^2$. So, $F(100 \times 10^3 \text{ m}) = \frac{1}{2}(1 \text{ kg})(20 \times 10^3 \text{ m/s})^2$. $F = [\frac{1}{2}(400 \times 10^6 \text{ kg m s}^{-2})]/(100 \times 10^3 \text{ m}) = 2 \times 10^3 \text{ N}$.

34. **A is the best answer.** According to Newton's Law of Universal Gravitation, the force of gravity is equal to $(GmM)/r^2$. Gravitational potential energy is commonly said to equal $F_g r$, or $GmM/r$. And, indeed, when gravitational force is nearly constant, as near the surface of the earth, gravitational potential energy is equal to the product of the force of gravity exerted by the earth on an object and the distance from the center of the earth to the object. However, strictly speaking, gravitational potential energy is equal to the area under the curve of gravitational force as a function of distance, $r$. Therefore, even as the magnitude of gravitational force exerted on a block decreases, its potential energy increases. In non-calculus based physics, is said that as an object moves from the surface of the earth to infinity, the value of its potential energy increases from a large negative number to zero. Recall that each movement against the force of gravity requires work and contributes the potential energy of an object. Blocks at the middle or top of the stack will have greater potential energy than those at the bottom of the stack.

35. **C is the best answer.** A simple technique for solving this and many other physics problems is to consider situations at their extremes." Here the examples are reasonably close in mass. What if object A were one million times as massive as object B? Imagine that object A is a piano and object B is a dime. Now place them on a spring and propel the piano one inch into the air. Will the dime be propelled one million inches into the air at the same time? Of course not. Mass is not proportional to the height. Since all the answers are given as such, only C can be the best answer.

36. **A is the best answer.** This is a proportions problem. Set the initial elastic potential energy equal to the final energy, $\frac{1}{2} kx^2 = mgh$, and notice that the square of the displacement of the spring is proportional to the height, $x^2 \propto$ h. Increasing the height by a factor of four requires increasing the displacement of the spring by a factor of two.

37. **C is the best answer.** Recall that a force directed perpendicularly to a displacement does not do work on the displaced object. Only the horizontal component of the 100 N causes the object to accelerate. The horizontal component of the force is $F\cos\theta = (100\text{N})(\cos(30°)) = 87$ N. To find the acceleration, use $F = ma$. $a = F/m = (87 \text{ N})/(10 \text{ kg}) = 8.7 \text{ m/s}^2$. Then, use $v = v_o + at$ to determine that $v = 17.4$ m/s. $v = 0$ m/s + (8.7 m/s²)(2 s) = 17.4 m/s.

38. **D is the best answer.** The rock starts out with gravitational potential energy. As it falls, it loses gravitational potential energy and gains kinetic energy. As the rubber band stretches, the rock slows to a stop and kinetic energy is transferred to the elastic potential energy of the rubber band; choice D reflects this transfer of energy.

39. **C is the best answer.** Kilowatts are a unit of power, which is a measure of energy transfer per unit time. 1 W = 1 J/s. Therefore, 1 kW = $10^3$ J/s and 1 kilowatt hour = $(10^3 \text{ J/s})(60 \text{ s/min})(60 \text{ min/hour}) = 3600 \times 10^3 \text{ J} = 3,600,000$ J. Choice C is the best answer.

40. **B is the best answer.** $P = \Delta E/t$. In this instance, change in energy is equal to work done and $P = W/t$. Notice that power and work are directly proportional to one another. If $P$ is doubled from 50 kW to 100 kW, then the work done in a given amount of time is also doubled. Therefore, choice A is a true statement and can be eliminated. Notice that, in this case, $W = mgh$, and $W$ is directly proportional to $m$. Choice C states that the new winch can raise an object with a mass of $2m$ in the same amount of time that the old winch can raise a mass of $m$. This makes sense since the new winch can do twice as much work as the old winch in a given amount of time. Choice C is a true statement and can be eliminated. Choice D suggests that, if the old winch can do work $W$ in time $t$, then the new winch can do work $W$ in time $t/2$. Again, this makes sense given that the new winch has twice the power of the old winch. Choice D can also be eliminated. Choice B, however, indicates that the power of the new winch is half that of the old winch. Therefore, it is a false statement. Because the question stem asks which statement is not true, choice B is the best answer.

41. **B is the best answer.** Like all ideal machines, the pulley changes only the force required to do a given amount of work in a given amount of time. It does not change either the amount of work done or the time during which the force acts. Recall that power is change in energy per unit time. In this case, $\Delta E = W = Fd = mgh = (30\text{ kg})(10\text{ m/s}^2)(2\text{ m}) = 600\text{ J}$. Therefore, $P = (600\text{ J})/t = (600\text{ J})/(60\text{ s}) = 10\text{ J/s} = 10\text{ W}$. Choice B is the best answer.

42. **B is the best answer.** Because the points of rotation of eccentric pulleys are off-center, they function as modified levers. Notice that, in position 1, the distance from point A to the point of rotation of the top pulley is greater than the distance from point B to the point of rotation of the bottom pulley. Therefore, in position 1, the lever arm for the tension at point A is greater than that for the tension at point B. If the components of the compound bow are stationary, then the sum of the torques acting on the components must be zero and the tension at point A must be less than the tension at point B. Therefore, choices C and D can be eliminated. In position 2, the distance from point A to the point of rotation of the top pulley is less than the distance from point B to the point of rotation of the bottom pulley. Therefore, if the components of the bow are stationary, then the tension at point A must be greater than the tension at point B. Choice A can be eliminated and choice B is the best answer. On the MCAT®, unless otherwise specified, assume that all pulleys are simple, rather than eccentric pulleys. That is, assume that their points of rotation corresponds with their geometric centers.

43. **B is the best answer.** Both ideal and non-ideal machines reduce the force required to perform a task; choices A and C can be eliminated. An ideal machine is a system in which the work done on the machine by an applied force is transferred, undiminished, into work done by the machine on the surroundings. Therefore, an ideal machine reduces the force required without changing the work required. By contrast, a non-ideal machine is a system in which some of the energy transferred as work done on the machine is lost to friction, deformation, and/or other inefficiencies. Therefore, more work is required than would be in the absence of the machine. Thus a non-ideal machine reduces the force required but increases the work required. Choice D can be eliminated and choice B is the best answer.

44. **A is the best answer.** While riding her bicycle up the hill, the rider applies a force to her bicycle pedals that is translated into the force required to counteract the force of gravity and propel the bike and rider a given distance up the hill. By zigzagging, the rider increases the distance over which she travels. However, she also decreases the incline at which she travels. In doing so, she reduces the force of gravity she must oppose in order to climb the hill. Recall that the force of gravity that accelerates an object down an incline is equal to $mg\sin\theta$. If, by zigzagging, she were to reduce the incline from 30° to 15°, she would decrease the downward force of gravity from $mg\sin30°$ to $mg\sin15°$. Therefore, less force would need to be applied to the pedals; choices B and D, which suggest that equal or greater force would need to be applied, can be eliminated. Because work is path independent, the amount of energy required to ascend the hill would remain equal to $mgh$, where h is the vertical displacement of the rider and her bike. Choice C can be eliminated and choice A is the best answer. Think of each zigzag path as a ramp that decreases the force required to do a given amount of work by increasing the distance over which it is applied.

45. **C is the best answer.** Again, machines decrease the force required to do a given amount of work by increasing the distance over which the force is applied; they do not change the work required. Therefore, $W = Fd = mgh$ and $d = mgh/F$. Because the question stem asks for distance over which the force is applied per meter that the object is raised, assume that $h$, the distance that the object is raised, is equal to 1 m. Therefore, $d = [(30\text{ kg})(10\text{ m/s}^2)(1\text{ m})]/(25\text{ N}) = (300\text{ J})/(25\text{ N}) = 3((100\text{ J})/(25\text{ N})) = 3(4\text{ m}) = 12\text{ m}$.

46. **C is the best answer.** In the case of levers, $F_1 l_1 = F_2 l_2$. The radii of the two pulleys act as the lever arms for the system, so increasing the diameter of pulley A will decrease the force required to pull rope A. Changing the lengths of the ropes will have no effect on the machine.

47. **B is the best answer.** The formula relating work done on and by machines is $F_{input}d_{input} = F_{output}d_{output}$, where $d$ is the distance over which the input and output forces act. If mechanical advantage is equal to (output force)/(input force), then it must also be equal to (input distance)/(output distance).

48. **C is the best answer.** For an inclined plane, $Fd = mgh$, so $(50\ \text{N})d = (1000\ \text{N})(1\ \text{m})$ and $d = 20\ \text{m}$.

## EXPLANATIONS TO QUESTIONS IN LECTURE 3

49. **D is the best answer.** Atmospheric pressure supports the column of fluid. The pressure at the bottom of the column must be equal to atmospheric pressure because atmospheric pressure is forcing the liquid into the column. If the pressure at the bottom of the column were not atmospheric, there would be a pressure differential and more liquid would flow into the column. The pressure is equal to $\rho gh$. If $\rho$ is decreased by a factor of 13.6, the height must be increased by the same factor. Notice that, given the choices, there is no need to do the math. Every other answer is less than 10 times as tall. Answer choice B can be eliminated immediately because the height of the column depends on the density of the fluid. Changing the density must therefore change the height. Likewise, answer choice A is incorrect because a less dense fluid will be pushed up the barometer higher than a more dense fluid.

50. **C is the best answer.** The only difference between the two discs is what they are covering. Ignore everything else. The first disc has atmospheric pressure pushing upward; the second disc does not. This is the difference between the forces necessary to lift them.

51. **C is the best answer.** The density of the brick is $1400\ \text{kg/m}^3$. The density of water is $1000\ \text{kg/m}^3$. In order to float, the brick must displace an amount of water equal to its weight. The density of the brick is 1.4 times that of water, so an amount of water 1.4 times the volume of the brick must be displaced. One half of the Styrofoam block is required to displace this water, so the volume of the water displaced is equal to half the volume of the Styrofoam and is also equal to 1.4 times the volume of the brick. Therefore, $0.5\ V_{Styrofoam} = 1.4\ V_{brick}$. Multiplying both sides by 2 results in $V_{Styrofoam} = 2.8\ V_{brick}$.

52. **D is the best answer.** The balloon rises because the buoyant force is greater than the weight. When these forces are equal, the balloon will stop rising. In other words, the balloon stops rising when $\rho_{air}Vg = \rho_{helium}Vg$. The volumes are always equal because the balloon is always fully submerged in the atmosphere. Another way to look at this problem is to see that the balloon is fully submerged in the fluid atmosphere. For the balloon to float, not rise or sink, use the floating equation: Fraction submerged = $\rho_{object}/\rho_{fluid}$. The entire balloon is submerged, so the fraction submerged is equal to one. Choice A is not the best answer because the temperature of the air and helium can be equal while their densities are not equal. Choice B is not the best choice because the mass of the air outside the balloon is undefined. Choice C can be eliminated because the volumes of the helium and the displaced air are equal at all times (as is true for any submerged object). Choice D is the most reasonable interpretation of the phenomenon in the question stem.

53. **C is the best answer.** Without the floating equation, the quickest way to do this problem is to take the example to the extremes. If the specific gravity of the toy were 0.999, the toy would be almost the same weight as water and, of course, only a very small part would float above the water; $(0.001/1) \times (100\%) = 0.1\%$. The specific gravity must be how much is under the water. Now look at the example in the question. 45% must be under water, so 55% must be above. To solve this problem mathematically, set the buoyant force equal to the weight of the toy,

$$\rho_{water}V_{\text{submerged fraction of the toy}}g = \rho_{toy}V_{toy}g.$$

Rearrange and end up with the ratio:

$$V_{\text{submerged fraction of the toy}}/V_{toy} = \rho_{toy}/\rho_{water}$$

The right side of this equation is the specific gravity, and the left side is the fraction of the toy submerged. To find the fraction of the toy above water, subtract the submerged fraction from 1.

54. **B is the best answer.** The pressure on both sides is the same. Force is equal to the product of pressure and area, so the force will be larger on the side with the greater area.

55. **A is the best answer.** The formula for fluid pressure is $P = \rho gh$. If the density is changed, the pressure will change by the same ratio. Since the specific gravity of ethyl alcohol is 0.8, the pressure will decrease by a factor of 0.8. 5000 Pa × 0.8 = 4000 Pa. Replacing the fluid with a less dense or lighter fluid must lower the pressure, so answer choice D can be eliminated. By remembering that pressure depends on density, answer choice C can be eliminated as well.

56. **D is the best answer.** Pressure depends only on depth and density ($P = \rho gh$), not on the shape of the container.

57. **D is the best answer.** This is a combination of the continuity equation and Bernoulli's equation. The cross sectional area $A$ is increased by a factor of 4 when $r$ is doubled: $A = \pi r^2$. Since area changes and $Q$ remains constant, the velocity decreases by a factor of 4, $Q = Av$. From Bernoulli's equation, we see $K = P + \frac{1}{2} \rho v^2$. When the velocity decreases by a factor of 4, the $\frac{1}{2} \rho v^2$ term decreases by a factor of 16; however, the actual amount is unknown, so the amount that P increases cannot be calculated ($P$ and $\frac{1}{2} \rho v^2$ are added, not multiplied, so the absolute values must be known).

58. **B is the best answer.** The fluid at A and D are exposed to the atmosphere, so they must be at atmospheric pressure. The fluid at C is at the same level and velocity as the fluid exposed to the atmosphere and just leaving the pipe near point D, so the fluid at C must also be at atmospheric pressure. The fluid at B is at atmospheric pressure plus the weight of the fluid above it. The pressure at B is 1 atm + $\rho gh$.

59. **D is the best answer.** The equation for velocity of fluid from a spigot is derived from Bernoulli's equation. The relationship is $2gh = v^2$, and $h$ is proportional to $v^2$, which is reflected in the graph in answer choice D.

60. **D is the best answer.** This is a two-part question, so first find the relationship of the velocities. The flow continuity equation states that larger areas correspond with lower velocities. The velocity at point 1 must be less than the velocity at point 2, ruling out choices A and B. From Bernoulli's equation, comparing two points at the same height, a larger flow velocity is offset by a lower static pressure to maintain constant mechanical energy. At point 1, there is slower velocity but higher static pressure compared to point 2. Choice D is the best answer.

61. **C is the best answer.** The question stem gives a key clue in the beginning, which is the narrow nature of the dispensers. In classic Bernoulli's equation tanks, pressure terms can be ignored because atmospheric pressure is the same on all sides of the tank. The velocity of the fluid at the top of the tank can also be assumed to be zero because its cross-sectional area is so much greater than the dispenser. The dispenser is usually at the lowest point of the tank, so it can be assumed to have zero height, and that term can be eliminated. Solving the equation for velocity at the dispenser gives $v = \sqrt{2gh}$. The only thing that affects rate of dispensing water is height, and these two characteristics increase and decrease together. The best answer is the one with the highest height. Information about the diameter of the surface is extraneous, and choice C is the best answer.

62. **B is the best answer.** Use Bernoulli's equation to solve this problem:

$$P_{arm} + \tfrac{1}{2}\rho v_{arm}^2 + \rho gh_{arm} = P_{leg} + \tfrac{1}{2}\rho v_{leg}^2 + \rho gh_{leg}$$

Since the surface area of the two vessels is equal the velocity of the blood will be equal as well ($Q = Av$). The 'velocity head' term, $\frac{1}{2}\rho v^2$, will be the same in the arm and the leg leaving,

$$P_{arm} + \rho gh_{arm} = P_{leg} + \rho gh_{leg}$$

The arm is higher than the leg, so the 'elevation head' term will be greater, $\rho gh_{arm} > \rho gh_{leg}$. To balance this, the pressure term $P_{arm}$ will be less than that of the leg $P_{leg}$. Blood pressure is slightly higher (<10 mmHg) in the legs than in the arms if the person is standing. Another approach to this problem is to think of the body as a column of blood. When standing, the blood in the legs must support all the blood above it, therefore the pressure will be higher.

63. **C is the best answer.** Recall that work, $W$, is equal to $Fd$, where $F$ is a force and d is the distance over which it is applied. Recall also that pressure, $P$, is equal to $F/A$. Therefore, the equation for work can be rewritten as $W = (F/A)(A)(d) = PV$. Because work is the area under the graph of pressure as a function of volume, $W = P\Delta V$ at constant pressure and $\Delta PV$ at constant volume. In this case, pressure changes by $10^{-3}$ atm and volume remains constant at 1 cm$^3$. Note that it is the pressure gradient that drives blood through the vessel. To calculate work done in joules, convert atm to Pa and cm$^3$ to m$^3$. Because 1 atm is approximately equal to $10^5$ Pa, $10^{-3}$ atm is approximately equal to $10^2$ Pa. Because 1 cm = $10^{-2}$ m, 1 cm$^3$ = $10^{-6}$ m$^3$. Therefore, W = $(10^2$ Pa$)(10^{-6}$ m$^3) = 10^{-4}$ J.

64. **C is the best answer.** Recall that $Q = A_1v_1 = A_2v_2$. Therefore, $v_2 = v_1 \ A_1/A_2 = [v_1 \ (\pi r_1^2)]/(\pi r_2^2) = [v_1 \ (r_1^2)]/(r_2^2)$. If the radius is decreased by 40%, then $r_2 = 0.60r_1$. Therefore, $v_2 = [(0.5 \text{ m/s})(r_1)^2]/(0.6r_1)^2 = (0.5 \text{ m/s})/(0.36) = 1.4 \text{ m/s}$. Notice, however, that you did not need to calculate an exact value to select the best answer. You simply needed to know that the exact value was somewhere between 1 and 2.

65. **A is the best answer.** Since the water is rising, it is *somehow* pulled up against gravity. The answer choices allow for only one explanation: the water must be grabbing the walls (the soil) around it and pulling itself upward. This 'grabbing' is an intermolecular bond between water and the soil. If it were weaker than the bond between water and itself, then the water would be pulled back down onto itself.

66. **D is the best answer.** Because $\Delta P=QR$, an increase in pressure difference ($\Delta P$) or a decrease in resistance ($R$) increases flow ($Q$). Increasing the pipe radius decreases the resistance to flow. Increasing pipe length increases resistance to flow and decreases flow rate.

67. **B is the best answer.** The drop with stronger intermolecular forces will have greater surface tension, which will cause it to bead up more. Drop A is beaded up more in this example so it will have stronger intermolecular forces, eliminating answer choices C and D.

68. **C is the best answer.** Do not be confused by the complicated question stem. The pulmonary artery is bringing blood from the body to the lungs where it will pick up oxygen and give off $CO_2$. The $CO_2$ will diffuse from an area of higher pressure to an area of lower pressure. If the $CO_2$ is moving from the pulmonary artery to the alveoli, then the partial pressure of $CO_2$ must be higher in the pulmonary artery than in the alveoli. Therefore, choice A can be eliminated and choice C is the best answer. If the pressure were the same in the alveoli and the pulmonary artery, no $CO_2$ exchange would occur; choice B is not the best answer.

69. **A is the best answer.** The aneurysm has a greater radius than the normal blood vessel. Therefore, it will also have a greater cross-sectional area ($A = \pi r^2$). The blood in the aneurysm will have a lesser velocity due to this greater cross-sectional area ($Q = Av$), eliminating answer choices C and D. By Bernoulli's equation (assume constant height), if the velocity is decreased, the 'velocity head' will also be decreased, and the pressure term will increase. Therefore, the pressure is higher in the aneurysm.

70. **D is the best answer.** Remember that flow rate, $Q = \Delta P/R$, where $P$ is pressure and $R$ is resistance. Since all tubes would be subject to the same driving pressure, the tube with the least resistance would experience the greatest flow rate. Resistance, $R$, is directly proportional to $L$, and indirectly proportional to $r^4$. Therefore, the tube with the lowest $L$ to $r^4$ ratio would experience the greatest flow rate. Choices A, B, C, and D are associated with ratios of 4, 2, 1/4, and 1/8, respectively. Choice D is the best choice. The fluid in the tube with a length of 2 cm and a cross-sectional radius of 2 cm would flow at the greatest rate.

71. **D is the best answer.** Remember Poiseuille's law,

$$Q = \frac{\Delta P\left(\pi r^4\right)}{8\eta L}$$

The volume flow rate is directly proportional to $r^4$. Therefore, doubling the radius will increase $Q$ by a factor of 16. Flow rate is inversely related to viscosity and length, so doubling these parameters will actually decrease the flow rate. Doubling the difference in pressure between the two points will increase the volume flow rate, but only by a factor of 2.

72. **A is the best answer.** In order for white blood cells to roll along the wall of the vessel, they must move slower at the wall than they do at the center of the vessel. In an ideal fluid we assume that the velocity of the fluid through a cross-section is constant. Choices B and C are not the best answers because the velocity cannot be different at different points in the same cross-section of an ideal fluid.

# EXPLANATIONS TO QUESTIONS IN LECTURE 4

73. **C is the best answer.** This is a units question. 100 N/C is equivalent to 100 V/m. The charged particle experiences 100 N of force. This is a measure of the strength of the electric field: 100 N/C. Another way to say 100 N/C is 100 V/m. The plates are one meter apart, so they must have a 100 volt potential difference.

74. **B is the best answer.** The forces are conservative, so if the picture is turned 90°, the situation will be more analogous to a gravitational field in which objects possess some gravitational potential energy $mgh$; the vertical distance $h$, and not the horizontal distance, is what matters. Likewise, in the question, the total length of the path does not matter because some of the movement is not against the electric field. Work is done only when the particle moves in the 10 cm direction against the electric field. The work required is the force times the distance parallel to the field or $Eqd$. W = (10 N/C)(8 C)(0.10m) = 8 J.

75. **A is the best answer.** The force is given by Coulomb's law, $F = k\, qq/r^2$. The electrostatic force changes with the square of the distance between the centers of charge. In this case, $3^2 = 9$. The force and the distance are inversely related. If the distance is increased the force must decrease, so choices C and D can be eliminated.

76. **B is the best answer.** This problem is about energy. The system has a total electric potential energy of $U = kqq/r$. Remember, the forces acting are conservative so mechanical energy is conserved. As the first particle is propelled away from the second, electric potential energy is converted to kinetic energy. When the first particle moves 25 cm, it has doubled its distance of separation. From $U = kqq/r$, the first particle has lost half of its potential energy to kinetic energy when $r$ is doubled.

   When the first particle is infinitely far from the second particle, it will have lost the rest of the electric potential energy to kinetic. In other words, it will have twice the kinetic that it had at 25 cm. From $K.E. = \frac{1}{2}\,mv^2$, if $K.E.$ is multiplied by 2, the velocity must be multiplied by the square root of 2, or approximately 1.4. 1.4 times 10 equals 14 m/s.

77. **C is the best answer.** The electric field above an infinitely large electric plate remains constant with distance. This can be visualized by imagining the electric field lines. The lines are perpendicular to the plate and have nowhere to spread. By bending in one direction or another, they would increase their distance from one line, only to decrease their distance from another line. Since the lines would remain at an equal distance from one another, the electric field would remain constant. If the electric field is constant, the force must also be constant as given by $F=Eq$.

78. **A is the best answer.** The field lines are directed away from both charges, so by definition they are both positively charged. If they were both negative, as in answer choice B, the field lines would be directed towards each charge. If they had opposite signs the field lines would go from one charge, the positive charge, to the other, the negative charge.

79. **D is the best answer.** An $E$ field describes the force that a charge experiences due to the presence of a source charge. It is given by the equation $E = KQ_{source}/r^2 = F/q_{charge}$. To solve this problem, pretend that the middle expression in this equation gives the initial strength of the $E$ field. After moving the cell, the $E$ field's new strength will be: $E = KQ_{source}/4r^2$ since $(2r)^2 = 4r^2$. In other words, doubling the distance $r$ between the cell and the $E$ field source will lead to four-fold decrease in the magnitude of the E field strength. This equation must remain equivalent to the force the charge experiences given by $E = F/q_{charge}$. Since $F = ma$, $E = m_{charge}a/q_{charge}$. Since $q_{charge}$ and $m_{charge}$ are constant, in order for these two equations to remain equal, the magnitude of the charged particles' acceleration must also decrease by a factor of four. Choice D is the best answer. The electric field force and, by extension, the acceleration of the charged particles within the cell, will decrease with increasing distance from the field source. Choices A and C describe the opposite and can be eliminated. Since $r$ has an exponential term, E-field strength cannot be inversely proportional to the distance from the source charge. Choice B can be eliminated.

80. **B is the best answer.** Electrostatic forces are conservative, so the work done by a force against them is conserved in potential energy. A volt is a joule/coulomb, so voltage can be determined by dividing work by charge. (90 J)/(10 C) = 9 J/C = 9 V. Choice B is the best answer.

81. **A is the best answer.** The electric field inside a capacitor is constant. By definition, a dipole has equal but opposite charges on either end. The force on each end of the dipole is $Eq$ and in opposite directions. The net force is zero.

82. **B is the best answer.** The effective resistance is 3 Ω. First, find the effective resistance of the two resistors in parallel, resistor A and resistor B.

$$1/2\ \Omega + 1/2\ \Omega = 1/R_{eff}$$

$$R_{eff} = 1\ \Omega$$

Then, attribute this resistance to a single resistor in series with resistor C and find the overall effective resistance.

$$1\ \Omega + 2\ \Omega = 3\ \Omega$$

The voltage divided by the effective resistance gives 4 amps coming out of the battery. The 4 amps split evenly at the node before A and B, 2 amps through each resistor.

83. **D is the best answer.** Increasing the voltage across the plates would increase the amount of charge on the capacitor but not the capacitance of the capacitor. Capacitance is defined by $C = Q/V$. All the other choices—distance between the plates, area of the plates, and the dielectric constant—change the capacitance.

84. **B is the best answer.** Remember the rules for circuit components in parallel. Each branch of a group of parallel wires will experience the same voltage drop. This means that choices C and D can be eliminated. Next, if the voltage is the same, then the current must be different. This is based on Ohm's Law: $V = iR$. If V is constant and R varies, then i must also vary. Choice B is the best answer.

85. **C is the best answer.** This is Kirchhoff's first rule: current flowing into a node must also flow out. Since the resistors have equal resistances, the current is the same in both parallel branches: 4 amps flow into the node from both branches. Therefore 8 amps must flow out of the node.

86. **C is the best answer.** Based on circuit analysis, the net drop in resistance across the four resistors is 10 V. Because all four resistors are in series and have the same value, then they have an equivalent voltage drop adding up to 10 V. This means the first resistor has a voltage drop of 10/4 = 2.5 V. Choice C is the best answer. Choice A states that the resistor has a voltage drop of 0 V, which is never the case while the battery is connected. Next, choice B is a weak answer since the total voltage drop would be 4 V with 4 equivalent resistors each with a 1 V drop. Choice D would be true if all resistors were in parallel, but not in series.

87. **A is the best answer.** The total charge that can be stored across a capacitor, like the cell, can be calculated by $Q = CV$. Next, the surface area of the spherical cell = $4\pi r^2 = 4\pi \times (10^{-3}\ cm)^2 = 1.26 \times 10^{-5}\ cm^2$. To find the total capacitance of the cell membrane, multiply capacitance/area by area: $C = 1.26 \times 10^{-5} \times 10^{-6} = 1.26 \times 10^{-11}\ F$. The total charge can be found by multiplying capacitance by the voltage given in the text: $Q = CV = 1.26 \times 10^{-11} \times 70 \times 10^{-3} = 8.82 \times 10^{-13}\ C$. Divide the total charge required by the charge per ion (for potassium, a singly charged ion): $8.82 \times 10^{-13}\ / (1.6 \times 10^{-19}) = 5.5 \times 10^{6}$ ions. Choice A is the best answer.

88. **A is the best answer.** Use any of the equations for energy stored in a capacitor.

$$U = \tfrac{1}{2}\ CV^2 = \tfrac{1}{2}\ (1\mu F/cm^2)(70mV)^2 = \tfrac{1}{2}\ (10^{-6}\ F/cm^2)(7 \times 10^{-2}\ V)^2 = 2.5 \times 10^{-9}\ J/cm^2$$

89. **A is the best answer.** The question stem asks which of the three conditions, if true, would necessarily result in a greater force on $-q_1$ than on $+q_2$. The movement of charge in an electric field will result in a force according to the equation $F = qvB \sin\theta$. Notice that it does not matter that the ions carry opposite charges because this question is only asking about the magnitude of force in the q term. Opposite charges will reverse the direction of force on moving charges. In option I, if $-q_1$ moved faster than $+q_2$, that would not guarantee a greater force on that charge. It could move in the direction of the magnetic field, and the sine term in the force equation would bring the magnitude of force to zero. Option I is insufficient, so choices C and D can be eliminated. Options II and III express opposite conditions, and given that choices A and B remain, only one of them must be true. Notice that, in the force equation, θ refers to the angle between the charge's velocity and the field. In the diagram, the θ describes the angle between the charges' velocities and the normal. The smaller $\theta_1$ is in the diagram, the greater the θ in the force equation for charge $-q_1$. Notice that as the θ in the force equation increases from 0° to 90°, the sine term must also increase. That makes option II true, eliminating choice B, and leaving choice A as the best answer.

90. **C is the best answer.** Choice A comes from $V = iR$, with $I$ replaced by C/sec. Choice B comes from $P = i^2R$. Choice D comes from $P = V^2/R$.

91. **C is the best answer.** The maximum voltage is given by $V_{max} = \sqrt{2}\ V_{rms}$

$$V_{max} = \sqrt{2}\ V_{rms} = \sqrt{2}(120\text{V}) = (1.4)(120\text{V}) = 168\text{V}\ \text{which rounds to 170V.}$$

92. **B is the best answer.** Remember to use the units. The flow of $Na^+$ ions per meter of axon per second is $5.5 \times 10^{11}$. The flow of $Na^+$ ions in one centimeter of axon is:

$$(5.5 \times 10^{11}\ Na^+\ \text{ions/ meter})(1\ \text{meter}/10^2\ \text{cm}) = 5.5 \times 10^9\ Na^+\ \text{ions/cm/sec}$$

Each $Na^+$ ion has a charge equal to the elementary charge, the charge of one proton. The total charge flowing across in one second is:

$$(5.5 \times 10^9\ Na^+\ \text{ions/sec})(1.6 \times 10^{-19}\ \text{C/}\ Na^+\ \text{ion}) = 8.8 \times 10^{-10}\ \text{C/s}$$

93. **D is the best answer.** Use Ohm's Law. $i = V/R$. The resistance of one cm of membrane in a neuron with multiple sclerosis is $0.7 \times (250\ \text{M}\Omega) = 175\ \text{M}\Omega$. Do not forget to convert to SI units.

$$i = V/R = 7 \times 10^{-2}\ V\ /\ 1.75 \times 10^8\ \Omega = 4 \times 10^{-10}\ A = 4 \times 10^{-4}\ \mu A$$

94. **A is the best answer.** The force on a charge moving in a magnetic field due to a magnetic field is $F = qvB \sin\theta$. Since the hydrogen ion is at rest its velocity is 0 m/s and it will not experience a force due to the magnetic field of the MRI.

95. **C is the best answer.** Faraday's law states that a changing magnetic field will induce an electromotive force (EMF) in a wire. The goal of this problem is to figure out which of the options given produce a changing magnetic field with respect to the wire. Changing the magnitude of the magnetic field, option I, certainly does this. Eliminate answer choice D since it does not include option I. Moving the wire loop out of the page moves it along the same magnetic field lines. This does not change anything about the magnetic field felt by the wire and will not induce an electromotive force. Rotating the wire will change the magnetic field lines around the wire and induce an EMF.

96. **D is the best answer.** All of these will change the magnitude of the force on the proteins and therefore, by Newton's second law, change how fast they accelerate from rest. The electric field, $kq/r^2$, and the charge are directly related to the electric force felt by the protein. Increasing the size of the pores will reduce the 'drag' caused by the gel and allow the proteins to move faster.

## EXPLANATIONS TO QUESTIONS IN LECTURE 5

97. **C is the best answer.** The frequency of the waves being sent is equal to the frequency of the waves being received. Every second, one wave is sent. In 10 seconds, 10 waves are sent. The other information is extraneous.

98. **B is the best answer.** Intensity level is related to intensity by a logarithmic scale: intensity level equals ten times the log of intensity. Therefore, an increase of 20 dB equals a 100-fold increase in intensity. Also, intensity is proportional to the square of amplitude, so a 100-fold increase in intensity is due to a 10-fold increase in amplitude.

99. **C is the best answer.** Frequency is inversely related to both wavelength and period; options I and II are true. There is no relationship between amplitude and frequency; option III is false. Therefore, choice C is the best answer.

100. **A is the best answer.** Decibel level, or intensity level, is related to intensity by a logarithmic scale. If the intensity is doubled, decibel level increases by about 3 dB, making choice A the best answer. Remember that an increase in intensity level of 10 dB means that intensity has increased by a factor of 10.

101. **D is the best answer.** The amplitude of a standing wave is constant; choice D is false and is therefore the best answer. Nodes are the spots that will not move. Resonating strings form standing waves at wavelengths corresponding to their harmonics.

102. **C is the best answer.** This question appears to require a nuanced understanding of acoustics, but fundamental knowledge of wave properties can allow that knowledge to be circumvented. Do not spend too much time mulling answer choices that are tricky – move on and evaluate them all. One might stand out. The presence of two nodes indicates that this pipe resonates at its second resonant frequency. It is possible that this pipe resonates at both the fundamental and third frequencies, so choices A and B are true and can be eliminated. Sound travels by longitudinal rather than transverse waves. Consider the motion of air molecules as sound travels. They compress and expand to propagate sound, which is the essence of longitudinal waves. This makes choice C false and a strong answer. Choice D could be tricky. Consider the range of human voices that are possible. How are humans able to distinguish voices from one another? Each voice contains a range of frequencies that mix to create a unique timbre. Instruments and tracheas often resonate at more than one frequency simultaneously, so choice D is true and can be eliminated. Even if that information were not known, knowing the distinction between longitudinal and transverse waves would allow for selection of choice C as the best answer.

103. **D is the best answer.** The frequency will only increase when the distance between the source and observer is decreasing, as is the case in choice D. Choice B is the opposite situation. Wind has no effect on the velocity of the source and the observer, and does not affect the observed frequency. Objects moving at the same velocity do not get closer together.

104. **D is the best answer.** The velocity is a function of the properties of the string and is not affected by the force of the hammer. The wavelength of a standing wave is determined by the length of the string. The frequency depends on the wavelength and velocity of the wave, and is therefore also constant. If you hit the same piano key with increasing force, you will play the same note, you will just play it louder (larger amplitude).

105. **A is the best answer.** The ray will turn toward the normal as it enters the glass and away from the normal as it exits the glass, as shown in the figure.

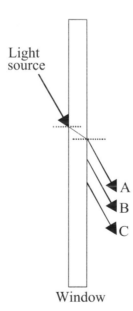

106. **D is the best answer.** Of the given choices, blue light has the highest frequency. If the bees perceive higher frequencies, perhaps they are more likely to be attracted to blue. The mnemonic ROY G BIV will help you remember the order of frequencies of different colored light.

**107. C is the best answer.** Attenuation is the decrease in intensity of a wave as it propagates through a medium. A major cause of attenuation is reflection as the wave passes through the medium. This is a particularly prominent issue in denser media. Choice C is the best answer. Choice A is inaccurate because refraction is the bending of waves when they pass through to a new medium. Diffraction is the bending of waves around a corner or slit, which does not decrease the intensity of the wave. Choice B can be eliminated.

**108. D is the best answer.** The observation that light is reflected could fit either the wave or particle theory of light. However, the other choices all provide support for the wave theory of light. Therefore choice D is the best answer.

**109. C is the best answer.** As shown in the figure below, changing the location of the glass will not alter the path of the light ray after it passes through the glass. However, changing the thickness of the glass will change the path of the light ray. Thicker glass will cause the ray to travel further along a path turned towards the normal. This could result in the ray of light passing through point A.

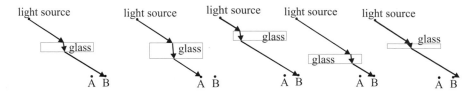

**110. D is the best answer.** As the dimmer is turned down, less energy is provided to the light bulb filament until, finally, the only visible light produced is red. A similar effect is seen at night in a dying campfire, when only red coals remain. Remember that light of all colors moves through a given medium at the same speed, therefore, choices A and B can be eliminated.

**111. B is the best answer.** The speed of light through glass can be found by using the index of refraction.

$$n = \frac{c}{v}, \text{ or } v = \frac{c}{n} = \frac{(3 \times 10^8)}{1.5} = (2 \times 10^8)$$

Once the speed of light in glass is known, use $x = vt$. Rearrange the equation to solve for $t$ and change cm into meters.

$$t = \frac{(1 \times 10^{-2})}{(2 \times 10^8)} = 0.5 \times 10^{-10} = 5 \times 10^{-11}$$

**112. A is the best answer.** A light wave bending as it enters a new medium is refraction, not diffraction. Diffraction occurs when waves bend around corners. Although the other answer choices may have been difficult to identify as diffraction, you should have been able to identify that choice A was an example of refraction.

**113. B is the best answer.** Remember that lenses do what they do because they refract, or bend, light. A magnifying lens creates images of objects that are larger than the objects, themselves, by bending the light from those objects. The extent to which light bends as it passes from one medium to another depends on the extent to which the speed of light changes as it passes between those media. Recall that refractive index, $n$, of medium is a measure of the extent to which the speed of light changes. $n = c/v$, where $c$ is the speed of light in a vacuum and $v$ is the speed of light in the medium. According to Snell's law, $n_1 \sin\theta_1 = n_2 \sin\theta_2$. Therefore, as $n_2$ approaches $n_1$, $\theta_2$ approaches $\theta_1$. In other words, light bends less when it passes between media with similar indices of refraction than it does when it passes between media with dissimilar indices of refraction. The indices of refraction of air, water and glass are approximately 1, 1.3 and 1.5, respectively. As the magnifying lens ($n = 1.5$) moves from air ($n = 1$) to water ($n = 1.3$), its index of refraction approaches the index of refraction of the surrounding medium. Therefore, the light is bent less and magnified less. Choice B is the best answer choice.

**114. A is the best answer.** A virtual image is formed by an apparent, rather than an actual convergence of light. Projecting an image onto a screen requires projection of the light that forms that image. Because no actual light rays form a virtual image, virtual images cannot be projected onto screens. Therefore, I is a false statement, and choices B, C and D can be eliminated. Choice A, III only, must be the best answer choice by process of elimination.

115. **A is the best answer.** An increase in the index of refraction of a lens would increase the bending of the light rays, which would increase the power of the lens. Therefore, I would increase the power of the lens; choice C can be eliminated. Since $P = 1/f$, an increase in $f$ would decrease the power. Therefore, II would not increase the power of the lens; choices B and D can be eliminated. Choice A, I only, is the best answer. To confirm, consider whether III would increase the power of the lens. Increasing the radius of curvature of one side of the lens would flatten the lens, reduce the degree to which it bent light, and decrease its power. For this reason, III would not increase the power of the lens, and choice A is the best answer.

116. **D is the best answer.** A converging lens forms a real, inverted image of an object outside its focal distance. If object distance is 4 cm and focal distance is 1 cm, the image formed must be real. Real images are images formed on the opposite side of the lens from the object. Therefore, if the object is in front of the lens, then the image must be behind the lens. Choice A, which states that the image is formed in front of the lens, can be eliminated. The thin lens equation states that $1/f = 1/d_o + 1/d_i$. Therefore, $1/d_i = 1/f - 1/d_o = 1/(+1 \text{ cm}) - 1/(+4 \text{ cm}) = 3/4 \text{ cm}^{-1}$ and $d_i = 4/3 \text{ cm} = 1.33 \text{ cm}$. Choices B and C can be eliminated and choice D is the best answer. Remember that, by convention, converging mirrors and lenses have positive focal distances and objects that are on the opposite side of a lens from an observer have positive object distances. On the MCAT®, assume that an object in a one lens system is in the opposite side of the lens from the observer.

117. **B is the best answer.** The question stem states that the mirror forms an inverted image. Only converging mirrors can form inverted images. Converging mirrors are concave mirrors. Therefore, choices A and C, which state that the mirror is convex, can be eliminated. Converging mirrors only form inverted images of objects positioned beyond their focal points. Therefore, since the object distance is 5 m, the focal distance must be less than 5 m. Choice D, which states that the focal distance is greater than 5 m, can be eliminated. Choice B is the best answer.

118. **A is the best answer.** Concave mirrors are converging mirrors. Converging mirrors form real, inverted images of objects outside their focal points. The focal distance of the mirror is 2 cm and the object is placed 4 cm in front of the mirror. The object is outside the focal point, and the image of the object formed by the mirror is inverted. Answer choices C and D, which state that the image is upright, can be eliminated. According to the thin lens equation, $1/f = 1/d_o + 1/d_i$. By convention, focal distances of converging mirrors are positive and object distances of objects on the same side of the mirror as the observer are positive. On the MCAT®, assume that objects in one mirror systems are on the same side of the mirror as the observer. Therefore, $1/d_i = 1/f - 1/d_o = 1/(+2 \text{ cm}) - 1/(+4 \text{ cm}) = \frac{1}{4} \text{ cm}^{-1}$ and $d_i = 4 \text{ cm}$. Magnification, $m = -d_i/d_o = h_i/h_o = -(4 \text{ cm})/(4 \text{ cm}) = -1$. Since the magnification has a magnitude of 1, the image height is the same as the object height, 1 cm. The negative sign confirms that the image is inverted. Therefore A is the best answer choice.

119. **D is the best answer.** No image is formed when an object is placed at the focal point of a lens. Therefore, choices A and C can be eliminated. To decide between choices B and D, first assume that the lens is a diverging lens. Recall that diverging lenses form only virtual images, and, by convention, virtual images have negative image distances. Therefore, if the lens were a diverging lens and the object and image were at the same distance from the lens, $d_i$ and $d_o$ would be equal in magnitude but opposite in sign. If $1/f = 1/d_o + 1/d_i$ and $d_i = -d_o$, then $1/f$ would equal $1/d_o + 1/(-d_o)$, which equals zero. If $1/f$ equaled zero, then $f$ would equal infinity. Only flat mirrors have a focal distance equal to infinity. Therefore, the lens cannot be a diverging lens and choice B can be eliminated. Choice D must be the best answer. To confirm, recall that converging lenses form real images of objects placed outside their focal points. By convention, real images have positive image distances. If the lens were a converging lens and the object were at twice the focal distance, then $1/f$ would equal $1/(2f) + 1/d_i$, and $d_i$ would equal $2f$, as well. In other words, if an object is placed at twice the focal distance of a converging lens, then the image formed will also be at twice the focal distance of the lens. Note that when the image is a real image, it will be on the opposite side of the lens from the object.

120. **C is the best answer.** According to the figure, the optical device forms an inverted image on the opposite side of the device from the object. Only converging mirrors and lenses form inverted images. Therefore, choice A, convex (diverging) mirror, and choice D, diverging lens, can be eliminated. Remember that inverted images are always real images, so the image formed must be a real image. Real images formed by mirrors are on the same side of the mirror as the object, whereas real images formed by lenses are on the opposite side of the lens from the object. Recall that a real image is formed by an actual convergence of light rays. Mirrors reflect light back towards objects whereas lenses refract light as they pass through to the opposite side of the lens from the object. Because the real image is on the opposite side of the optical device from the object, the optical device must be a lens. Choice B, concave (converging) mirror can be eliminated and choice C, converging lens, is the best answer.

# Photo Credits

## Covers

Front cover, Explosive start of athlete with handicap.: © filrom/iStockphoto.com

## Lecture 1

Pg. 7, Student walking: © Dana Kelley

Pg. 8, Winding road: © Nicolas Raymond/www.freestock.car, adapted for use under the terms of the Creative Commons CC by 3.0 license (http://creativecommons.org/licenses/by/3.0/legalcode)

Pg. 9, Female carving skier: © ultramarinfoto/iStockphoto.com

Pg. 15, Projectile follows follows a parabolic path: © Ted Kinsman/Science Source

Pg. 20, Hand and book: © Dana Kelley

Pg. 22, Isaac Newton: © Science Source

## Lecture 2

Pg. 37, Airplane jump: © Drazen Vukelic/iStockphoto.com

Pg. 37, Skydiver: © Aleksander Trankovi/iStockphoto.com

Pg. 49, Cowboy with wagon: © Doug Berry/iStockphoto.com

## Lecture 3

Pg. 62, Cruiser: © Nasowas/iStockphoto.com

Pg. 63, Small buckets: © Dana Kelley

Pg. 63, Scale: © cjan/Veer.com

Pg. 83, Dripping faucet: © Eric Delmar/iStockphoto.com

## Lecture 4

Pg. 89, High voltage: © Vladimir Popovici/iStockphoto.com

Pg. 99, Firefighter fighting a fire: © Tatiana Belova/iStockphoto.com

Pg. 107, Turbines of Hydroelectricity Power Generator at Hoover Dam: © YinYang/iStockphoto.com

## Lecture 5

Pg. 115, Neurospin MRI Research Center: © Phillipe Psailla/PhotoResearchers

Pg. 116, Liberty Elementary School: © Dana Kelley

Pg. 121, Scanned ECG strip: © czardases/iStockphoto.com

Pg. 121, Nurse performing an EKG: © nyul/iStockphoto.com

Pg. 125, Five young people grimacing at something they hear: © Don Bayley/iStockphoto.com

Pg. 126, Guitar: © Dana Kelley

Pg. 127, Sympathetic resonance: © Efran/Gettyimages.com

Pg. 134, Muzzle blast: © Gary S. Settles/Photo Researchers, Inc.

Pg. 134, F-18 Super Hornet Vapor Cone © skinman/iStockphoto.com

Pg. 136, Sigmund Freud: © Georgios Kollidas/iStockphoto.com

Pg. 137, Thermogram of incandescent and compact fluorescent lamps: © GIPhotoStock/Photo Researchers, Inc

Pg. 145, Fiber optics: © Henrik Jonsson/iStockphoto.com

Pg. 145, Total internal reflection: © GIPhotoStock / Science Source

Pg. 146, Prism: © Dimitri Vervitsiotis/Gettyimages.com

Pg. 147, Bubble: © Mikkel William Nielsen/iStockphoto.com

Pg. 152, X-ray diffraction of platinum crystal: © Erwin Mueller, Pennsylvania State University/Science Source/Photo Researchers, Inc/Colorization by: Mary Martin

Pg. 154, Mirror from a school bus: © ConradFries/iStockphoto.com

Pg. 154, Mirror Concave: © stevegeer/iStockphoto.com

Pg. 158, Refraction images: © David Parker/Photo Researchers, Inc.

# Index

electromagnetic waves 110, 116, 153

electromotive force (EMF) 100, 112, 246

energy 33, 42-51, 56, 59, 61-64, 75, 78-79, 82, 87, 89 – 90, 93-95, 99-105, 107, 109, 111, 115-116, 123-124, 126-127, 129, 136-139, 143, 145, 153, 174, 182-186, 190, 192, 198-199, 209, 215, 217-224, 226-227, 231, 238-240, 242, 244-245, 248

equilibrium 33-38, 40-41, 53-54, 79, 84, 120, 182, 187, 218-219, 221-222, 238

equipotential surfaces 95

eyepiece 166

# F

far-sighted (hyperopia) 167

First Law of Thermodynamics 42, 45, 47

floating object 68-71

fluid 26-27, 61-72, 75-87, 89, 98-101, 103, 106, 128, 191-194, 209, 223-225, 231, 241-243

fluid pressure 64-65, 75, 79, 223-224, 242

fluorescent light 137

focal length ($f$) 154, 156, 159-161, 165-168, 171, 207-208, 230

focal point 115, 154, 156-157, 159, 160-161, 163, 166, 168, 249

fracture point 27, 217

frequency ($f$) 117, 135, 153

friction (static and kinetic) 20, 23, 25-27, 30, 76, 81

# G

gauge pressure 66, 82

gravitational field 49, 92 – 94

gravitational force 16-17, 20-23, 37, 62, 70-71, 89-91, 93, 111, 239

gravitational potential energy ($U_g$) 43

# H

heat (q) 42-48

Hooke's law 27-29, 48-49, 237

hydraulic lift 52, 67, 73

# I

ideal fluid 76-79, 80-82, 85, 106, 191, 193, 223, 243

ideal waves 116

image 115, 149, 154-155, 157, 159, 160-163, 166-167, 169, 208, 211, 230, 232, 248-249

incandescent light 137

inclined plane 23-24, 29, 52, 56, 217, 237, 241

incompressible 63, 65, 67, 76-77

index of refraction ($n$) 142, 153

inertia 16, 22, 59, 118-119, 178, 217

infrared 137, 139-140, 184-185, 208, 230

in parallel 89, 102, 105-108, 113-114, 199-200, 227-228, 245

in series 89, 102, 105-108, 113-114, 227-228, 245

instantaneous speed 7

instantaneous velocity 7, 11

intensity 121, 124-125, 129, 135, 143, 183, 246, 248

intensity level 125, 246

intermolecular forces 83-84, 118, 243

in vacuo 116, 139

inverted image 159-164, 166, 169, 208, 210, 230, 232, 249

inverted wave 126, 142

irrotational flow 76

isolated system 42, 44

# J

joule (J) 43

# K

kinetic energy ($K$) 49

# L

laminar flow 76, 85, 193, 223

Law of Conservation of Mechanical Energy 48

lens 136, 142-143, 154-163, 165-169, 171, 207-209, 230-232, 248-249

lens aberrations 165

lens strength 156

lever 52-55, 57, 183, 219, 222, 239, 240

lever arm ($l$) 34, 36, 39

light 45, 101, 110, 115-117, 122, 126, 129-130, 133, 136-150, 152-161, 165-168, 171, 207-210, 220, 230-232, 247-249

like charges 90

lines of force 92, 110, 200, 227

logarithmic scale 125, 229, 246

longitudinal waves 116, 128

# M

machines 52, 55, 219, 240-241

Mach number 134

magnetic field (**B**) 92, 110-112, 136, 139, 201-202, 227-228, 245-246

mass (m) 3-4, 15-17, 19-22, 24, 27, 29-30, 33-36, 38, 41-44, 50-57, 61, 63, 70-73, 77, 82, 87, 89-95, 101, 112, 118-119, 174, 180, 184-187, 192, 203, 215, 217, 220-223, 225, 236, 238-241, 253

mechanical advantage 52, 57, 219, 241

mechanical energy ($\Delta E_m$) 43, 48-49, 94, 111, 184, 219, 242, 244

mechanical waves 116

medium 115-121, 124, 126-127, 129-131, 139, 141-148, 172, 177, 201, 227, 231-232, 248

metallic conductors 98

multimeter 107

upright reflection  126, 142

## V

vector  4-7, 9-10, 21, 23, 25, 27, 34, 48, 54, 93, 95, 130, 215, 217, 235, 238

velocity  3-5, 7-15, 18-20, 22, 27, 29, 35, 37, 40, 48, 50-51, 56, 59, 62, 64, 76-82, 85, 87, 97, 103, 111, 117-119, 121, 124, 127, 129-135, 142, 145, 148, 174-177, 182-183, 187, 191-195, 210, 215-219, 221-229, 231-232, 235-239, 242-247

Venturi effect  79, 223

Venturi meter  79

Venturi tube  79

virtual focal point  156

virtual image  159, 232, 248

viscosity  76, 81, 84-86, 190, 192-193, 222-223, 243

voltage (V)  89

voltmeter  107

volts (V)  94

volume flow rate  77, 81, 84-85, 223, 243

## W

water  153, 169

wave  115-122, 124, 126-136, 138-139, 142-145, 147, 149, 152-153, 206-208, 210, 229-232, 246-248

wavelength ($\lambda$)  117, 135

wave pulse  126

weight  16, 21, 23, 25, 29, 40-41, 62, 64-65, 68-72, 82-83, 174, 183-184, 187, 218-219, 221, 236-237, 239, 241-242

work-kinetic energy theorem  46

work (W)  4, 42

## X

x-ray diffraction  152

## Y

yield point  27

Young's double-slit experiment  150

## About the Author

Jonathan Orsay is uniquely qualified to write an MCAT® preparation book. He graduated on the Dean's list with a B.A. in History from Columbia University. While considering medical school, he sat for the real MCAT® three times from 1989 to 1996. He scored above the 95th percentile on all sections before becoming an MCAT® instructor. He has lectured in MCAT® test preparation for thousands of hours and across the country. He has taught premeds from such prestigious universities as Harvard and Columbia. He has written and published the following books and audio products in MCAT® preparation: "Examkrackers MCAT® Physics", "Examkrackers MCAT® Chemistry", "Examkrackers MCAT® Organic Chemistry", "Examkrackers MCAT® Biology", "Examkrackers MCAT® Verbal Reasoning & Math", "Examkrackers 1001 questions in MCAT® Physics", "Examkrackers MCAT® Audio Osmosis with Jordan and Jon", all of which have evolved when the MCAT® has changed, and which continue to be the number one bestselling MCAT® materials available.

## A Student Review of This Book

The following review of this book was written by Teri from New York.

*"The Examkrackers MCAT® books are the best MCAT® prep materials I've seen-and I looked at many before deciding. The worst part about studying for the MCAT® is figuring out what you need to cover and getting the material organized. These books do all that for you so that you can spend your time learning. The books are well and carefully written, with great diagrams and really useful mnemonic tricks, so you don't waste time trying to figure out what the book is saying. They are concise enough that you can get through all of the subjects without cramming unnecessary details, and they really give you a strategy for the exam. The study questions in each section cover all the important concepts, and let you check your learning after each section. Alternating between reading and answering questions in MCAT® format really helps make the material stick, and means there are no surprises on the day of the exam-the exam format seems really familiar and this helps enormously with the anxiety. Basically, these books make it clear what you need to do to be completely prepared for the MCAT® and deliver it to you in a straightforward and easy-to-follow form. The mass of material you could study is overwhelming, so I decided to trust these books—I used nothing but the Examkrackers books in all subjects and scored in the 99th percentile in all sections. Thanks to Jonathan Orsay and Examkrackers, I was admitted to all of my top-choice schools (Columbia, Cornell, Stanford, and UCSF). I will always be grateful. I could not recommend the Examkrackers books more strongly. Please contact me if you have any questions."*

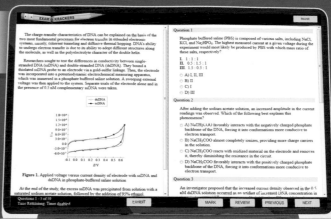

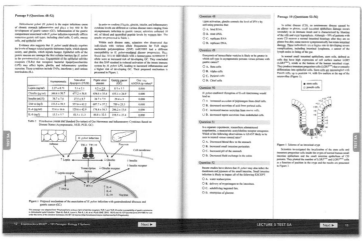

**DIRECTIONS.** Most questions in the Physical Sciences test are organized into groups, each preceded by a descriptive passage. After studying the passage, select the one best answer to each question in the group. Some questions are not based on a descriptive passage and are also independent of each other. You must also select the one best answer to these questions. If you are not certain of an answer, eliminate the alternatives that you know to be incorrect and then select an answer from the remaining alternatives. A periodic table is provided for your use. You may consult it whenever you wish.

## PERIODIC TABLE OF THE ELEMENTS

| 1 H 1.0 | | | | | | | | | | | | | | | | | | 2 He 4.0 |
|---|---|---|---|---|---|---|---|---|---|---|---|---|---|---|---|---|---|---|
| 3 Li 6.9 | 4 Be 9.0 | | | | | | | | | | | 5 B 10.8 | 6 C 12.0 | 7 N 14.0 | 8 O 16.0 | 9 F 19.0 | 10 Ne 20.2 |
| 11 Na 23.0 | 12 Mg 24.3 | | | | | | | | | | | 13 Al 27.0 | 14 Si 28.1 | 15 P 31.0 | 16 S 32.1 | 17 Cl 35.5 | 18 Ar 39.9 |
| 19 K 39.1 | 20 Ca 40.1 | 21 Sc 45.0 | 22 Ti 47.9 | 23 V 50.9 | 24 Cr 52.0 | 25 Mn 54.9 | 26 Fe 55.8 | 27 Co 58.9 | 28 Ni 58.7 | 29 Cu 63.5 | 30 Zn 65.4 | 31 Ga 69.7 | 32 Ge 72.6 | 33 As 74.9 | 34 Se 79.0 | 35 Br 79.9 | 36 Kr 83.8 |
| 37 Rb 85.5 | 38 Sr 87.6 | 39 Y 88.9 | 40 Zr 91.2 | 41 Nb 92.9 | 42 Mo 95.9 | 43 Tc (98) | 44 Ru 101.1 | 45 Rh 102.9 | 46 Pd 106.4 | 47 Ag 107.9 | 48 Cd 112.4 | 49 In 114.8 | 50 Sn 118.7 | 51 Sb 121.8 | 52 Te 127.6 | 53 I 126.9 | 54 Xe 131.3 |
| 55 Cs 132.9 | 56 Ba 137.3 | 57 La* 138.9 | 72 Hf 178.5 | 73 Ta 180.9 | 74 W 183.9 | 75 Re 186.2 | 76 Os 190.2 | 77 Ir 192.2 | 78 Pt 195.1 | 79 Au 197.0 | 80 Hg 200.6 | 81 Tl 204.4 | 82 Pb 207.2 | 83 Bi 209.0 | 84 Po (209) | 85 At (210) | 86 Rn (222) |
| 87 Fr (223) | 88 Ra 226.0 | 89 Ac= 227.0 | 104 Unq (261) | 105 Unp (262) | 106 Unh (263) | 107 Uns (262) | 108 Uno (265) | 109 Une (267) | | | | | | | | | |

| * | 58 Ce 140.1 | 59 Pr 140.9 | 60 Nd 144.2 | 61 Pm (145) | 62 Sm 150.4 | 63 Eu 152.0 | 64 Gd 157.3 | 65 Tb 158.9 | 66 Dy 162.5 | 67 Ho 164.9 | 68 Er 167.3 | 69 Tm 168.9 | 70 Yb 173.0 | 71 Lu 175.0 |
|---|---|---|---|---|---|---|---|---|---|---|---|---|---|---|
| = | 90 Th 232.0 | 91 Pa (231) | 92 U 238.0 | 93 Np (237) | 94 Pu (244) | 95 Am (243) | 96 Cm (247) | 97 Bk (247) | 98 Cf (251) | 99 Es (252) | 100 Fm (257) | 101 Md (258) | 102 No (259) | 103 Lr (260) |